WILD NEW ZEALAND

Wild New Zealand

READER'S DIGEST   SYDNEY

Published by Reader's Digest (Australia) Pty Limited (Inc. in NSW)
26-32 Waterloo Street, Surry Hills, NSW 2010

First edition, fourth revise
© 1990 Reader's Digest (New Zealand) Limited
© 1982, 1985, 1990 Reader's Digest (Australia) Pty Limited
© 1982, 1985, 1990 Reader's Digest Association Far East Limited
Philippines copyright 1982, 1985, 1990 Reader's Digest Association
Far East Limited

National Library of Australia cataloguing-in-publication data

Wild New Zealand
  Index
  ISBN 0 949819 95 6
  1. New Zealand — Description and travel — 1951 —
  I. Reader's Digest Services
919.31'0437

Wild New Zealand was edited and designed by Reader's Digest (Australia) Pty Limited

The editors gratefully acknowledge the collaboration of the following:

Consultants

Maxwell Gage, DSc, FRSNZ
Former Professor of Geology
University of Canterbury

F. J. Newhook, MSc, PhD, DIC, FRSA
Professor, Department of Botany
University of Auckland

Gordon R. Williams, BSc (Hons), MSc, PhD
Former Professor, Department of Entomology,
Lincoln College, Canterbury

Photographers

Philip Temple made a notably
extensive contribution. For detailed
photographic credits see p. 318.

Contributors

Errol Brathwaite

J. W. Cole, BSc, PhD
Department of Geology
University of Canterbury

Gordon Ell

Philip Holden

Philip Houghton

Michael King

Guy Salmon

Maurice Shadbolt

Michael Short

Brian Turner

Mary Varnham

Contents

Introduction 8

Origins of the New Zealand landscape 10

550 million years in the making of New Zealand 12

The origins of New Zealand's rocks 14

A land thrust up and worn down 16

Unique remnants of ancient types of forest 18

How New Zealand acquired and lost unique plant life 20

Animal life transformed by extinctions and introductions 22

Great landscape regions of New Zealand 24

Northland 26

Hauraki Gulf.................................... 38

Auckland's west coast 46

Coromandel Peninsula......................... 52

Rotorua 58

Lake Taupo 70

Tongariro National Park 78

East Cape 92

Urewera National Park 100

Egmont National Park 106

Hawke's Bay and Wairarapa coast 112

Marlborough Sounds 120

Golden Bay 128

Nelson Lakes National Park 136

The Kaikouras 146

Arthur's Pass National Park 156

Banks Peninsula 168

Mount Cook National Park 178

Westland National Park .204

Mount Aspiring National Park 218

Central Otago 236

Fiordland National Park .254

The Catlins 274

Stewart Island 282

Touring and walking in wild New Zealand

Touring and walking in wild New Zealand 296

Visiting the wild regions 298

Walking in the wild regions 304

New Zealand Walkway system 308

Safety and survival in the bush 310

Index 312

Acknowledgments 318

Introduction

'Wild' has several meanings. 'Untamed', 'uninhabited', 'disorderly', 'desolate' and 'lacking restraint' are some that the dictionary offers. In any of these senses the word 'wild' justly describes the New Zealand that is celebrated in this book.

Much of the country remains untamed. Much is uninhabited, and most of the remainder is inhabited only sparsely. The natural landscape can seem disorderly by contrast with neatly fenced rectangles of agricultural or pastoral land. Places where erosion has taken control, in the wake of destruction of the plant cover by settlers or introduced animals, are desolate indeed. Above all, wild New Zealand is magnificently lacking in restraint.

It is a land where 20 mountain peaks soar to heights greater than 3000 m, and where mountain ranges seem to rise steeply from the sea. Volcanos smoulder ominously and, through the ages, occasionally erupt with devastating force. Mud spits and gurgles in boiling pools. On long coastline, from which no inland place is more than 110 km, beaches of golden sand stretch endlessly away to the horizon. In other places towering cliffs are battered by huge waves.

The vegetation is perhaps even more diverse than the landforms—from dripping, moss-festooned rainforest to near-desert. In the primeval forests there are ancient trees of enormous height and girth. On the alpine slopes tiny plants survive freezing cold and biting winds.

All these are but a few aspects of the wild beauty of the New Zealand landscape displayed in this book, which is divided into three parts. The first part explains why and how New Zealand came to occupy its isolated position on the globe, and it tells of the processes and events that, over millions of years, gave the islands a unique natural inheritance.

The second and largest part of the book depicts and describes the landscapes of 24 regions, from the northern tip of the North Island to the southern tip of Stewart Island. Some of these regions are famous beyond New Zealand, but others are little known even to most who live in the country.

Those who are stimulated to see any of these regions at first hand will find practical guidance on visiting all of them in the third part of the book. There are suggestions too, for walking in the wilderness.

A land thrust up and worn down

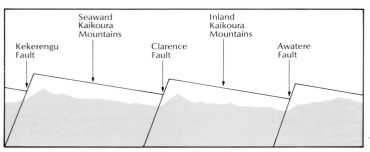

No upstanding feature of land can survive indefinitely. Rain, wind, ice and sun and agents of decay in the atmosphere and soils will erode it. It will be reduced to low relief unless there is compensation by either uplift of the crust or addition of new material, such as volcanic lava, to the surface.

The ridges and spurs of a mountain range are merely the parts that have not been worn away by the erosion process that has formed the details of the relief, the peaks and valleys.

In New Zealand erosion has engraved valleys upon continually rising blocks of crust. Long strips of the earth's crust, mostly parallel to the boundary between the persistently moving Indian-Australia and Pacific plates, have been thrust up above adjacent tracts upon which material eroded from the heights has accumulated.

Variations in the form of the uplands reflect differences from place to place in the nature and internal structure of underlying rocks, in the vigour of the movements of the crust, and in the climates prevailing during the development of the landscapes.

The face of New Zealand is on the whole very young, even though underlying rocks in places are very old. This is because erosion constantly modifies and lowers upland surfaces and some of the products of the erosion build up valley floors. In the last few ten thousand years major changes have occurred in stream patterns and prominent features have come into existence. There have even been major changes in the land during the last 10 000 years in places reached by extended glaciers during the last ice age.

Some regions are exceptions to the general youthfulness of the land surface—the far north, some eastern parts of the South Island and Stewart Island—but even these may have remained little modified for no more than about 10 million years.

The boldest scenery in New Zealand is in Fiordland, where glaciers have carved steep-sided troughs in tough, coarsely crystalline granites and gneisses which were vigorously uplifted in late geological times. These troughs have been drowned by the invading sea, or by lakes dammed by glacier moraine.

Most of the higher mountainous tracts of both islands are made up of ranges carved by streams from the harder, older greywacke and metamorphic schists. In many parts of the South Island glaciers have also shaped these ranges. Away from the glaciated areas, the drainage patterns are often complex and confusing, streams and tributaries are closely spaced and ridge crests are sharp. Valleys that were once filled with ice are straighter and simpler in plan, the distinctive forms of glacier scour having been more or less obliterated by weathering since the ice departed.

Mountains sculpted from granite differ from the greywacke and schist ranges mainly in their simpler pattern of more widely spaced streams. Such mountains, in Nelson and Westland, are bold and abrupt, especially the row of isolated granite mountains standing above the Westland plains.

In the softer terrain of the younger rock cover relief is more subdued because of weak resistance to erosion, except where recent uplift has been more than enough to compensate. The rapidly rising Kaikoura Ranges are an example; there young rocks extend to well above 1000 m. Valleys eroded by streams in

the younger rocks vary from steep-walled gutters to open, rolling dales. The tributary streams are usually closely spaced and many-branched.

Folding and other internal rock structures can often best be seen where layers of the more resistant types of younger rock, especially limestone, tend to stand out from surrounding softer ground as ledges and ridges.

In the eastern districts of both North and South Islands some remarkable landscapes have been produced by the exceptional combination of weak rocks being made even weaker through being crushed by shearing along faults in a region of rapid uplift. In such places, the slopes are gentle, modelled almost entirely by gravitational slumping and flowing, and streams are widely spaced. The land is also chronically unstable and any surface disturbance, such as removal of forest cover, is likely to speed up the movements and start off severe gullying.

Landscape features of volcanic origin take a variety of forms. The more obvious are volcanic mountains, in the form of cones or domes, and scoria cones, such as those that pimple the landscape of Auckland. Less obviously volcanic in origin are tablelands built up by successive outpourings of sheets of fluid lava, as in the region west of the Bay of Islands, and the ignimbrite plateaux of the central North Island.

'Block mountain and trough' landscape—a succession of broad, parallel ridges and val-

Land-shaping events during the last 2 million years

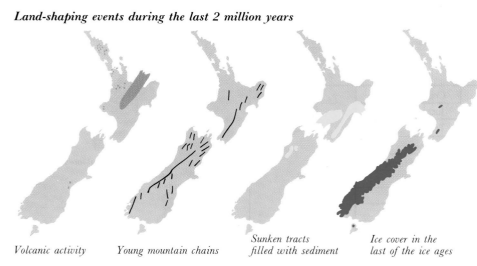

Volcanic activity   *Young mountain chains*   *Sunken tracts filled with sediment*   *Ice cover in the last of the ice ages*

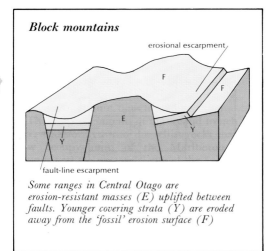

Block mountains

Some ranges in Central Otago are erosion-resistant masses (E) uplifted between faults. Younger covering strata (Y) are eroded away from the 'fossil' erosion surface (F)

leys is characteristic of Central Otago. It was once thought that this landscape was due to the raw effects of recent tilting and rising of blocks of crust along faults. But it is really a 'fossil landscape', an ancient eroded surface, buried under younger rocks, broken by faults and folded, and finally upheaved and exposed again.

The deposits left by vanished glaciers have left landscape features whose full magnitude is hard to appreciate from the ground. In the upper Waitaki and upper Clutha basins there are long, sinuous ridges of moraine, up to 100 m high, and broad sheets of gravel deposited by meltwater rivers. These features are also found in the eastern fringe of Fiordland and in the lowlands of central and southern Westland. Loops of moraine have impounded lakes—both large lakes such as Lake Pukaki and tiny ones such as Lakes Ianthe and Matheson.

The most extensive flat areas of New Zealand, and the most valuable agricultural land, are broad, gently sloping fans of alluvium built by rivers entrenched within them. The Canterbury Plains are built of gravel produced by the intense erosion from glaciers and severe frost during the ice ages and carried by the Waimakariri, Rakaia, Rangitata and smaller rivers.

New Zealand scenery is also remarkable for the giant stairways of terraces flanking the larger valleys of both islands, and for gorges, like the Manawatu Gorge, which conduct a river from one side of a mountain range to another. Cataclysmic fracturing of the mountain range, allowing the river to flow through, was once a popular explanation of this phenomenon. The real explanations are various but less dramatic. In some cases the gorge was already established before the range arose and the uplift was so slow that the river could keep cutting its course.

◄Steep fans of coarse debris, like this one in the Tasman Valley, South Canterbury, are a distinctive feature of New Zealand mountain scenery

▲Glacier ice steepened and scalloped these mountains in western Otago and erosion by frost and gullying has finely etched the surface since the glaciers departed

▼Blue-grey silt rock known as 'papa' underlies much of the North Island. The Rangitikei River has carved its valley out of papa, and terraced it into gigantic steps

▲Erosion of a gully, near Wellington, produces debris which *is building a fan and causing the coast to advance*

Unique remnants of ancient types of forest

In 1910, one of New Zealand's greatest botanists, Leonard Cockayne, wrote words that still apply: 'However little the average New Zealander may know about the plants of his country, few there are who cannot raise some enthusiasm regarding the "bush" as the forest is everywhere called. To young and old it is a delight: the stately trees; the birds, fearless of man; and, above all, the wealth of ferns, appeal to all. But that this forest is a unique production of nature, found in no other land, is not a matter of common knowledge, though truly it has many claims to be considered a priceless possession.'

The unique New Zealand bush takes many forms, because plants have grouped themselves into many different communities.

Botanists have given names to the main types, but more as a matter of convenience than precise description. Kauri forest, for example, is rarely pure kauri. The jungle-like warm temperate rainforest, dominated by podocarps and various hardwood trees, varies so enormously in its composition that a particular tract is named according to its dominant podocarp. If *Dacrydium cupressinum* is dominant, the forest is rimu forest; if *Podocarps dacrydioides,* kahitatea forest; if *Podocarps totara,* totara forest. Other podocarps, such as miro and matai, seldom form stands, but contribute to mixtures.

New Zealand podocarp-hardwood forest is probably the best surviving example of a type of vegetation which was widespread in the middle latitudes of the Southern and Northern Hemispheres before the great ice ages. It has a complex stratification. Hardwood trees form the canopy. Over them tower, to almost twice their height, the mature podocarps, often joined by the huge northern rata. Tawa is the main hardwood in the North Island and kamahi in the South Island, but they are joined by pukatea, hinau, maire and others.

Below the canopy is a layer of small trees, tall shrubs and tree ferns. Then come smaller shrubs, juvenile trees, and ferns, mosses and liverworts on the ground. Numerous climbing plants, the lianas, bridge all these layers.

The close similarity with tropical rain forest is completed by the prolific epiphytes, plants which perch on others. Most noticeable amongst them are plants from the lily family, *Collospermum* and *Astelia*, which in turn provide perching space and humus for other epiphytes. The broadleaf *Griselinia lucida* and northern rata, eventually send liana-like roots to the ground.

The fate of the remaining podocarp forest has been the subject of recent controversies. At the rate of cut of the mid-1970s the resource would not have lasted seven years in some places or 15 years in others. Now government policy for indigenous state forests eliminates clearfelling and replacement by exotic pines and aims to perpetuate native forests on a 'sustained yield' basis.

There are pressures to retain all or most of what is left of the podocarp-hardwood forest, and debates about the ability of dense stands of tall podocarps to tolerate selective logging. In the scales are, on one side, retention of forest tree communities that have taken millions of years to evolve and, on the other side, employment and social stability for human forest communities over the short term before pine logs can replace indigenous timber in the mills.

Kauri forest

Many associated species are shared by podocarp and kauri forests, but the kauri forest is quite distinct, and not only because of the gigantic kauris. Several plants in the middle and lower storeys give the kauri forest a special character: kauri 'grass' *Astelia trinervia*, the tall 'cutty grass' sedge *Gahnia xanthocarpa*, the tree daisy *Senecio kirkii*, the fragrant *Alseuosomia* and *Phebalium* and the dwarf tree fern

◄ *These trees in the Whirinaki Forest belong to one of the finest stands of podocarps— rimu, matai, miro and totara—left in New Zealand. The foreground has been cleared of trees and undergrowth and podocarp seedlings planted to replace the forest under the policy of 'sustained yield'*

The plant life as it was

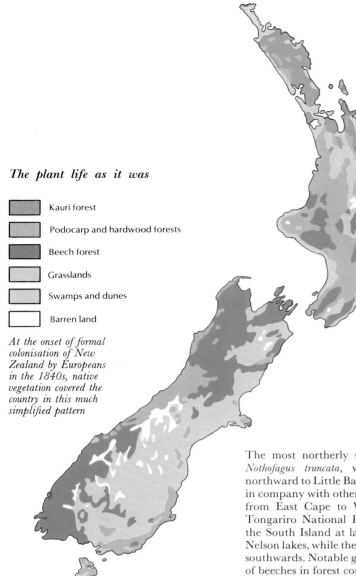

Kauri forest

Podocarp and hardwood forests

Beech forest

Grasslands

Swamps and dunes

Barren land

At the onset of formal colonisation of New Zealand by Europeans in the 1840s, native vegetation covered the country in this much simplified pattern

►*Evergreen beeches, usually clothed in moss, are dominant, or even alone, in the most extensive type of New Zealand forest*

Blechnum fraseri, which is less than a metre tall. Kauri grows in dense groves in some places, but the northern kauri forests often display great diversity, involving podocarps, taraire and tawa.

There are large areas of regenerating kauri forest and government policy is to reserve many of these. In the original kauri forests there are a dozen or so colossal trees, more than 1000 years old, to which the Maori gave individual names. These giant kauris are comparable in age and size to the great sequoias of California.

Beech forest

Moisture-loving, evergreen forests dominated by one or more of the five New Zealand kinds of *Nothofagus* beech together form the most extensive native forest in the country. In places the beech is purely one species; in others it is mixed with other beeches, or with hardwoods or softwoods or sometimes both.

There are three main reasons why so much beech forest is left. First, beech had limited usefulness as a timber tree until the modern age of chipping and pulping. Second, much of it grows at altitudes about 600–750 m and therefore ranks as protection forest. Third, much of it is in national parks.

The most northerly species is hard beech *Nothofagus truncata*, which alone extends northward to Little Barrier Island. It is found in company with other beeches in the ranges from East Cape to Wellington, including Tongariro National Park. It disappears in the South Island at latitude 42°S, near the Nelson lakes, while the other species continue southwards. Notable gaps in the distribution of beeches in forest country are Mt Egmont, central Westland and Stewart Island.

Hard beech and black beech *Nothofagus solandri solandri* belong to the lower altitudes. Red beech *Nothofagus fusca*, silver beech *Nothofagus menziesii* and mountain beech *Nothofagus solandri cliffortioides* are mountain trees, disappearing from the slopes in that order as altitude increases.

Beneath the canopy in a beech forest there is only a single shrub layer, most commonly *Coprosma*. The floor is carpeted with ferns, mainly crown fern *Blechnum discolor* and prickly shield fern *Polystichum vestitum*. Mosses and liverworts, also grow copiously.

Beech-podocarp forest

Some of the major timber resources of the South Island are composed of beech-podocarp forest—a dense canopy of beech from which emerge podocarps, mainly rimu. It occupies foothills and middle altitudes.

Coastal forest

The remaining major forest type is impossible to standardise. On Stewart Island southern rata and tree daisies reach out over the water. In Fiordland, beech forest tumbles from the heights to the sea. But in the northern half of the North Island a distinctive coastal forest comes into its own. Pohutukawa (New Zealand Christmas tree),

puriri, kohekohe and karaka all play important roles. Sometimes there is a characteristic understorey, but often this coastal forest is very open because little grows in the dense shade beneath the canopy.

Alongside estuaries, as far south as Tauranga, the forest gives way to New Zealand's only species of mangrove, which grows extensively on tidal mud flats. Elsewhere the coasts are rocky and adorned with perching pohutukawas, or flanked with sandhills where the sand-binding sedge pingao—which has no near relative anywhere—and spinifex grass prepare the way for tough scrub, tolerant of salt and wind-blown sand.

High mountain communities

At its upper limits true forest gives way rapidly to a narrow belt of subalpine forest, where the trees are low, twisted and gnarled. The upper bush line, dictated by the climate of a region, is dramatically straight.

The New Zealand flora has burgeoned in the subalpine and alpine communities, showing a tremendous range of adaptation to a wide variety of often harsh habitats, including fell fields, herb fields, shingle slides and alpine bogs. Hebes, celmisias, gentians, eyebrights, ourisias, spaniards and the world's smallest conifer, the ground-creeping pygmy pine *Dacrydium laxifolium*, all excite botanists and nature-lovers.

Grasslands

New Zealand has no native sward-forming pasture grasses. In 1840 tussock grassland occupied nearly half of the South Island, but it has since steadily given way to improved pastures. Now about 15 per cent of New Zealand's surface is in indigenous grassland and about 30 per cent is in exotic grasses.

19

How New Zealand acquired and lost unique plant life

New Zealand's plant life is outstanding in its variety and its uniqueness. Visitors from countries where they are accustomed to fairly uniform vegetation—such as beeches, elms, conifers or eucalypts—are struck by the great diversity of plants and plant communities in New Zealand. They are also struck by the number of plants they have never seen before, because 84 per cent of New Zealand's flowering plants are found nowhere else.

On the other hand, only 11 per cent of the genera to which New Zealand flowering plants belong do not have members in other lands. Until recent years this strong relationship between the New Zealand flora and those of other lands was difficult to explain. There were, it was true, some plants whose seeds could have been accidentally carried to New Zealand by birds, or blown on the winds or swept on ocean currents. But there were many that could not have reached the isolated archipelago by such means.

Geology provided the answer to the puzzle when comparisons between rocks of matching portions of continents and meticulous magnetic mapping of the ocean floor clinched the evidence in favour of the theory of continental drift. New Zealand had been connected with Australia and Antarctica, and united with them and India, Africa and South America in the super-continent of Gondwanaland about 150 million years ago.

About 70–80 million years ago New Zealand separated from its last neighbour, Australia, and the enormously long period of isolation since then has contributed to the development of unique species. The plants and the way in which they assemble into populations, communities and ecosystems are what they are today as the result of surviving the battering of geological and climatic events. They have survived by competing and adapting.

The fossil record tells the story. Before the Tertiary period began 65 million years ago, New Zealand already had forerunners of its important conifers—*Agathis* (kauri), *Dacrydium* (rimu) and several *Podocarpus* species—and of *Nothofagus* (beech) and *Knightia* (rewarewa). The New Zealand beech fossils show close similarity to those of Antarctica and also to present-day beeches of South America, Australia and New Guinea.

Fossil *Metrosideros* (rata) and *Leptospermum* (tea-tree) have been recognised in rocks about 60 million years old, and *Dracophyllum* (spider wood) and *Dysoxylum* (kohekohe) in rocks 50 million years old. In the Oligocene era, about 35 million years ago, *Coprosma* and members of the daisy family appear, and about 20 million years ago, *Beilschmiedia* (tawa) and *Weinmannia* (kamahi).

During the Miocene era, which lasted from 26 to 7 million years ago, much of New Zealand supported tropical forest which had migrated along the Norfolk Ridge and Lord Howe Rise. These routes had by then, however, foundered. Had the land connection with the north remained, New Zealand would have received snakes and land mammals.

Not all the plant immigrants survived. Violent movements in the land along the New Zealand archipelago during the Tertiary period (65–2 million years ago) extinguished some species and encouraged others to evolve into new species. Thirty million years ago the ancestors of New Zealand's present plants were taking refuge on a few isolated islands occupying New Zealand's site. Since then general land levels have risen, mountains have been formed and eroded, massive ice sheets have come and gone, and the shore line has risen and fallen 100 m or more.

The greatest losses probably came during the ice ages, which started about 2 million years ago and continued until 11 000 years ago. There were perhaps six periods of intense glaciation, each lasting tens of thousands of years, during which glaciers and a fringe of continental ice extended out to sea. So much water was locked up in ice that sea levels dropped by 100 m or more. Beyond the ice, a belt of exposed sea bed was added to the land mass and plants colonised it. Cook Strait was dry land and offshore islands around the Northland coast became part of the mainland. Between the glaciations, there were mild periods with climate as warm as, or warmer than today's.

Sea bed exposed

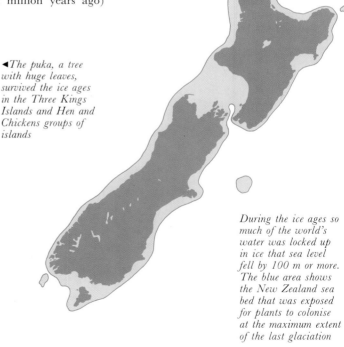

During the ice ages so much of the world's water was locked up in ice that sea level fell by 100 m or more. The blue area shows the New Zealand sea bed that was exposed for plants to colonise at the maximum extent of the last glaciation

◄The puka, a tree with huge leaves, survived the ice ages in the Three Kings Islands and Hen and Chickens groups of islands

◄*One of the world's rarest plants,* Tecomanthe speciosa *was discovered on one of the Three Kings Islands. Only one plant was left in a species which was not known elsewhere*

The glacial periods affected plant life disastrously. Whereas during a warming cycle, vegetation boundaries would simply have moved upwards by natural means of dispersal, during a cooling cycle, plants on an island were trapped. As the increasing cold lowered the altitude of vegetation boundaries, plant species were 'driven' northwards and seawards. New plant communities were formed on the newly exposed sea bed, but many were eliminated and lost. This is why the flora of lowland (below 350 m) New Zealand is poor in species, with an average of only 1.3 species per genus, compared with a world average of 12.5. The fossil record shows that the lowland survivors represent a poor range of the flora that existed before the ice ages.

The richer flora in the northern half of the North Island, with remnants of sub-tropical forest, is evidence that plants found refuge there. An important refuge for tropical plants that failed to survive on the mainland was provided by the offshore islands of Northland. Some of the rarest plants on earth were discovered some 30 years ago on the Three Kings Islands, off the northern tip of the North Island. There were one plant of *Tecomanthe speciosa*, one of *Plectomirtha bayiana* and a handful of *Elingamita johnsonii*. All three species were unknown elsewhere. The giant leaved puka tree *Meryta sinclairii* survived slightly less precariously on several islands in the Three Kings and Hen and Chickens groups.

Alpine plants, on the other hand, would have tolerated glaciation. In fact the changing climate probably stimulated the development of new species and hybrids by opening up new habitats and bringing together groups of species that had been isolated for a long time. Alpine valley communities normally separated by frozen ridges would have been linked by 'bridges' of former ocean bed during glaciations and by mountain summits during warm periods. Consequently four of New Zealand's largest genera, *Hebe*, *Celmisia*, *Ranunculus* and *Coprosma* provide a substantial proportion of the high-altitude species and exhibit great variety of form.

For many years botanists were puzzled by the absence of beech trees from a long stretch of Westland—almost two degrees of latitude—although there are extensive beech forests to the north and south. Now it is generally accepted that during the last ice age an enormous sheet of ice obliterated all plants from the present land surface of Westland but left lowland refuges to the north, in Nelson and Marlborough, and to the south, in Fiordland and Southland.

When the ice disappeared the devastated area was colonised by podocarps, with the help of birds attracted to their succulent fruits. Podocarps have indigestible seeds which can germinate after being eliminated by birds, but beech seeds are nuts which do not survive being eaten. Even in 11 000 years beech has made little progress in closing the gap. It is a slow traveller and it finds the closed podocarp community almost impossible to gatecrash.

During the period covering the evolution of higher plants up to the present day, volcanic action, burying vast areas in ash and lava, has also had a big impact on plants. Devastation must have come to Northland and the central North Island several times in the last few hundred thousand years. Study of the great Taupo eruptions of less than 2000 years ago shows that effects on vegetation must have been considerable. Charred tree trunks visible in road cuttings testify to the succession of showers of hot ash that buried ancient forests.

Another recent cause of destruction and modification of the plant cover is man. Tales of the 'great fires of Tamatea' and burnt logs testify to destruction by humans long before European settlement began. It was perhaps these fires that destroyed the forests which once covered Canterbury and Otago.

Exploitation of the forest for timber and clearing for agriculture began and intensified throughout the 19th century. By 1900, some 1.2 million hectares of kauri forest had been reduced to 200 000 hectares. Today there is less than 5000 hectares of virgin kauri. Fires in 1881 and 1887 destroyed almost 6000 hectares in Puhipuhi Forest alone.

These are just a few examples of man's destructive impact by direct means, but man has also destroyed the forests by indirect means. In the course of turning New Zealand into a rich agricultural and tree-growing country, almost 2000 species of plants, many of them serious pests, have been introduced. Gorse, blackberry, briar, rose and heather are a few of them.

In a more insidious way, introduction of animals for sport—rabbit, deer, thar, chamois, possum, goat and pig—has had an impact on almost all native plant communities.

Forest

Exotic plantations

Tussock grassland and scrub

Pastures and arable land

Swamp

Sand dunes

Barren

Vegetation in early Polynesian times, about 700

Vegetation at the advent of European settlers, about 1800

Vegetation in modern times, mid-1970s

When Polynesian settlement began, eruptions from Lake Taupo had deprived much of the central North Island of its forest cover. When Europeans arrived the forest had regrown, but elsewhere forest had been destroyed. Since then forests have receded and grassland has been replaced by sown pastures

Animal life transformed by extinctions and introductions

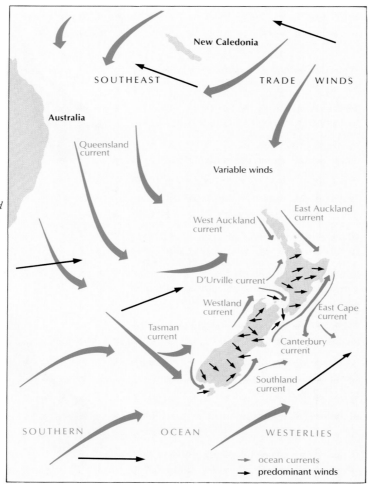

New Caledonia

SOUTHEAST TRADE WINDS

Australia

Queensland current

Variable winds

West Auckland current

East Auckland current

D'Urville current

Westland current

East Cape current

Tasman current

Canterbury current

Southland current

SOUTHERN OCEAN WESTERLIES

→ ocean currents
→ predominant winds

►Many species of animals, especially invertebrates and birds, have been brought to New Zealand by the ocean currents from the northwest and west and by the winds blowing from the west

When the first Polynesian settlers arrived in New Zealand, no more than 1500 years ago, they found a country a little larger than Great Britain, unpopulated by humans. Perhaps three-quarters of the land was covered with evergreen forests of three main kinds—the kauri forests of the northern third of the North Island; the podocarp-hardwood forest of much of the rest of the North Island, part of the south and southeast of the South Island and Stewart Island; and the beech forests of the higher parts of the North Island and most of the forested parts of the South Island. Elsewhere there were expanses of scrub, grassland and swamp vegetation.

The country had only one kind of land mammal—two species of small and inconspicuous bats. It had numerous birds, a high proportion of them flightless or possessed of only limited powers of flight. Some of the flightless birds, the moas, were enormous.

The few reptiles were all lizards—skinks and geckos—except the tuatara, which, although lizard-like, is a direct descendant of the dinosaurs.

Three species of frogs, very small and well camouflaged, lived in the forests so retiringly

that it is believed few Maoris knew they existed. The lakes and rivers supported about 30 species of freshwater fish, most of them rather small, though the two species of eels and the now-extinct grayling were of reasonable size and valuable as food.

The marine plants and animals of the New Zealand coasts were to a considerable extent unremarkable local representatives of the life in the Indo-Pacific region of the world's most continuous habitat, the ocean.

The lack of variety and occasional peculiarity of the animal life was largely due to 70 millions years of isolation since much of it had originated in the supercontinent of Gondwanaland.

Until humans arrived, the additions to the New Zealand fauna of Gondwanaland origin fell into two groups. The more important were the animals that arrived here from the west or north-west on ocean currents or winds or by island-hopping. New Zealand's biological history has much to do with the country's location for millions of years downwind of Australia, in the belt of ocean currents and winds that almost uninterruptedly flow westward around the world north of the

Antarctic Circle. The other group of animals originated from cosmopolitan species that seem to have no trouble finding their way round the world.

The first Polynesian settlers, who came by canoe, brought with them the Polynesian dog (now extinct in New Zealand) and the Polynesian rat, or *kiore*, and some food plants. They probably brought by accident a few insects as well.

The Polynesians, from whom the present-day Maoris are descended, wrought no inconsiderable changes in some 1000 years of occupation of New Zealand before the advent of Europeans. Primitive agriculture requires the use of fire to clear the land, and the Polynesians used it extensively, especially in the north, east and south of the North Island and the east of the South Island. Much of the lowland forest was reduced to scrub and grassland by mostly uncontrolled burning.

The same Polynesians also took their toll of flightless birds, and by hunting played an important part in at least the final stages of the extinction of the moas and some Chatham Islands species. They also perhaps reduced the range and numbers of others.

But a new era began with Captain James Cook, who intentionally introduced pigs, goats, fowls and various crops species—few of which probably survived—and may have accidentally introduced black rats and, no doubt, some weeds. Later explorers and sealers and whalers acted similarly and did not confine their well-meant introductions to the main islands.

The sealers and whalers also committed other serious offences against the natural order. At the time of European discovery, New Zealand had three species of seals—the New Zealand fur seal, the New Zealand sea lion and the elephant seal—all abundant on the coasts of the southern South Island and subantarctic islands. Five species of commercially important whales—the southern right, southern blue, southern hump-back, southern sei and sperm whales—where all common in New Zealand seas. All these animals were exploited so greedily that in 25 years near-extinction of the seals made sealing uneconomic and in about twice as long the whaling industry was virtually exhausted too. The story was repeated about a century later in the equally ruthless over-exploitation of the Chatham Islands crayfish.

In the first quarter of the 19th century, settlement began in earnest, and so did introductions and local modification and destruction of the environment. The early settlers, usually of comfortable middle-class English stock, found themselves in a rugged but by no means inhospitable country with a better climate than their homeland. But it was sin-

▶ *The black swan was introduced to New Zealand from Australia as an ornamental bird. Its numbers increased so greatly that it has become the principal waterfowl in places*

gularly lacking in animals to hunt and fish for, and in the familiar farm and household birds of home. Few native species became numerous in the newly-established English pastures and gardens because the natives were tied by long adaptation to the retreating native vegetation.

Something had to be done. With the encouragement of the Government and the example of the Governor, Sir George Grey, public-spirited citizens founded numerous acclimatisation societies dedicated to importing from Europe, North America, Australia, Asia and elsewhere species that appeared to be suitable for listening to, looking at, fishing for and hunting.

Later, more introductions seemed to be necessary to control the earlier ones that were showing signs of becoming pests. That was how New Zealand acquired its stoats, ferrets, weasels and hedgehogs. In the heyday of acclimatisation, 1855 to 1880, almost everything was tried, including nightingales, robins, gnus, zebras, llamas and Tasmanian devils. Acclimatisation societies paid high prices for European house sparrows. Only snakes and foxes were forbidden entry by act of Parliament. By the beginning of the 20th century the main effort to transform New Zealand into a latter-day Noah's Ark was almost spent, but the process has gone on sporadically, intentionally and accidentally, almost until the present day.

Now New Zealand has the following introduced wild animals of Polynesian, European, North American, Asian and Australian origin: 33 species of mammals (all pests to some degree); 34 species of birds (perhaps one-third of them distinctly pests at times); one species of Australian lizard and four species of Australian frogs (both groups are harmless); 14 species of freshwater fish (about half of them sporting assets) and at least 1000 species of insects (mostly pests).

◀ *An ancient reptile directly descended from the dinosaurs, the tuatara, has survived only in New Zealand. It is a relic of the fauna of Gondwanaland*

▼ *The welcome swallow is a recent immigrant to New Zealand from Australia. Since the late 1950s its numbers have grown rapidly. It usually makes its nest, a cup of mud and grass, on man-made structures*

Great landscape regions of

New Zealand

From the sub-tropical farthest north to the bleak farthest south, from the coast to the summit of the highest mountain, this part of the book presents New Zealand's finest landscape regions. There are 11 regions in the North Island, 12 in the South Island and the whole of the little-known, little-inhabited third main island of the country. These regions do not exhaust New Zealand's stock of scenic splendours, for there are many splendid localities and individual features elsewhere, but each is a substantial area with a host of features. Some of the national park regions have been extended to encompass associated districts beyond the formal boundaries of the park. New Zealand has a number of classic walking tracks and some of these—even some that are strictly for the fit and expert—are described and depicted to convey something of the experience to those who are unable to undertake these walks or who have yet to yield to the lure of the wilderness.

Northland

The pristine character of Northland, a region long altered by the work of man, now resides most pleasantly in places where land meets and mingles with sea. Elsewhere, the leafy vaults of the surviving kauri forest contain the original sorcery of the ancient Northland wilderness

Humans have been marking, trimming and taming wild Northland for more than a thousand years. Few eminences in the region have not been refashioned by prehistoric Maori defensive earthworks. Few forest groves, hills and wastes never knew the tread of pale-skinned pioneers. Often these latecomers unstitched the vast forest cover, in pursuit of profit or pastoral valleys.

Northland is rugged. There are few plains, except along rivers, and multitudes of rocky hills, though these are modest by New Zealand measure, seldom rising more than 700 m. Unlike New Zealand's loftier regions, Northland is no longer in active mountain-building movement, nor at apparent risk of reshaping by earthquake or eruption. Most of its crust has been stable for 30-40 million years.

By New Zealand standards, the land surfaces of Northland have been exposed for an unusually long time to weathering in a warm, moist climate. The oldest rocks are mainly in the east. The remainder are widespread volcanic rocks, and marine sandstones and mudstones. In later geological times volcanos have spread extensive lava sheets over the Kerikeri district and built scoria cones near Kaikohe and Whangarei.

When the sea level rose with the ending of the last ice age, 10 000 years ago, valley after valley was flooded in Northland, leaving sometimes serene, sometimes dramatic harbours. Wind has worked with tide. The prevailing westerlies have bent exposed vegetation, and driven ever-changing shoals across those harbours open to their whims.

When man first breached its primeval peace, Northland was green, virtually from end to end, with some of the tallest forest on earth. The immense and aristocratic kauri tree stole sun and sky from those afoot in the forest. The kauri germinates naturally no further south than a few score kilometres. The coast is likewise clad distinctively in growth of tropical ancestry which needs a kindly clime to flourish. The mangrove grips Northland's tidal estuaries. The no less labyrinthine pohutukawa tree clings to seaside cliffs, rooted deep in stony fissures.

The Maori largely left Northland's wilderness alone. The forest was abundant with birds which could be snared for the earth oven, and the mighty trees of the forest god Tane were felled selectively for fashioning into canoes. Cove and river could be harvested lightly for fish and mollusc, gifts of the sea god Tangaroa. The wilderness was mother and father of man.

For Europeans, who arrived soon after Captain Cook's pathfinding voyage in 1770, the wilderness was a storehouse to be ransacked. British sailors began calling for kauri masts and spars, inaugurating a trade which was to leave Northland with sadly few remnants of its native cover by the end of the 19th century. Nor were the wastes neglected. Swamps and iron-hard hills were tugged apart in quest of fossilised residue of long-dead kauri, a gum which had value as a constituent of varnish and linoleum.

In the second half of the 20th century deforestation has been arrested and sometimes reversed as conservationists have had their say. Forests of exotic pine for commercial purpose grow in districts once dominated by sand dunes and barren hills. In 1989, 900 hectares of radiata pine trees were planted on sand-dune land.

▶Sand dunes reach far inland along Ninety-Mile Beach. The beach itself is firm enough to support motor vehicles but there is access only in the south. The length of the great sweep of sand is nearer 90 km than the 90 miles of its name

▼A highway figure-8 makes Northland an ideal touring region. The sea is nowhere far away, though easy, direct access to the coast is limited

Cape Reinga
Spirits Bay
Cape Maria van Diemen
Parengarenga Harbour
Ninety-Mile Beach
Rangaunu Bay
Whangaroa Harbour
HIGHWAY 10
Kaitaia
Kerikeri
Waitangi
Bay of Islands
Cape Brett
Whangaruru Harbour
HIGHWAY 12
HIGHWAY 1
Hokianga Harbour
Opononi
WAIPOUA FOREST PARK
Hikurangi
Whangarei
Whangarei Harbour
Tasman Sea
Dargaville
Kaipara Harbour

Nature and history in the Bay of Islands

◀ *The Hole in the Rock moved Captain Cook to an unusually whimsical mood, in which he punningly named Piercy Island, ostensibly after Sir Piercy Brett, a Lord of the Admiralty*

▼ *Nearly 150 islands dot the Bay of Islands. The shore of the bay meanders for a total of some 800 km*

Nowhere in Northland has the sea's invasion of land, after the ice ages, had more dramatic effect than in the Bay of Islands. The inundated hills resisted as the sea took their flanks and torsos, and they survived in truncated form, as islands. There are nearly 150 of them in the Bay of Islands—some just seawashed stumps of land; others substantial enough to be farmed. Fish had a region rich in life-giving reefs. Humans, when they came, had a breathtaking harbour of a hundred safe havens, with deep-water channels and anchorages along the drowned valleys.

Captain Cook, in 1770, was the first European voyager to take advantage of the Bay of Islands, and he named it. Cook thought the bay blessed with 'every kinds of

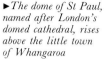
◄Mangroves flourish in the beautiful hill-girt Whangaroa Harbour

►The dome of St Paul, named after London's domed cathedral, rises above the little town of Whangaroa

refreshments', a verdict still fair two centuries later. Intimacy with the Bay of Islands is best established, as in Cook's time, under the silence of sail, as pohutukawa-garlanded islands, crammed with quiet coves, parade past the voyager.

The bay, even with summer at its height, can never really be crowded. There is virtually a deserted beach for every visitor.

It was not always peaceful. When Cook came, canoes pushed out from the islands, and from mainland bays, for their occupants to wonder at the white canvas sails—and booming firearms—of the 18th century European. The Maori population was large, and pas studded the bay.

Other early voyagers were less lucky. Marion du Fresne, in pursuit of the noble savage and perhaps fresh land for France, arrived in the Bay of Islands two years after Captain Cook. He was a gentle man, whose attitude to the Maoris was implicit in his pronouncement: 'As I only do good to them, assuredly they will do me no evil.' He glimpsed the marine potential of the kauri tree and had one felled for spars, but he apparently overstepped the mark by violating the Maori law of *tapu* in some way. Du Fresne and a number of his men were slain.

By the early 1800s the bay was harbouring whaler and trader and timber-seeker, and New Zealand's first unkempt European outpost grew at Kororareka, now Russell. One visitor was Charles Darwin, in 1835. He was unimpressed by the human prospect ('the very refuse of society') but found the natural world much less vile, especially in a kauri grove. 'The noble trees stood up like gigantic columns of wood,' he wrote.

The whale herds, taking their migratory path past New Zealand's northerly extremities, were fast plundered; so also was the kauri forest garbing the bay's low hills. The timber was taken to Sydney, but some can be seen, still substantial today, in the historic buildings which dignify cove and estuary—for example, the Kemp house at Kerikeri, which was built in 1821; and Christ Church in Russell, built in 1835.

The bay's quiet waters lapped tapestries of oysters on the rocks at Rangihoua while New Zealand's first Christian sermon was preached by Samuel Marsden, on Christmas Day 1814. Seabirds wheeled over the sunlit sea,

while New Zealand was ceremonially taken as a British colony at Waitangi in 1840. Among the mangrove-girt upper reaches of the bay, Governor Hobson planted the country's first capital at Okiato and named it after Lord John Russell. It's eminence was brief. Hobson's masters in Sydney disapproved of the site and in 1841 Auckland was made the capital. In 1842 the name Russell was transferred to nearby Kororareka. With colonial bureaucrats and aspirant businessmen finding more interest elsewhere and with European settlement centring increasingly on southern landscapes, the Bay of Islands gently reverted to character.

In the 20th century, with sheep and cattle grazing swards of green here and there

among hills patched with remnant forest and scrub, the bay has been marked slightly by tourist invasion. Tourists first came in pursuit of the bay's abundant marine life, especially big-game fish. Marlin, mako, tuna, thresher and hammerhead shark flourish in formidable size out to the open sea, in the vicinity of Cape Brett and Piercy Island.

The celebrated Wild West romancer Zane Grey began establishing the bay's many world records for big-game catches from lonely camps in the 1920s. Now there are luxurious hotels and motels for those who wish to pit their energy and patience against the largest fish in the sea, or to sample simply and quietly the other native pleasures of the Bay of Islands.

►The coast between the Bay of Islands and Whangaroa Harbour is steep and the shores are mostly rocky

▼Erosion-resisting cores of ancient volcanos rise above pastoral landscapes in many parts of Northland. These are north of Whangaroa Harbour

Sands and legends of the farthest north

▶*Motupia Island lies off Ninety-Mile Beach, near its northern end. Maori myth says the pierced islet was Maui's anchor stone*

▲*Godwits gather on the beaches of the far north in March before beginning their great migration to the Arctic*

▼*Te Paki Stream, near the northern end of Ninety-Mile Beach, once provided the only access to Cape Reinga*

The straggling, glittering northernmost extremity of New Zealand has been firmly part of New Zealand only in recent geological times. When the sea level began to rise again at the end of the last ice age, the North Cape hills became a diminutive archipelago. Then sand, continually carried up the west coast by northerly inshore currents, joined up the islands and connected them to the mainland by a long spit. Prevailing westerly winds built up large dunes. As waterways receded, vegetation took grip here and there and gradually sand changed to fertile soil.

Sand pervades the peninsula for almost its entire length. Captain Cook, voyaging past, dismissed it as 'Desert Coast'. That description still serves the magnificent emptiness of Ninety-Mile Beach (actually nearer 90 kilometres), seen from any eminence, as it

stretches out of sight. Some 29 000 hectares of sand have drifted inland. Travelling up the centre of the peninsula, the visitor can observe dunes rearing from east and west. Marram grass has been planted to hold the dunes, and lupins to fix life-giving nitrogen in the sand. A forest of exotic pines, for future industry, now grows where once was waste.

For the Maori the great curve of Ninety-Mile Beach, with its fine marine mists and muttering winds, was a both literal and poetic highway. It was this route the phantoms of the dead travelled, and looked their last upon New Zealand, before embarking on the submarine road to the lost but never-forgotten Polynesian homeland of Hawaiki. On the hill of Hauma, to the north, they knotted wild grasses to point the direction for those soon to follow. On the hill of

►*Parengarenga Harbour is lined with brilliant white sands which contrast with golden dunes on the west coast. The sand, almost pure silica, is mined for glassmaking*

Maringi-noa they shed their tears of farewell. Finally, after crossing a creek called Waioterata, beyond which there was no return, they leapt from the limbs of an aged pohutukawa tree burgeoning from a cleft in rock at the tip of Cape Reinga. There great doors of kelp parted to reveal the way to the hereafter. A last terrestrial breath might be taken at the Three Kings Islands, distant upon the horizon.

It was said that after battle the numerous passing slain sounded like a great flutter of birds overhead. A great flutter can distinctly be heard in the farthest north in March, when the *kuaka*, or eastern bar-tailed godwit, gathers on the dunes of the district before making its migratory journey to its breeding grounds in the Arctic tundra of Siberia and Alaska, in the northern hemisphere. The author James Buckland has left a vivid account of the godwits departing from Spirits Bay in the 1890s: 'The beach was covered with kuaka . . . thousands hovering overhead to find a footing . . . an old cock uttered a strident call, clarion clear, and shot straight into the air, followed by an incalculable feathered multitude. Higher and higher the host rose until it was just a stain in the sky.'

The godwit is far from the only living thing to lend the region distinction. Because of its former isolation, it has plants and shrubs that are unknown or rare in the rest of New Zealand. Most intriguing, though, is a large, rare native land snail, *Placostylus ambagiosus*, which forsook the sea to live on land. It survives in only tiny colonies, but its fossilised shells can be found in the sand.

Another creature, which did not forsake the ocean, is often as elusive—the toheroa. This bivalve mollusc was once described by the British author Eric Linklater as tasting like oysters 'fed for a season on asparagus tips'. It burrows deeply into the sand of Ninety-Mile Beach, fattening on plankton derived from brackish water in the dunes behind the beach.

Maori legend says that the toheroa was bestowed by the gods on a famished war party. Europeans found it a gift of the gods too. It was popularised by the uncrowned King Edward VIII, who discovered this king of clams when he visited New Zealand as Prince of Wales in 1920. By 1940, 75 tonnes a year were being canned to gratify aristocratic tastes. Soon afterwards, the shy shellfish vanished—as it had in 1888, 1900, 1917 and still does to this day. When it returns, it is not slowly, by infant thousands, but suddenly by mature millions. Where has it been, and why? The comings and goings of the toheroa remain a mystery.

To conserve the shellfish the toheroa-taking season is a week or two at most, and in some years non-existent. By way of compensation, the toheroa's less temperamental cousin, the small, sweet tuatua, still flourishes along Ninety-Mile Beach.

There is more to the far north than sand, shellfish, birds and sea. Upon a plateau above Ahipara, the small settlement nestled at the southern end of Ninety-Mile Beach, there is as stark a stretch of gumland as any to be glimpsed in Northland. This is land that has been leached hard as the floor of long-departed kauri forest, and now is virtually barren of all but scrappy fern and skinny manuka scrub. In it the fossilised gum of that forest was once found in plenty.

Hundreds of diggers, largely from the Yugoslav region of Dalmatia, once dwelt on the bleak Ahipara plateau, seeking the gum for their livelihood. In the 1890s it was one of the country's major exports, outshining gold. Unlike other gumland in the north, the Ahipara plateau has not been fired, disced and fertilised for agricultural use; it has been discreetly preserved by the National Historic Places Trust for posterity's gaze. Few birds are heard in this desolate forest graveyard; the wind whines in from the ocean; the surf's thunder is faint over the hills.

The sea is seldom more than a kilometre or two away in the far north. Harbours like Rangaunu, Houhora and Parengarenga finger far into the peninsula from the east. Cape Reinga, with the Pacific crashing at its foot, is a dramatic arena for legend. To its west, golden sand swerves away to Cape Maria van Diemen, named by the Dutch discoverer of New Zealand, Abel Tasman in 1642. He also named the Three Kings Islands, 50 km to the north. Tasman noted that the rocky islands were inhabited by natives 'of very large size, taking prodigious long strides'. The islands have not been inhabited since 1840.

Much of the farthest north is now government reserve. There wild Northland—with its mighty beaches, its lonely coves and creeks, its dunes and gumland clay—remains quiet, and as precious as it was to the myth-making Maori.

►*The steep ridge of Cape Reinga provides a dramatic finale to the far north. Off shore, the Tasman Sea and the Pacific Ocean meet in impressive turbulence. The most northerly point of the North Island, however, is on the Surville Cliffs, about 32 km eastward*

Mangrove-lined harbour reaching far into the hills

▶On the north head of Hokianga Harbour huge sand dunes move inland, piled up and driven by the westerly winds. The dunes also stretch far up the coast to the north of the Hokianga Harbour

For the Maori every encounter of the natural world was raw material for mythology. The Hokianga Harbour—or river, as casual locals often like to have it—proved a feast for the imagination. This fiord-like arm of the Tasman Sea forces its way between bulky hills for more than 50 km—almost half way across the Northland peninsula. Tall surf crashes over immense and perilous shoals at the harbour entrance. The Maori called this seething water Kaiwaka, or the 'canoe-devourer', and European vessels have found its appetite quite as voracious.

The south side of the harbour is steep and green, with patches of farmland and rags of the once dense forest cover. To the north, golden sand dunes, heaped up to 170 m high by energetic westerly winds, march theatrically inland. Up harbour, swift tides battle through massed armies of mangroves. Racing still farther into serene valleys, the sea threads a vivid motif through carpets of native reed, or raupo, from which shags rise to feed upon tiny yellow-eye mullet.

The mightiest of marine creatures in Maori mythology was the taniwha. Some-

times fearsome, sometimes friendly, it probably had its imaginative origin in the dolphin or whale, though its character could be distinctly dragonish. At all events it was an amiable and very pregnant female taniwha which guided the first famished and sea-weary Polynesian voyagers into a then diminutive Hokianga. The humans moved on; the taniwha settled in a cave and gave birth to 11 lusty junior monsters. Chafing at the confines of a cave, they finally burst out and began shovelling back the landscape with their noses, digging a dozen fresh channels for the sea, until the Hokianga found its present irregular form.

The Hokianga's waters can still nourish myth. The founding taniwha seems to live again in the haunting tale of the wild dolphin which arrived at the tiny seaside community of Opononi from the open sea in the summer of 1955-56 and befriended humans by the teeming thousand. They called it Opo. No dolphin since classical times has made affection for man so plain, nor been mourned in its death by so many as Opo.

The kauri forest, bristling on almost every Hokianga horizon, brought timber-seekers

◀Low tide and sunrise at Opononi. This village, a few kilometres up the Hokianga, is quiet most of the year but becomes a busy resort in summer. In 1955-56 thousands came to watch a wild but amiable dolphin frolic with children

◄The largest moth found in New Zealand is the puriri moth. The female's wing span is up to 150 mm. The larvae bore into puriri and other trees

►The weta, a kind of grasshopper, occurs in some spectacular forms, including this northern giant, which can be up to 75 mm from tip of ovipositor to head

▼The mangrove is often maligned but in tidal creeks and estuaries it provides important habitats for marine animals

from Sydney across the harbour shoals in the early 19th century. Curiosity brought others, like the talented young English artist Augustus Earle in 1827. He worked with both pen and paint-brush to convey the quality of the Hokianga. 'After crossing the bar,' he recorded, 'no other obstacle lay in our way; and floating gradually into a beautiful river we soon lost sight of the sea, and were sailing up a spacious sheet of water, which became considerably wider after entering it; while majestic hills rose on each side, covered with verdure to their very summits. Looking up the river, we beheld various headlands stretching into the water, and gradually contracting in width, till they became fainter and fainter in the distance, and all was lost in the azure of the horizon.' Farther up harbour, Earle went afoot into 'a wood so thick that the light of heaven could not penetrate the trees that composed it'.

He also witnessed the beginning of the end for so much of that forest. In the year of his visit there was a small shipyard at Horeke, where marine builders were exploiting the virtues of kauri. The shipyard did not last long; but the kauri continued to go. Soon there were rough timber towns to feed the needs of shipbuilders in Sydney and farther afield. One durable if dubious Hokianga tradition says that kauri spars were blooded as early as 1805, at the Battle of Trafalgar.

Later, small armies of diggers arrived to attack the inland wastes of the Hokianga, in pursuit of kauri gum. When that trade also diminished, so did the Hokianga's economic importance; the population thinned to a few farmers scattered across indifferent land, and to such tiny harbourside communities as Rawene and Kohukohu.

So in the end history seems to have been no more than a passing dream on the Hokianga. It is still the intricate tidal terrain carved by the taniwha. The retreat of man leaves spaces which only nature can efficiently fill. Poor farmland has been abandoned, ceded to the realm of the returning forest. Jetties crumble

to stumps on which oysters and mussels proliferate. Mullet swarm where once waterborne Maori tribesmen battled, or timber barques glided.

The mangrove forests, marine sanctuaries never violated by man, are still secretive and sibilant, with a sighing and rustling of water in which flounders and stingrays feed. The mangrove tree, which flourishes and reaches its greatest New Zealand height in the far north, displays its fascinating adaptations to its watery habitat. It breathes through vertical roots above the mud, propagates by

floating embryos and has developed a means of excreting salt from its leaves.

Let the last word be left with another early English visitor, the roguish if poetic adventurer Edward Markham. In 1834 he could as well have been writing of the Hokianga in the 1980s: 'There is something so beautiful in the rivers in this Country. A Stillness, fine sky over head! no Noise! now and then a Fish will leap or King fisher dart down and a beautiful little Bird . . . who flutters about a flower more like a Butter fly with all his feathers spread . . .'

►The rocky south head of Hokianga Harbour is in striking contrast to the sand dunes on the opposite head, from which a dangerous bar runs out. Small vessels can enter the harbour, however, and navigate about 24 km inland

Home of the huge and ancient kauris

◄The kauri is dominant in the Waipoua Forest, but many other species of trees also grow luxuriantly there

South of the Hokianga is a stand of tall forest which becomes more and more precious with the passage of time. It is one of the last mature samples of the 13 million hectares of kauri forest that once distinguished the entire length of the Northland peninsula. In prehistoric times the far north saw more than one generation of kauri forest. A combination of milling and land clearance for farming has reduced the great forest to mere remnants. The largest of these is Waipoua Forest.

The New Zealand Government plucked a large part of Waipoua Forest from the jaws of the kauri millers early in the 20th century, so that the timber might be harvested with some discrimination. Later, after public protest and petition in the 1940s, the Waipoua Forest became a sanctuary for the kauri tree which has become as beloved a symbol of New Zealand as the ubiquitous silver fern.

Any track through Waipoua Forest leads to awe. Groves of giant kauris suffer little competition. Around the kauris the undergrowth clears. A thick litter of bark and leaves crunches underfoot. Sunlight filters feebly through overhead verdure. Even the birdsong seems hushed; an ecclesiastical calm prevails under the soaring stone-coloured columns and arches of foliage.

The kauri is one of the dinosaurs of the vegetable world, second in size only to the giant sequoia of California. (As timber tree, in terms of usable volume, the kauri has been second to none.) Its age, which research seems to push farther and father back, can be

up to 2000 years, maybe more. Its height can be up to 55 m, its girth 16 m.

To encounter Te Matua Ngahere, ('father of the forest'), is like walking toward the pocked, silvery-grey face of a cliff—until one realises that this is living texture, not dead rock. As for Tane Mahuta, ('god of the forest'), one must retreat, marvelling, to comprehend its height. At 51 m, it is by no means the bulkiest kauri in the Waipoua Forest, merely one of the more accessible.

There is room for the belief that somewhere in this vicinity, hidden deep in difficult terrain and dense foliage, live fabled trees of still greater girth and height. No matter—the known trees are enough.

The kauri belongs to the Araucaria family, which also contains the Norfolk Island pine

and the monkey puzzle of the Andes. In its genus *Agathis* it has six less spectacular sisters in Malaysia, the Philippines, Australia and Fiji and other Pacific islands. Its leaves are thick and leathery and its timber is straight-grained, silky, honey-coloured and tough. The kauri exudes a resin which—bled from the living tree or dug from sites where aged trees had fallen—once had a commercial value rivalling that of the timber itself.

It is the physique of the full-grown kauri which lends the tree its greatest distinction. As the kauri climbs skyward and sunward, rising above the forest's olive-green canopy, its trunk does not taper off. If anything its girth can be greater at the point where the first limbs push out, and that point can be more than 20 m above the ground. A grove of kauris has no peer. California's largest sequoia may be twice as old and nearly twice as high as any known living kauri, but by comparison lacks majesty.

New Zealand's early history is embedded in the plunder of the kauri. In the mid-19th century, kauri timber was for a time New Zealand's largest export. Half the kauri forest was gone by 1885, and three-quarters by 1900. Now New Zealand has special policy designed to protect not only mature kauris but also regenerating stands. A small commercial release of the timber will ensure continuity for ship-building and minor special purposes. As timber, the kauri is more attractive and durable than most. As a vast living tree, its presence emphasises that people remember their role as guardians of the natural world.

▲The kauri, related to the monkey puzzle of the Andes, has distinctive scaly bark

►A quartet of tall kauris, the 'Four Sisters', stand in the Waipoua Forest

▶Tane Mahuta, the 'god of the forest', has a girth of 14 m. It is 51 m high and the first branch is 12 m up from the great platform of debris which the tree has built up over the centuries. The tree is believed to be about 1200 years old

Island refuge for rare and tropical species

► *High vertical cliffs distinguish the Poor Knights Islands even across 25 km of water from the mainland*

◄ *This twin-boled kauri tree is one of several big kauris to be seen in the Ngaiotonga*

Scenic Reserve, in forested hills between the Bay of Islands and Whangaruru Harbour

Northland's west coast is either sandy and symmetrical, or muddy and untidy; its geologic origin has been disguised by the action of wind and tide. The origin of the fretted east coast is always conspicuous—volcanic flow has here and there left rocky inlets, peninsulas and islands contesting the sea's supremacy. Evocative sandstone heights, seemingly sculpted for legend, also give character. Peaceful coves washed by transparent tides alternate with long white surf beaches.

And those offshore islands are more than simply attractive decor in the shimmering light of dawn; they are also often sanctuaries for forms of life from an older, wilder New Zealand. Undersea reefs and caves flutter with vividly coloured fish riding a warm current down from the tropics. Big-game fish like marlin and mako also abound. This is Northland at its Pacific best.

Captain James Cook, in dogged pursuit of a great southern continent—and still trying to decide whether New Zealand filled that fabled bill—nevertheless found time to leave a witty name or two here as he voyaged past in early 1770. The Hen and Chicken Islands, for example. And the Poor Knights— apparently named for a European dish, which is now better known as French toast, of fried egg-soaked bread.

Two centuries later marine life remains luxuriant here and nowhere more so than about the Poor Knights—remnants of once vast lava domes corroded and perforated by the sea. Around this flotilla of steep-sided islands swirls a sub-tropical current 1.5–2.5 °C warmer than adjoining coastal waters. That degree or two of temperature, along with lucid water and desirable plankton—and an abundance of sheltering reef—allows tropical fish to prosper. There is a theory that these islands function as a gateway through which the marine animal life of New Zealand can constantly be enriched by once distant and colourful species.

The rock faces of the Poor Knights are intricately penetrated by sea, making a congenial environment of arches, caves and tun-

▼*Many spectacular sea creatures live on the underwater cliffs of the Poor Knights Islands, like these feather stars*

▼*The scarlet urchin is another of the Poor Knight's invertebrates*

nels. One tunnel travels 400 m inland. Others have vast trapped air bubbles in which exploring divers can shed masks, breathe and conduct conversation. There is sometimes up to 60 m depth of water. Within the caves are rich meadows of multi-hued sponges—ranging from red and pink to mauve and purple, yellow and orange to green and blue.

In such settings fish gush past in spectacular shoals—blue maomao, golden snapper, kingfish, bronze whaler sharks, flights of gliding stingrays, tropical gropers, black-yellow butterfly fish, iridescent pigfish, blue drummers and yellow-banded parrotfish. Scorpionfish and moray eels move across the ocean floor. New immigrants to New Zealand waters—such as rainbowfish, lizardfish, cleanerfish and combfish—can also be glimpsed. Hardly a year seems to pass without a fresh arrival identified. The planktonic larvae of many varieties of sub-tropical fish and invertebrates have drifted here on the warm current and colonised the waters, where galaxies of fish now graze.

The Poor Knights, in prehistoric time, formed a natural fortress for Maori tribesmen. Cook noted that 'the land hereabouts is rather low and pretty well cover'd with wood and seems not ill inhabited'. Maori occupation ended in the 1820s, with the arrival of the musket in New Zealand.

Since then, the Poor Knights have remained a fortress for species rare, extinct or embattled on the mainland of New Zealand. They are the home of the spectacular red-flowered Poor Knights lily, or *raupo-taranga*, a

relic of a prehistoric tropical flora which otherwise grows wild only on Hen Island—Taranga—of the Hen and Chickens group, offshore from the entrance to Whangarei Harbour. Its only sister species grows in the mountains of New Caledonia. The Poor Knights lily grows profusely on exposed flat rocks, forming compact clumps, sometimes several metres across, and copiously building up its own humus. The flowers are made up of nectar-filled florets crowded on a horizontal stalk almost in the manner of a bottle-brush. Other threatened species on the Poor Knights are whau, parapara, tawapou and broad-leaved maire.

The islands are the home of eight species of

petrels, notably the handsome and strikingly patterned Buller's shearwater, considered a rare bird elsewhere, but so prolific on the Poor Knights that its excavations make the earth hazardous for walkers. It is among the most common of birds on the Poor Knights. In the thickly regenerating forest cover, bell-birds chime, parakeets and crakes flitter. Five species of skinks and two of geckos make a lively reptilian diet for swooping kingfishers. Little blue penguins nest on the shore.

But the star of creation's grand parade on the Poor Knights, as on other New Zealand offshore islands, is the shy and durable tuatara. It has survived the dinosaurs; it has seen it all in 60 million years.

◄*Erosion has produced curious crenellated forms in outcrops at the Waro Limestone Reserve, near Hikurangi. Many of the rocks are much higher than these*

Hauraki Gulf

A multitude of diverse and fascinating islands, hazy panoramas and clear, sparkling waters are among the ingredients from which is distilled the amiable charm of the sheltered Hauraki Gulf

The Hauraki Gulf holds more than 100 islands and islets with names. Seen from sea level they sometimes float on a silver haze, but more often they merge into one another as a green and dun horizon across the sparkling waters off the suburbs of Auckland. Approach that horizon and further horizons of islands appear.

The real gulf lies inside the protecting wall of the Coromandel Peninsula but the islands spill from it, out into the teeth of ocean winds. The Hauraki Gulf Maritime Park gathers in the outlying islands as well—the Poor Knights, the Hen and Chickens, and even the Mercury Islands in the Bay of Plenty. There are dramatic contrasts between

▼ *The Hauraki Gulf Maritime Park includes most islands in the gulf, plus several distant outliers*

the islands, even those within the gulf itself.

Geologically this is a drowned countryside, where the tops of volcanic hills and older landscapes stand proud as islands. The Firth of Thames and the Hauraki Plains together occupy a sunken block of crust, bounded by roughly parallel major faults, which are about 220 km long. In the south it can be traced nearly as far as Tirau. Since the trough began to subside it has fallen by perhaps as much as 2 km, but sediment has kept it well filled. This has come not only from erosion of neighbouring highlands but from the pumice lands of the Taupo-Rotorua volcanic region, carried by the Waikato River, which in past ages has emptied into the Hauraki depression by way of the Hinuera Gorge.

The sea floor tilts to the Coromandel side, where the ranges are lifting above the eastern fault. The rivers of the Hauraki Plains once ran along the foot of these ranges to the sea, to be joined by other rivers like the Tamaki, Waitemata and Mahurangi. But the gulf now covers their meeting places. The sea rose at least 100 m with the melting of the ice and the plains and rivers were drowned in the gulf, while several harbours invaded the mainland. One count measures the length of this coastline at 800 km, with another 450 km of island shores.

Much of the Hauraki Gulf is difficult to reach. Launches serve only the inner islands and charter planes to the outer islands are expensive. Permits to land are required on some islands because they are the last refuge of birds, other animals and plants which have vanished from the mainland or are unknown there. Little Barrier Island, for example, has been the only home for the stitchbird for 100 years. Its forest floor, long unaffected by introduced animals, is one of the few places where bush regenerates naturally. Native bats and a giant weta survive there, and rare petrels breed on the island's mist-shrouded peaks.

The Hen and Chickens group, also an absolute sanctuary, was once the last home of the North Island saddleback, or *tieke*. Today it has been successfully introduced to other islands, such as Cuvier, northeast of the Coromandel Peninsula, and on Fanal in the Mokohinau Islands, north of the Barriers.

Closer inshore, rock stacks and islands are also homes for thousands of birds safe from predators and people. Whereas most oceans have only one or two species of petrels, or shearwaters, this comparatively tiny stretch of water has breeding colonies of 12.

Even the islands closest to the mainland have peculiarities. Rangitoto, a gently-sloping cone of basaltic lava, has more than 200 native ferns and flowering plants which appear to survive without soil. Kawau Island boasts Australian wallabies, kookaburras and introduced plants, relics of the pioneer era, when Governor Sir George Grey, established his own exotic paradise there.

At the western extremity of the Hauraki Gulf, the Pacific ends on the white-sand sweep of Pakiri and the cliffs of Cape Rodney. Offshore, Little Barrier Island is close

enough for its great cliffs to be distinguished, while 30 km farther away, stand the peaks of Great Barrier Island, a large island of poor farms and reverting bushland. To the southeast, on the other side of the gulf, the hump of Mt Moehau and the dorsal ridge of the Coromandel Range can be seen.

A string of little islands, some farmed and private, runs southwards from Cape Rodney. They have remnant patches of coastal scrub and forest, similar to the adjacent mainland, where cliff-binding pohutukawa, stolid puriri, bushy coprosmas and gangly kanuka —all trees and shrubs with hard leaves and strong bodies—withstand the salted lashing of tropical cyclones which die in the gulf.

Tiritiri Matangi Island, formerly farmed, is reverting to natural cover and harbours large numbers of the seed-eating Polynesian rat *kiore*, and the spotless crake, a bird which usually skulks in swamps but thrives here in a dense tangle of rank grasses. Another farm park is Motutapu Island, hitched by an isthmus to Rangitoto. Across a breezy channel is Motuihe, which can be reached by an occasional ferry. Nearby Browns Island is a volcanic cone, where the earthworks of a Maori pa are visible. Farther out to sea lie The Noises, a cluster of rocks and islets, and the David Rocks, where there are petrel colonies.

Eastward, the islands of Waiheke and Ponui, have many farms. Waiheke has a number of settlements and a carefree atmosphere. Only scenic reserves show what it was

▲*Auckland's island, Rangitoto, rises from the gulf beyond the entrance to Waitemata* *Harbour. It is a young volcanic cone which may have been active only 300 years ago*

like in the past. Beyond the resort island of Pakatoa, off towards the Coromandel Peninsula, are rocks where gannets and spotted shags breed, but these can be approached only by private boat.

The heel of the gulf is the shallow Firth of Thames. At low tide it presents a vast sea of mud covered with thousands of wading birds, feeding on crabs, worms and molluscs. More than 12 migratory species come here each spring. Miranda, where the shellbanks come closest to shore, is the best place to watch as high tide drives the birds in.

A barren volcano repossessed by plants

►*Rangitoto Island is joined by a narrow causeway to Motutapu Island. Beyond are Rakino Island and a group of islets called The Noises*

Near the mouth of Auckland's Waitemata Harbour lies a volcano which archaeological research has suggested was possibly active as recently as 300 years ago. The Maoris called it Rangitoto, 'bloody skies'.

Nearly every Aucklander sees Rangitoto every day, but few visit it, even though it is only a half-hour ferry ride away. It looks much the same from any angle—not very tall (only 259 m), sloping very gradually out of the sea, and dusky khaki in colour, its details smudged by the blue haze that hangs over the islands of the Hauraki Gulf. From the distance it seems to be bush-covered, but from the Rangitoto wharf it is immediately clear that the island is a vast rockery where plants grow out of scoria boulders apparently without the benefit of soil. A century-old painting shows vastly more rock than now.

From the wharf a track rises to the summit and another track winds round the coast to Islington Bay, where Rangitoto Island joins Motutapu Island. It passes sharp-edged lava flows near the sea, where thousands of black-backed gulls breed in October and November. At sunset vast flocks return from feeding on the city rubbish dumps to roost among the rocks. A road which loops around the south-ern part of the island runs across to Motutapu.

There is almost no soil on Rangitoto, and there are no surface streams. The temperature of the face of the lava rock can climb to more than 70°C on a hot day. In these conditions plants do not conform to norms. The roots of trees must penetrate crevices and openings in the lava rock in their search for moisture. Between the rocks, scoria and fallen leaves provide a kind of humus in which mosses and ferns flourish.

Plants have adapted to the inhospitable stones of Rangitoto and they grow in unusual profusion of species. The cover includes more than 200 species of native plants and as many introduced species brought in by wind, birds and visitors.

Delicate ferns grow from the ledges of the rocks. Lichens and algae cover the rock surfaces. Even orchids appear in the shade of some trees. Epiphytic lilies and daisies also grow from crevices in the rocks, because they cannot find huge trees upon which to perch.

At the height of summer Rangitoto is man-tled in the red blooms of pohutukawa trees. Even these are unusual, as many are hybrids, crossed with the northern rata, which favours the rainforest. The hard shiny leaves of the resulting plant deflect some of the heat of the summer. In the late winter and spring, algae 'bloom' pale blue on the dull purple of the scoria fields.

Lichens and mosses are the first plants in a succession that ultimately leads to pohu-tukawa and native honeysuckle trees estab-lishing themselves in favourable places. Once established, patches of bush expand, growing outwards into their own shade. The bush reclaims the lava beds very slowly. It is expected to take centuries in some raw cor-ners of the island.

Regeneration is not helped by animals—wallabies, possums and fallow deer—which crop the fan-tips of the astelia plant and chew the young shoots from the pohutukawa. Some gaunt tree skeletons bear witness to these depredations. Man has also modified the environment, but the Hauraki Gulf Maritime Park Board is acting to bring about restoration. Pine trees, self-sown from wind-blown seeds from the mainland have been eliminated. Animals are being trapped. There is no longer a right to sell properties, and permits for repairs to baches are refused. As a result, miniature manuka and kanuka, pin-leaved mingimingi and koromiko, rise through cracks in the ground where cottages and tennis courts once stood.

Near the top of the island there is still a gentle grove of evergreen oaks. There is soil

◄*The rocky shore of Rangitoto can be followed partly by tracks and partly by a road built by prisoners between 1925 and 1936*

▼*Browns Island, south of Rangitoto, is an extinct volcano. It was the site of one of the earliest farms in the Auckland district*

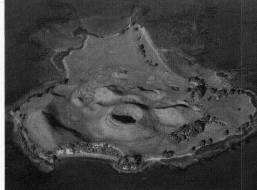

◄The harsh volcanic rock of Rangitoto is a difficult environment for plants but trees are gradually colonising the island

▲Plant debris in lava crevices on Rangitoto Island provide humus in which plants flourish

▼Kidney ferns growing on Rangitoto Island

here now, on the oldest of the scoria summit cones. Then the final steep slope of the most recent cone is reached. On top of this slope stands a concrete forward-command post, the operational eyes of mainland gun emplacements in the days before radar. Glass windows have replaced the observation slits, to provide a sheltered view of the scrub-filled hole of the latest crater.

South, across the channel from Rangitoto, is the tip of another volcano, renamed Browns Island from the more sonorous Maori *Motukorea*. In the ice ages it stretched across the dry land into the mouth of the Tamaki River. It was an extensive volcano, but now the sea is more than 30 m above the old Tamaki and the lava flows are drowned. Only a cluster of craters stand above the sea. They are grassed now and marked by the walls and trenches of former Maori settlement. There is no ferry to the island.

Kawau Island, which has a ferry service, gains most of its interest from its introduced species. The island lies in what was once the mouth of the Matakana River. It is bordered by low orange cliffs with rocky platforms where rock oysters and crayfish live.

An early Governor of New Zealand, Sir George Grey, bought Kawau from copper miners in 1862. He wanted it to display animals from the places he had visited in his colonial service. The zebras that were to pull his carriage died, but he was more fortunate with his wallabies and kookaburras. The wallabies flourished, and the kookaburra, an Australian kingfisher, soon spread to nearby parts of the mainland as well.

By the 1960s eradication of the wallabies began, and Kawau was found to have some of the last survivors of the rare parma wallaby. Four other kinds are on the island and are protected in the area around Mansion

House Bay. The most common of these is the dama or tammar wallaby, about 500 mm high, silver-grey in colour, and with a short rat-like tail. The brush-tailed rock wallaby jumps about the cliff-tops and the black-tailed swamp wallaby—locally miscalled 'wallaroo'—can still be seen. The black-striped wallaby, however, may now be extinct on Kawau.

Wallabies, possums and fire have ravaged Kawau's natural bush. Dead giants, puriri and pohutukawa, rim the seaward cliffs. Manuka has overrun much of the farmland, yet the island retains its charm, and tracks full of interest lead from the Mansion House to other parts of the island.

Little Barrier, where rare birds find safety

◀Little Barrier Island lies at the mouth of Hauraki Gulf, 90 km from Auckland. Great Barrier Island is 18 km to the east

Standing high at the mouth of the gulf, Little Barrier Island is known in Maori as *Hauturu*, the resting-post of the winds. Its andesite cliffs rise sheer for more than 400 m to form a hog-backed island. Dangerous ravines, choked with bush, lie between the island's steep ridges, and only two permanent tracks exist. Both tracks start on the only flat land, a boulder beach, and finally reach the 722 m high summit.

Little Barrier, 2817 hectares in area, is a nature sanctuary. Rare and endangered birds find safety there, and the stitchbird, or

▼*Little Barrier Island does not welcome casual visitors. Cliffs surround stony shores and the island is a wildlife reserve which may be visited only with the permission of the Hauraki Gulf Maritime Park Board*

hihi, has made this its home for nearly 100 years. The forest remains intact, unharmed by the depredations of deer, goats or possums, and the forest floor is carpeted with the seedlings of great trees. The undergrowth is prolific and dense, often impassable.

But it is not virgin bush. About a third of the forest was cleared or burnt by its Maori owners in the 1880s in a race to fell as much kauri as possible and frustrate government intentions to declare a reserve. The Government made several attempts to prevent the despoliation but was unsuccessful until 1895, when it purchased the island from the Maoris. It declared the island a sanctuary for the unique animals it harboured in 1897.

Little Barrier Island is now managed by the Hauraki Gulf Maritime Park Board and

access is limited to those with a demonstrable interest in wildlife and tramping. Apart from its extensive bird life, the island numbers at least ten species of native worms among its biological interests. One of these, a giant earthworm which lives in the subsoil, often reaches 1300–1400 mm in length and is sometimes 11 mm thick. An investigator trying to measure a tunnel made by one of these worms gave up digging at 3.5 m.

The island also boasts at least 42 kinds of tiny (2–3 mm) bush snails, and the spectacular giant weta. This grasshopper with long armoured legs and twitching feelers is, at 225 mm, New Zealand's largest insect.

Because there are few tracks, much of the exploration of Little Barrier Island must be done by boat. There are few landing places,

◄The forest covering of Little Barrier Island grows thickly from the shores of the island to its summit

▼Te Titoki Point, the island's only flat land, is formed of stones deposited by opposing ocean currents

and even making a landing can be difficult, as it demands a leap from a dinghy onto slippery stones, with the swell lifting the stern of the boat against the shore. Rough weather isolates the island. Visitors are rowed ashore from launch or seaplane to a curious triangle of land which the meeting of two ocean currents has built out from the side of the island. The banks enclose 26 hectares of stony flat, where the resident ranger lives, with a visitors' bunkhouse hidden in the orchard.

An ancient forest of pohutukawas grows from the massive boulders of Te Titoki Point. The branches meet in gothic arches above a boulder field where the skeletons of long-dead Maoris lie. Further along, the low stone walls still shelter wild Maori vegetables.

About the homestead and bunkhouse rare and unusual birds appear. Some of them are no longer seen on the nearby mainland even though it is only 25 km away. The red-crowned parakeet, or *kakariki*, cackles in the treetops. Sparrow-sized whiteheads, rarely seen in mainland forests, are common here. The bellbird—with a song not unlike the plentiful tui—sings in anticipation of the dawn, and laconically on through the day; and it is a bird which the northern reaches of the North Island see no more.

At dusk, the high-pitched shrieks of the petrels may be heard as they fly into the shrouded peaks at Hauturu, to their nesting-burrows in the moss. At night, the brown kiwi, introduced to the island, hunts about the home paddock near the ranger's cow.

Despite its modest height, Little Barrier Island presents a succession of vegetation similar to that on higher mainland mountains, though falling short of alpine flowers. On the coast are pohutukawa and giant kanuka, often bare-stemmed and whipped by the wind. The ascending bands of forest are narrower than in the mainland mountains, so that the track to the top offers a rapid succession. About 150 m—which is often cliff-top height on the steep-sided island—the kauri trees begin. Manuka covers many flat-topped ridges where the kauri was cleared last century. Gradually, about 300 m, beech trees intrude, along with the red-flowering northern rata. The ridge trees stand above deep ravines of rata and tawa. These forest ridges, with their abundant food, are alive with birds.

The kaka, a large, rust-brown bush parrot, calls with its harsh voice, as it slashes with its curved bill at decaying trees for grubs and insects. Flocks of red-crowned and yellow-crowned *kakariki* swoop high over the gullies. In summer, the soft slurring call of the shining cuckoo blends with the songs of little bush birds which may become unwitting foster-parents to its young. Robins and tomtits flick along the track, while tiny green riflemen flit up the trunks of trees.

The remarkable feature of Little Barrier's bird life is its profusion. Stoats and weasels are unknown there, although feral cats present a menace. The only other mammals are *kiore*, the Polynesian rat—basically a seed-eater—and the short-tailed native bat.

Rangers and volunteers have been trying to eradicate the cats since the beginning of the century, and only now does the end appear in sight. The damage done by cats only becomes obvious at altitudes between 450 m and 600 m, where the track passes from rata to tawa and tawhero forest, hung with mosses and ferns. Even on the track itself the remains of Cook's petrel, or *titi*, provide grim evidence of the threat to thousands of birds who make Little Barrier Island their home in the breeding season.

Petrels are especially menaced, as they dig breeding burrows among the tree roots, from an altitude of 300 m right up to the summit of the island. They were in danger of extinction until the predator cats were removed from the island. This bird nests below the

summit, where the track actually clambers along the trunks of huge southern rata trees, so overgrown with mosses, lichens, ferns and parasites that the ground lying several metres below is not visible.

Finally the track emerges into montane scrub, and a view that takes in the whole of the gulf, with the industrial haze of metropolitan Auckland beyond. The physical distance from the city is as little as 80 km, but in biological time the distance is far greater. Comparatively undisturbed, Little Barrier Island remains a living museum.

◄A huge rockfall lies at the foot of 430 m high cliffs at Hingaia Point. The enormous blocks of stone are now largely covered by a pohutukawa forest

Recovery from exploitation on Great Barrier Island

Sometimes when the weather changes for the worse in the Hauraki Gulf and the haze dissolves into a leaden sea, watchers in Auckland can see four islands on the northeast horizon. In reality these are not islands but the mountain peaks of Great Barrier Island, about 100 km from Auckland. Geologically Great Barrier Island is a continuation of the Coromandel Peninsula, but the waters of the Colville Channel, a 20 km wide strait between peninsula and island, now cover what was once the northern part of Coromandel.

Erosion of mainly volcanic rock has shaped Great Barrier Island and mining here and there helped to reshape the details. The terrain matches the Coromandel mainland, rising abruptly and high on the western shore, with great cliffs and rugged ridges, falling to easier country, and the drowned bays and islands in the east. Great Barrier's main peak, Hirakimata, or Mt Hobson, is 621 m high. The island, the biggest off the North Island, has an area of 285 km². The climate is mild and agreeable, with most of the rain falling in the winter season.

The island has a small permanent population—approximately 800—which is swelled in summer by Aucklanders who arrive by light aircraft, big launches or yachts. Boats shelter in pohutukawa-fringed bays which pierce the western cliffs. These western harbours—Katherine Bay, Port Fitzroy, Whangaparapara, Okupu and Tryphena—are connected by roads but their condition makes the sea the inevitable highway for Great Barrier. Only 85 km of road are either formed or metalled. The remaining 100 km are unformed. Visitors to the island need to be ready to walk.

On Great Barrier Island most of the land is administered by the Department of Conservation, which was established in 1987. It was preceded by the New Zealand Forest Service, which in 1942 took over 4452 hectares of cut-over kauri land. As the soil has proved unsuited to exotic pines, the Greater Barrier Forest has been dedicated to re-establishing the kauri forest.

The rape of Great Barrier Island is thought to have begun in 1794 when the first kauri spars were taken from the shores of Port Fitzroy. But not only timber attracted the European newcomers; miners dug at Whitecliffs in a search for silver and gold. A copper lode which vanished into the sea towards Coromandel was mined, but it petered out and mining was abandoned early this century. Kauri-gum diggers had their turn as they probed the centre of the island. Settlers burnt down the forest to clear the land for now-defunct farms.

But worse was to come. In 1925, The Kauri Timber Company set out to mill commercially every kauri tree 30 cm or more thick—mere saplings by kauri standards. Only 40 hectares of kauri were left untouched, around the rugged peak of Mount Hirakimata.

Thirty years passed before the Forest Service began the work of restoration, and nature assisted this. After the burning of the forest, manuka and kanuka brush appeared, and amongst it young kauri, rimu and totara.

►Port Fitzroy, one of the settlements on Great Barrier Island, shelters within this maze of peninsulas, islands and islets

It took 15 years of ringbarking and scrub-cutting to eliminate this nursery cover and let the future giants see the light. Now 2000 hectares of young kauri, mixed with rimu, totara and tanekaha, are rising—a forest for the centuries to come.

Apart from an island in Port Fitzroy which has fallow deer, Great Barrier is free of deer, possums, stoats, weasels and ferrets. The rich bird life is evidence of this. The upper ridges of Mount Hirakimata remain one of the last homes of the black petrel, which flies in by night to nest in burrows.

Below, in the Kaitoke Swamp, a nocturnal duck, the brown teal, survives, safer there than in many other places where it is a threatened species. On Great Barrier considerable numbers of brown teal skulk in the shelter of swamps or shaded creeks during the day and come out to feed on the open ground at night.

The trusting robin, pied tit and whitehead may have gone—there are feral cats at large—but the big grey kokako with its blue wattles still persists in the northern forests. And the forests are home to most common species, as well as the kaka parrot, and the kakariki parakeet, slim and green among the leaves.

Among the sea birds of Great Barrier Island there are several petrels and shearwaters, breeding about the western cliffs and isles with the little blue penguin. On Mahuki, a rocky islet off the same coast, hundreds of gannets nest.

The ocean beaches on the east coast are backed by two estuaries where dotterels, rails, and migratory godwits and oystercatchers abound. Farther back in the swamp, shy and well-camouflaged, are bitterns.

Reminders of the island's history remain. Whangaparapara was the site of the last shore whaling station in New Zealand. It started in the late 1850s but only lasted until the next decade. Close to the migration route of whales, Great Barrier Island could count blue, fin, sei, and killer whales as regular visitors. The mighty humpback was another of the whalers' targets, often passing only 15 km offshore on its way to the Pacific breeding-grounds. They killed more than 100 humpback whales off Great Barrier Island one year.

The abandoned whaling station, like the flooded mineshafts, the rotting kauri-dams and the scrub-covered farms, symbolise an island attacked and exploited, and then left.

◄The sandy crescents of Oruawharo Bay, in the foreground, and Kaitoke Beach are on the eastern side of Great Barrier Island

▼The peaks of the island carry most of the forest. Much was spoilt but regeneration has brought the area to more than 7670 hectares

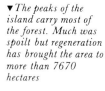

Auckland's West Coast

To the west of New Zealand's largest city the Tasman surf pounds rocky headlands of the Waitakere Ranges, which interrupts a long sequence of dunes and broad, placid harbours

Auckland city sits at the narrowest point of New Zealand, where the arms of the Hauraki Gulf in the east almost meet those of the Manukau Harbour in the west. Out beyond the Manukau Heads the Tasman Sea crashes into the steep shore of Auckland's wild west coast. The contrast with the gentle beaches of the Hauraki Gulf is so great that the Maoris used to refer to the west as masculine and the east as feminine.

The Auckland isthmus had its origins 26 million years ago, when a chain of offshore volcanos, long since eroded away, extruded lava under the sea. Mountain-building shocks lifted these lava flows and volcanic rubble and sand to create the Waitakere Ranges. Uplift of the neighbouring Hunua Range, the Port Waikato Hills and the more distant Coromandel Peninsula was part of the same process. This assemblage of uplifted crustal blocks now forms the boundaries of the Auckland region. Other blocks pushed downwards, like the Firth of Thames and the Hauraki Plains in the east, and Manukau Harbour in the west, complete the picture.

During the ice ages when much of the world's water was locked up as ice, the sea level fell to at least 100 m lower than at present. Rivers and streams carved their courses into the exposed land, but when the ice melted and the sea rose again, about 10 000 years ago, these valleys were flooded. The Hauraki Gulf and the Kaipara and Manukau Harbours were both ultimately formed in this way.

Within the last 100 000 years Auckland has gained some 60 volcanos, forced up by shifting pressures 50 km under the surface. As well as the cones which pimple the city, there are flooded craters, forming lakes and basins like Orakei and Pupuke, and giant reefs of lava. Hot springs on the isthmus are a constant reminder that volcanic action may yet reshape the region.

In comparatively recent times the volcanos of the central North Island have played a major role in forming the land south of Auckland. Eruptions have affected the course of the mighty Waikato River at various times, forcing it to deviate on its northern journey to the sea, through country razed by the accompanying storm of pumice thrown out by the volcanos. Sometimes the Waikato has reached the ocean at the Firth of Thames; at other times it has debouched into the Manukau and flowed out past the blockade of the Waitakeres. Recent volcanic action in the Pukekohe-Bombay area has been viewed by some geologists as responsible for the river's present course.

The region north of the Manukau can only be entered by a series of tortuous, shingle roads which wind through the ranges.

The recesses and coastal slopes of the Waitakere Ranges remain wild places. As much as 130 km² of steep ridges and stone gullies are covered with bush. In the bush reserves some kauri trees grow. Some, too hard to bring out of the gullies, were left by the early millers, but others are part of the regenerating bush. Large rimus, kahikateas and totaras also rise here while the occasional northern rata towers above the tawas of the valleys, fighting for pre-eminence in the forest canopy. The Waitakeres shelter a variety of bush birds and the weka and the brown kiwi have both been released in the ranges recently. Waterbirds flourish in lagoons and coastal ponds.

North and south of the Waitakeres, sand dunes rise to heights of 100 m or more. These were formed more recently, thrown up by the surge of the sea and the assault of great winds. These sandhills often crept over the countryside, smothering the land, before pine forests were established to bind them. The 50 km reach from Muriwai Beach to the South Head of Kaipara Harbour is all sand dune country, and the coastal hills running south from Manukau Harbour are quite similar to these dunes.

Black sand dominates the beaches along the western coast and the main component of the dunes is titanium-rich ironsand. It is a vast resource, running more than 150 km northwards from Taranaki. In some places the beds are several hundred metres thick, and they are often more than half iron. The original source of the ironsand was largely Mt Egmont, but other coastal volcanos have contributed. In summer these ironsand beaches are hot and uncomfortable to walk on. The mountain-backed Waikato coast is largely inaccessible and almost devoid of resorts, except the Raglan, Aotea and Kawhia Harbours, where large flocks of wading birds feed on wide mudflats, and the channels run with fish.

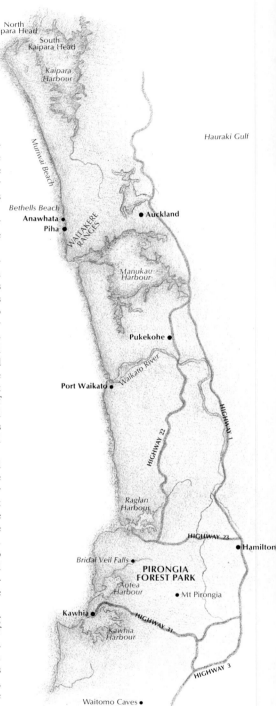

▲*Few roads provide access to the Auckland west coast and few of these are sealed highways. But inland there is much to see that can be more readily reached*

▶*At the Bridal Veil Falls, near Raglan, the Pakoka River drops in gauzy sheets past a 50 m high cliff of columnar basalt*

Rugged cliffs, wild seas and a precious wetland

▶ *The famous surf of Piha Beach rolls in between Lion Rock and Te Whawha Point farther on*

The Waitakere Ranges present a face of patchy bush to the invading houses of the Auckland suburbs. Outside the safety of Manukau Harbour, the great breakers of the Tasman Sea pound the Waitakere shore and fill the air with salty mist. Here the Waitakeres are all bush gully and cliff buttress. The sea's assault upon the ancient rocks has drilled caves and blowholes and in places piled black sand into a rock-girt beach cushioned by dunes.

The wildest and remotest point on the Auckland west coast north of the Manukau is perhaps Whatipu, where the picturesque wooded shore of the harbour gives way to the

▼*Lion Rock, a former headland, has resisted the erosion of wind* *and ocean and now rears up in the middle of Piha Beach*

severe coast of the open sea. Out to sea lies the Manukau sandbar, treacherous and shifting, upon which many ships have foundered. Huge deposits of ironsand front the cliffs, where the waves sometimes uncover a rusty tangle of sleepers and spikes, relics of a bush railway. It is more than 60 years since timber ships sheltered in this tiny cove to carry away kauri. Windswept coastal scrub now tops the cliffs, and the original bush has been further depleted by gum-digging and fire.

This is an area with few roads, all distant from one another. A visit to more than one west coast beach may mean time-consuming backtracking over the ranges. There is a network of walking tracks, but conditions are often tough, especially in the wet months. There are gentler introductions to the bush,

especially along the Scenic Drive. In the rougher areas, maps and experience of similar country are vital; the search-and-rescue teams are often called out in these parts.

The road runs to the coast again at Karekare, where cliffs drop more than 200 m to the sea. Karekare itself is a narrow black sand beach, approached through a gully choked with pohutukawas. In sheltered places behind the cliffs groves of nikau palms and kowhais grow, near little swamps where the air is warm and windless, yet still within the sound of the sea.

The road to Karekare is a branch of the road to Piha, 5 km on. Piha is famous for its surfing and fishing, but this is a treacherous coast which has claimed many lives fishermen swept off the rock platforms by

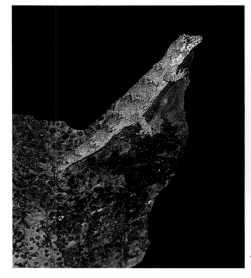

◄The forest gecko is one of several species living in the Waitakere forests. The other two species here are green geckos. These soft-skinned, granular-scaled lizards have great climbing ability and feed on insects on trees

unexpected monster waves, and swimmers carried away in the angry sea. Piha is also well-known for its remarkable landmark, the Lion Rock, which the active enjoy climbing. The Piha road leads on to other beaches. At Anawhata the cliffs call a halt and private land bars access to the shore.

Farther north is Bethell's Beach, or Te Henga, where the black ironsands reach inland for more than a kilometre. Modelled by the westerlies, they run right up against the bush and form a basin for Lake Wainamu. Many stones and pebbles worn smooth by the action of wind and sand lie on the surface and are often mistaken for Maori cutting-stones. This is understandable as conspicuous fortifications remain along this coast, the remains of strong Maori pas built close to

ready stocks of fresh fish, shellfish and birds.

At Te Henga, conservationists have managed to reserve the Lake Wainamu area and have bought part of the Bethell's Swamp, the last wetland in the Auckland region. The deep swamp here has such secretive species as the bittern, the banded rail, the spotless crake and the fernbird amongst its inhabitants. On the outer ramparts of the nearby coast one of the few northern colonies of spotted shags is found; and banded dotterels and New Zealand dotterels can be seen scuttling across the high black dunes.

The conjunction of rugged cliffs and wild seas ends gloriously at Muriwai Beach. Various features typical of undersea eruption are displayed in the cliffs at Muriwai. In Maori Bay deposits of pillow lava create what look

like curious carvings on the cliff-face. The truncated ends of the old lava flows create circles of rock, not unlike huge stone hibiscus flowers. Quarrying here was halted by conservationists but not before the coast had been badly scarred.

North of Muriwai Beach the surf is just as strong but it builds rather than attacks and for 50 km to South Kaipara Head the sands have been piled into dunes as big as hills. Pines bind the shifting dunes, which form a retaining wall for the southern part of the vast Kaipara Harbour, but the balance is fragile. The sand is white here because the coastal drift is no longer from terrain that is predominantly volcanic.

Hidden away in the dunes are a series of little lakes where the bittern, the spotless crake, the banded rail and the dabchick are found. Their survival is sometimes threatened by moving sand and changes in the water table. The dabchick, in particular, needs secluded water upon which to feed and breed.

The northerly part of Auckland's west coast ends at South Kaipara Head, near an air force bombing range. Beyond the high white sandhills lies the dangerous bar to New Zealand's largest harbour. There the tide flushes through a 6 km gap to rise up creeks almost on the other coast of the North Island, and makes their water brackish even into the hills of Northland. North Kaipara Head stretches away into the clouds of spray.

◄The dangerous Piha coast has claimed many lives—fishermen swept off rocks, swimmers carried away

▲High cliffs surround White Beach, a small cove between Te Whawha Point and Anawhata

Black sands and pale limestone formations

◄*The Bridal Veil Falls are the centrepiece of a beautiful scenic reserve between Raglan and Kawhia. The falls can be viewed from the top or the bottom, as a track leads through the bush to the base*

Much of the charm of the lonely expanses of the Manukau Harbour seems to go by default. In Auckland most people look east to the islands and sparkling waters of the Hauraki Gulf. Yet the broad mudflats of the Manukau, so little disturbed today, provide a special environment which the Maoris recognised when they aptly named the harbour—as *manukau* means 'wading birds'. These mudflats attract thousands of migratory birds from Siberia, Alaska, and the estuaries

and rivers of the South Island. The southern shore of Manukau Harbour is composed of soft green fields, all neatly farmed but penetrated by mangrove-fringed tidal creeks. The mangrove is near the southern end of its range here and its gnarled roots support a much smaller plant than in Northland. In the far northern harbours the mangrove grows to 3–4 m high, but here it has diminished to 1–2 m. Farther south, at Kawhia, the same tree which chokes rivers in the tropics

has become a miniature shrub, still hard-leaved and tangled, but only a few centimetres high among the rushes.

The coast which separates Manukau Harbour from the Tasman is, like the Kaipara coast, made up of huge sandhills. These rise to more than 100 m, and there was a time when they moved inland at 20 m or more a year, swallowing up farmland in their path; but pine forest now binds the sand together.

Low hills on the southern Manukau shore turn the Waikato River from its northward course. The river, the longest in New Zealand, runs slowly near the end of its 425 km journey. It falls only 41 m after its junction with the Waipa, 90 km upstream at Ngaruawahia. The tidal stretch is over a kilometre wide and birds mass there to feed—shags, pied stilts, white-faced herons, grey duck, mallards, and black swans—all denizens of the local peat swamps and shallow lakes which lie near the sluggish river.

The west coast can be reached by road in and around the Raglan, Aotea and Kawhia Harbours, where the forbidding march of cliffs and black sand is interrupted by shallow, wandering arms of the sea, which find shelter among quiet hills.

The languid western harbours contrast with the ridges of greywacke sandstone and shale and dominating volcanic peaks which divide them from Hamilton and the market

▲*Rocks near Kawhia*

◄*The Marokopa Falls, near Te Anga in Waitomo district, are among the most beautiful waterfalls in New Zealand*

►*The Te Puia hot springs rise to the surface at low tide on the black sand beach west of Kawhia*

towns of the Waikato and the King Country. In this region the bush is so dense that there are few tracks, but Mt Pirongia, 962 m high, is a popular climb. Some ornithologists believe that the rare kokako is more numerous there than anywhere else, along with a variety of birds which prefer dense forest.

The Pirongia Forest Park, of 17 000 hectares, covers a volcanic mass, about 2 million years old, which dominates the western horizon of the Waikato basin. Several peaks rise to about 900 m, with The Cone, at 945 m, being Pirongia's twin. Together they form a basalt mountain with a base 17 km across. Giant bluffs stand high above the bush, wet in the mists and covered with moss forest or bog vegetation. There are also plateaux near the tops of Pirongia and The Cone. One of these is nearly 2 km wide, at a height of 480 m, and boasts a thick broadleaf forest, where the fresher green of huge old rimu and miro caps tawa and tawari.

Near the windswept summit of Pirongia, the botanist Cheeseman found the growth of stunted kamahi and mountain scrub had been lashed by the wind into a rigid canopy 2–3 m above the ground. So tightly woven were these stunted trees that he crawled over their tops as he kept his eyes on the view.

A narrow road winds across the coastal edge of the Pirongia Forest Park and a short walk from it leads to the lip of the Bridal Veil Falls, where the water drops 50 m in lazy sheets among ferns and forest. Nearby, Lake Disappear lives up to its name. Covering several hectares of land in wet weather, it drains out of the valley through fissures in the rock, and is no more.

Limestone country reappears south of Pirongia. This district is called Waitomo, a Maori name meaning 'water running out of a hole', and it has been adapted locally to refer to hundreds of caves and sinkholes as 'tomo'.

The caves run through a block of limestone, up to 150 m thick, overlain by sandstone and mudstone. Caves are formed as a result of surface water, containing carbon dioxide dissolved from the atmosphere, finding its way into the limestone mass by way of faults, bedding planes and fractures. The water corrodes the limestone, enlarging small cracks into fissures which conduct ever-increasing flows of water. Where water saturated with calcium carbonate in solution persistently drips from a cave roof, stalactites grow downwards. Beneath persistent drips, stalagmites grow upward from the cave floor. Seepage produces surface encrustation. The formations in the Waitomo caves have been built up over 50 000–100 000 years.

The galleries of the Waitomo cave systems generally run parallel with the predominant direction of joint fissures in the limestone bed. This has helped to establish integrated, connected underground drainage systems which have diverted surface streams from parts of their valleys.

The Waitomo, Raukuri and Aranui Caves are well lit for tourists, but these three are only a small part of a large system. So far 85 km of caverns and passages have been surveyed. Gardner's Gut, near Waitomo, branches into 11.4 km of passages and is the longest cave in New Zealand. It is very likely that there were formerly more caves and that some limestone bluffs in the King Country are really the walls of caverns now collapsed and lost. For example, erosion and collapse of the surrounding limestone explains the formation of the Mangapohue Natural Bridge, a 15 m high arch over a stream off the Marakopa road.

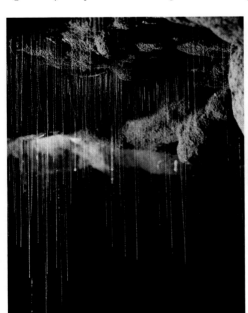

◄*Glow worms dangle sticky threads in which they entrap prey. The glow worms are the larvae of gnats which live in the Waitomo Cave*

▲*Limestone formations in the Waitomo Caves, like these 'straws', have built up over as many as 100 000 years*

Coromandel Peninsula

Exploiters have assaulted the Coromandel Peninsula since the earliest days of European settlement, but the intricate coast remains calmly beautiful and the craggy ranges still shelter dense rainforest

◄*Ancient volcanic plugs rearing above rainforest endow the landscape of the Coromandel Range with a character unlike any other part of New Zealand. Volcanic islands elsewhere in the Pacific—Hawaii or Tahiti, for example—are called to mind*

The dramatic Coromandel Peninsula is a sea-bound mountain range cut through near its southern end by the Karangahake Gorge. It culminates in the great hump of Mt Moehau and continues out into the wide Pacific as Great Barrier Island.

A fault separates the Coromandel Range from the sunken block of land that comprises the Hauraki Plains and the Firth of Thames. South of Manaia Harbour the range has risen against the sunken block, but to the north the peninsula has fallen too, turning river valleys into extensive harbours and hilltops into chains of islands.

The peninsula itself has many of the characteristics of an island. The sea is always close at hand, and the mountain backbone is tall and narrow. Even the plant life has more similarity to that on the neighbouring islands than to other mainland regions. Geographically isolated, with a mild oceanic climate, the Coromandel Peninsula has plants which begin their northward range within its embrace and others which are at the northern limit of their distribution. The variety of plants is much richer than normal—the peninsula claims more than 350 species.

Yet man has not been kind to this peninsula and only the toughness of the terrain has protected it. In fact, it all appears more untouched than it is. Mining and farming have ravaged the hills, and much of the original bush has been milled and burned.

Most exploration by car on the Coromandel Peninsula must be done on shingle roads which test a driver's skill, but the road running northward up the picturesque western shore is sealed as far as Coromandel township. From the start of the road at Thames there are pohutukawas, remnants of old coastal forest, retaining the roadside.

Along this western coastal road five other roads branch off, leading to the valleys and ridges where substantial areas of native bush remain. The ridges grant views of Auckland across the shimmering gulf, or out to the offshore islands in the Bay of Plenty. The eastern coast is less easy to visit. There is no continuous road to the north.

Exotic conifer forest is rapidly covering hills that once carried scrub, but Coromandel Forest Park contains surviving rainforest. On the harbour flats there are still sedge and mangrove swamps where bitterns, fern-birds,

rails and crakes make their natural homes.

The Coromandel Range is the refuge of many rare creatures. In pockets of bush visited by few, the North Island kokako, or blue-wattled crow, can still be heard. Primitive native frogs, which bypass the tadpole stage, develop in the damp shelter of rocks on the forest floor.

Among the remoter places near the Coromandel Peninsula must be counted offshore islands like the Mercury and Aldermen groups, and Cuvier Island. Though set in the Bay of Plenty, they form part of the Hauraki Gulf Maritime Park and permits are needed to land. In any case, many of the offshore islands have coasts that intimidate even the intrepid; and it is well, because some of them give security to bird species the mainland has lost, and the ancient tuatara makes its nocturnal forays among the rocks.

▼*Coromandel Forest Park runs intermittently along the whole peninsula. At a number of points its forests have been opened for visitors. Kauaeranga Valley, for instance, provides camping places and gentle walks*

On the coast of Coromandel where pohutukawas grow

▶This pohutukawa tree, its gnarled roots half exposed, clings to the Coromandel shore on the high-tide mark

The western hills of the Coromandel Peninsula fall abruptly to the sea. The road along their seaward edge skirts the rocky headlands and stony beaches of the Firth of Thames.

On these beaches, semi-precious stones—carnelian, agate, jasper and chalcedony—lie scattered among the pebbles. They have been washed down the ravines and along the creek beds. At the top of the range, behind Coromandel, quartz crystals and amethysts can be found in dumps beside abandoned mine-shafts and drives. The shafts make deviation from well-used tracks very risky. Often hidden by scrub, they fall to depths of 100 m, and they claim a victim regularly.

The range was built up over nearly 20 million years by repeated volcanic episodes which buried an older landscape of greywacke under andesite and rhyolite. Since eruptions ceased some 20 million years ago, the solidified lava that once filled the feeding pipes resisted erosion more than the rest of the ancient volcanos and now stands like fortresses on the crests of the range.

The peninsula itself was permanently scarred by exploitation in the 19th century and much of its regenerated wilderness is merely scrub. Huge kauri trees, with trunks rising 20 m or more, provided materials for the surge of British shipbuilding after the

Napoleonic Wars. Only remnants of the kauri forest survive today. From the 1860s to the 1880s gold-miners reworked the land with drives and shafts, clearing and burning as they went, and often triggering landslides.

In winter many kingfishers migrate to this coast because it has ready food when frosts elsewhere have killed their normal insect prey. Flashing electric blue and gold, they dart from the pohutukawas in search of tiny marine creatures on the beaches.

Beyond Coromandel township the road rounds a number of bays and then clambers over the hill to Colville, another drowned valley. From there the road takes a spectacular course, travelling past the foot of Mt Moehau. The Coromandel Farm Park provides

camping sites amongst the pohutukawas at Fantail Bay. The tortuous Port Jackson hill road ends at Fletcher's Bay and a track leads to The Needles, a 152 m high headland with exciting views, and then down to the eastern coast of the peninsula and Port Charles. The eastern coastal roads are not continuous and to explore the bays of the north-east means patient retracking on one-way roads.

Offshore lies Cuvier Island, part of the Hauraki Gulf Maritime Park. Landing is by permit. A significant population of the North Island saddleback has been built up on Cuvier since it was re-introduced in the 1960s from Hen Island, then its only known habitat. Red Mercury Island, farther south along the eastern coast, now also has North

▲*The day's last light silhouettes distant Mt Moehau and some of* *the many islands, the tops of drowned hills, off the west coast*

Island saddlebacks. The seven Mercury islands are all in the Hauraki Gulf Maritime Park. Permission is needed to land on Great Mercury, which is privately owned.

The Aldermen Islands continue the offshore line of rock stacks and hilltops. Captain Cook named them because to him they appeared like a court of aldermen, three islands in a triangle, with a chain of pinnacle rocks around them. The Shoe and Slipper Islands, closer inshore, are private.

Back on the peninsula, exotic pine forests run south to the resort of Whangamata and ultimately Waihi Beach.

◄*The Cathedral Cove Reserve at Hahei, south of Mercury Bay, protects three bays separated by high cliffs. At low tide it is possible to pass through this great sea cave from one beach to another. When the tide is ebbing at nearby Hotwater Beach it is possible to scrape a hollow in the sand and bathe in a hot spring*

Plundered forests on castellated ranges

▲*Many huge kauris have survived the logging of the Coromandel forests. This is one of several in the Waiau Valley, below Castle Rock*

▶*Enormous tree ferns are a striking feature of the Coromandel forests. The steepness of the terrain makes it easy to appreciate their delicate shapes from viewpoints above*

The Coromandel Forest Park begins close to the southern boundary of the region, where the twisting Karangahake Gorge separates the Coromandel Range and the Kaimai Range, and extends, with interruptions, to the end of the peninsula. The park consists of several great blocks—areas of regeneration and control—which are divided by land not in the forest park area. Declared in 1971, the park came too late to save all the virgin bush but it probably saved the ranges, as the steep ravines and mountain ridges are eroded quickly once they have been cleared. And when the smaller reserves are added, Coromandel Forest Park offers at least 72 814 hectares of wilderness.

The remnants of the Coromandel bush can present an arresting sight, with the huge, shaggy heads of mature kauri still standing above some of the ridges. Where it was difficult to climb or work, patches of the untouched forest survived. Manaia Sanctuary is one of these, with 400 giant trees, including Tane Nui, a kauri 47 m high and ten metres in girth, the fifth largest tree in New Zealand.

Millers tried to log Manaia. They felled noble kauri trees and floated the logs in water dammed behind a great wall of timber. But when they released the flood to send the logs to the coast they were splintered as they were sent crashing over a 60 metre high waterfall.

Nearly 8000 hectares are now planted in young kauri, grey-poled 'rickers' with caps of conical green. And on the sides of the valleys and in the gullies, the hardwoods rata, tawa, rewarewa and kohekohe mix with the deep foliage of podocarps—tall-standing rimu, matai, miro and tanekaha. This is Northland rainforest, but higher up in the ranges southern trees and plants intrude, including hard beech, and this conjunction of southern and northern plants lends additional interest to tramping and exploring.

The past has left its telltale marks. Old mining tracks probe in from the Karangahake Gorge, past abandoned mineshafts and on to the southernmost area, Maratoto. And in the Kauaeranga valley, near Thames, the remains of a bush tramway, high above the ground, and 50 or more logging dams still hidden in the bush all speak of a productive if damaging period. A more distant era is revealed by Table Mountain. Rising to 794 m, this steep-sided, flat-topped ridge crowns the broad, broken crest of the Colville Range northwest of Thames. Early in the century geologists described it as the worn-down remnant of a large dyke of andesite rock, the once-molten filling of a vertical fissure in older rocks which have been stripped down

▲Remnants of ancient volcanos give the
Coromandel Range a dramatic skyline which has
no counterpart in New Zealand

to lower levels by erosion. Alternatively it
could well be a remnant not of a vertical
mass, but of a horizontal sheet of andesite
from which erosion has removed the surroundings. Some of the pinnacles on the Coromandel Range may also be erosional remnants of lava sheets.

Low land around Colville separates the
main Coromandel Range from the northernmost part of the peninsula, where the
Moehau Range rises steeply from the sea. Its
damp, exposed peaks display not only the
archetypal kauri and towai of the north but
plants more characteristic of more southern
regions. As on other high peaks on the Coromandel Peninsula, there are 'islands' of
mountain broadleaf and five-finger, shrubs
more at home on the southern ranges of the
North Island, and there is also a herb field
where alpine plants flourish.

Entry into the Coromandel forests is gained by roads which wind steeply to the summit of the range. Highway 25A over the Kiri-
kiri Saddle offers the easiest driving, but the
Tapu-Coroglen road and others take one
closer to the forest. The more challenging
way to encounter the forest is to tramp in
from the ends of roads that penetrate narrow
valleys from the coast, wary of dangers hidden in the labyrinth of hills.

▲Northern rata adds
its crimson flowers to
the Coromandel forests
in summer, echoing the
pohutukawa blossom
down on the coasts

▶High in the
Coromandel Range,
crags and bluffs
dominate even the
gigantic old trees that
emerge from the canopy
of the forest

Rotorua

Boiling mud, hot springs and geysers have made the Rotorua thermal region famous, but it offers much more, including a chain of lovely lakes and landmarks created by a devastating eruption

Legend has it that people from *Te Arawa,* one of the canoes that brought the Maoris to New Zealand centuries ago, discovered the Rotorua region and its volcanic activity.

One group of the Arawa people was led by Ihenga, grandson of Tama-te-Kapua, chief of *Te Arawa.* He first came upon a lake which he called *Te-roto-iti-kite-a-Ihenga*, 'the little lake seen by Ihenga', and is now called Lake Rotoiti. Later he reached *Roto-rua-nui-a-Kahu*, 'second and big lake of Kahu', after his uncle. But he discovered an old *tuahu* or sacred shrine—others were there first.

The wily Ihenga exchanged the old posts and nets of the original *tuahu* for new ones he had brought and used the old ones for his own *tuahu.* When he met the chief who was in residence, Ihenga claimed the land as his own. When challenged, he suggested they compare *tuahu* to see whose was the older. The plan succeeded and Ihenga took possession of the Rotorua area. His *mana*—a 'presence' some Maori people are considered to be born with, which is increased or de-creased by their way of life—is still held in high esteem by the Arawa people of today.

The city of Rotorua, with its ever-present but soon-unnoticed odour of hydrogen sulphide, is at the heart of a region offering a wealth of sights, ranging from the awe-inspiring volcanic craters of Mt Tarawera to tranquil lakes. The most famous spectacles, though, are probably the numerous hot springs, mud pools and geysers.

The forests surrounding Rotorua are largely introduced. Within a 100 km radius of the city there are about 430 000 hectares of forestry plantation—more than half of it government-administered—which is being expanded to meet the needs of the 1990s. Some of the most productive man-made forest in the world is centred to the east of the city. The climate and soil allow radiata pine to reach maturity in only 25–30 years.

▼*Rotorua city is surrounded by an area of numerous lakes, forests, volcanic craters and thermal activity*

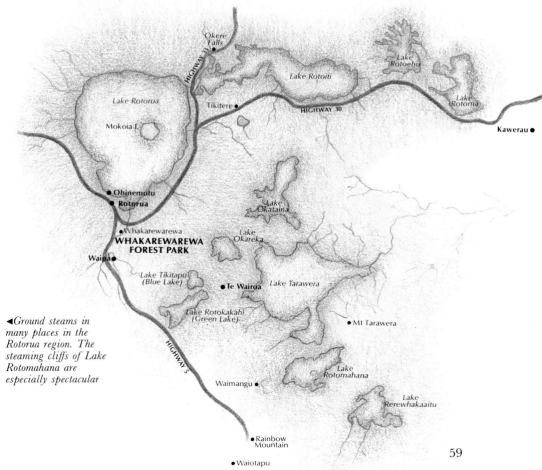

Geysers and hot springs at Whakarewarewa

◄*Pohutu geyser erupts to 18 m on average but sometimes it reaches twice that height. Its eruptions are frequent but irregular*

More than 500 hot springs bubble and spurt at Whakarewarewa, on the southern side of Rotorua city. Ranging from clear bubbling water to boiling mud, they occur in a zone only 1 km long by 500 m wide.

There are two main types of hot springs—chloride and sulphate. In chloride springs the water runs clear and is discharged, usually near boiling point, containing high concentrations of silica and chloride. The water is nearly neutral deep down but becomes slightly alkaline near the surface because of the release of gas. At the surface small amounts of silica in the water come out of solution and over a long time build up into sinter terraces. There are excellent examples of springs and terraces at Whakarewarewa.

All geysers are chloride springs. The reason for geyser activity is open to argument, but it basically involves the ability of water to contain more dissolved gas or steam when under high pressure than when under low pressure. The principle is the same in a bottle of champagne. Carbon dioxide remains in the wine while under pressure in the bottle, but once the cork is pulled pressure is reduced and the gas bubbles out of solution, sometimes in a miniature geyser of champagne.

The best examples of geyser activity at Whakarewarewa are Pohutu, which erupts to 18 m or higher, the Prince of Wales Feathers and Waikorohihi. Activity by one geyser seems to affect the others and this suggests that there may be some underground connection between them.

Chloride springs are formed when the water table—the level below which the ground is saturated with water—is at or near the surface. If the water table is well below the surface, however, sulphate springs are formed. These are highly acid and tend to form turbid water or pools of mud. Acid gases are given off and they alter the rocks to form clay, particularly kaolin, the grey material of mud pools. This can, however, become stained by iron or other metals, producing a multi-coloured array. Sulphate springs occur particularly on the northern and southern sides of the Whakarewarewa thermal area.

This thermal area lies at the southern end of the Rotorua caldera, a basin-like structure, 16 km in diameter and 300 m deep, formed nearly 150 000 years ago. Its formation began when violent eruptions poured out huge amounts of ash and pumice, which spread over the surrounding district to form the Mamaku Ignimbrite. The eruption of so much volcanic debris partly emptied the underground reservoir where the molten magma had accumulated before the eruption. The overlying rocks collapsed into the hole, forming a nearly circular caldera.

After the formation of the Rotorua caldera, quieter eruptions built up rhyolite domes, such as Mokoia Island in the centre of Lake Rotorua. Small explosions also formed craters such as Ngawha Crater at Whakarewarewa. This was caused by hot water held within sediments and volcanic rocks suddenly changing to steam. When this process, known as 'flashing', happens, there is an increase in volume and a hydrothermal eruption results. No lava is ejected but blocks of rock from the crater are scattered around.

Radiocarbon dating of the Ngawha Crater explosion gives a minimum age of about 42 000 years for Whakarewarewa as a thermal area, although it is probably much older. The thermal activity at Whakarewarewa is associated with the northeast-trending faults which have provided passageways for the hot water to rise from the depths. For the passageways to remain open, there must have been periodic movement on the faults.

Much of the ground between the hot springs at Whakarewarewa is warm, with steam issuing from many small fissures. There are well marked and maintained tracks through the thermal area and it is vital to keep to them, whether walking through on one's own or on a tour conducted by a Maori guide. In some places the ground is only a thin crust over boiling mud. If it is broken severe burns can result.

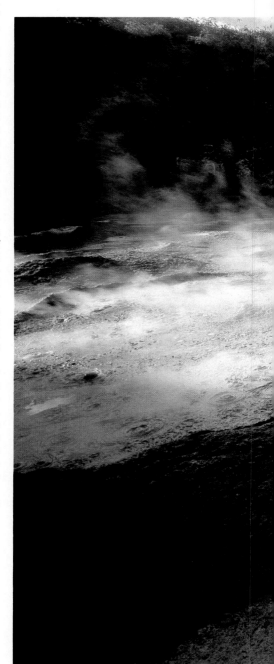

►*The largest mud pool at Whakarewarewa is called the Frog Pond, because after rain mud spurts up like frogs jumping. The mud reached 96°C but it boils only rarely*

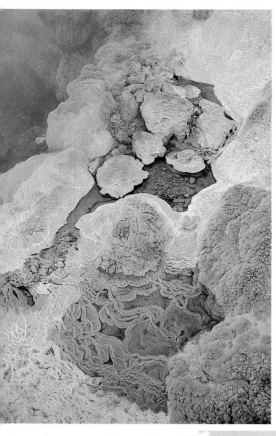

◀Silica encrustations form around geyser vents, usually as cones or mounds, and these remain to mark extinct geyser sites

▲In dry weather, mud becomes thick and cones build up around steam vents. In wet weather the mud becomes less viscous

Destruction and death when a mountain exploded

◄*The famous Pink and White Terraces, which were painted here by J. B. C. Hoyte, were later destroyed by the great eruption of Mt Tarawera. The silica terraces were a widely-known tourist attraction—of even international fame, it was said at the time*

At first sight Mt Tarawera does not look like a volcano, for it lacks the classic conical form, but one winter morning in 1886 it erupted with devastating result. In four hours it transformed itself and much of the surrounding landscape, destroyed three settlements and killed more than 100 people.

That eruption, the most violent and destructive by any volcano in New Zealand since European settlement began, was the latest in a series of major eruptions of Mt Tarawera. According to radiocarbon dating, it erupted 19 000 years ago, 14 700 years ago, 11 250 years ago and about 900 years ago. During the last of these eruptions the present skyline of Wahanga, Ruawahia and Tarawera peaks was formed.

Most of these eruptions produced rhyolite, the light-coloured lava that forms much of the Rotorua region. An eruption of a rhyolite volcano is very different from that of an andesite volcano such as Mt Ngauruhoe. At the beginning of the eruption, lava oozes out of a vent, quickly solidifies and plugs the vent. As the eruption continues lava is unable to break through this plug. The volcano bulges into a dome like a gigantic upturned pudding-basin. (An example is Wahanga Dome on the northern side of Mt Tarawera, 1.75 km in diameter and 300 m above the surrounding volcanic rocks.) As a volcanic dome forms, gas builds up and white ash and pumice explode out of the volcano. The finer

ash spreads over the surroundings, forming a deposit of tephra—ancient Greek for 'ash'.

After each of its eruptions Mt Tarawera lay dormant, as it was when Europeans first settled in the district in the mid-19th century. But in the early morning of 10 June 1886, apparently with very little warning, there was a violent eruption, quite different from any that had gone before. At 12.30 a.m. earthquakes began, and increased in intensity for an hour until there was a small explosion from the northeastern end of the mountain. At 1.45 a.m. the main eruption began. There was a roar from near Ruawahia

peak, and a black column, glowing with reflections from red-hot rocks, blew straight upwards.

At 2.10 a.m. the southwestern end of the mountain exploded, emitting a deafening roar and a cloud estimated from Gisborne, about 140 km away, to have been about 10 km high. At 3.30 a.m. violent explosions produced a chain of craters across the mountain. The Rotomahana basin burst into eruption too, hurling out a column of steam even higher than that from Mt Tarawera and covering surrounding lands with thick mud.

About 5.30 a.m. the eruption ended as

►*The spectacle and terror of the eruption of Mt Tarawera are well recorded in this old lithograph. The huge eruption was quite brief—only four hours—but it soon devastated a wide expanse of land*

abruptly as it had begun, leaving a chain of nine deep craters across the mountain and black basalt scoria and mud spread over most of the Bay of Plenty district and eastwards as far as Hawke's Bay. The Maori settlements of Te Ariki and Moura, on the shores of Lake Tarawera, and the European settlement of Te Wairoa were destroyed. At least 116 people were known to be dead, and the toll may have been as high as 155.

The Rotomahana Basin also suffered severe changes. The famous Pink and White Terraces, marvels of natural architecture in shining silica, were destroyed forever. Pieces of sinter, presumably from the terraces, can be found in the fragmentary volcanic rocks surrounding Lake Rotomahana.

▲*Colossal forces left this awesome cratered rent, 19 km long, across Mt Tarawera. The eruption in 1886* *destroyed all the vegetation on the mountain, but forest has regenerated rapidly on the lower slopes*

This lake was itself created by the eruption, which also caused Lake Okataina to rise some 12 m, presumably by blocking its outlet. Lake Tarawera, to the south, rose at the same time, but in 1904 the ash barrier broke, the excess water flooded the Kawerau district and the lake dropped to slightly below its pre-eruption level. To the west of Lake Tarawera there are three very picturesque smaller lakes—Okareka, Tikitapu and Rotokakahi—filling probably not old craters but newer basins which were formed at that time by

the extrusion of the lava domes and flows.

Lakes Tikitapu and Rotokakahi are commonly known as the Blue Lake and Green Lake respectively. The contrasting colours of their waters can be seen most strikingly on a fine day from the isthmus between them. Both lakes border the Whakarewarewa Forest Park, and tracks through it provide periodic glimpses of the lakes and in some places follow the shore.

Southeast of Lake Rotomahana, Lake Rerewhakaaitu lies in a basin between the volcanic area and the Kaingaroa Plateau. It has no surface outlet and has overflowed onto the ash-covered plain. There is a small explosion crater, probably about 11 000 years old, on its northwestern side.

A mosaic of lakes

▶ *The dabchick, a small relative of the crested grebe, is common on lakes in the Rotorua volcanic region*

The city of Rotorua stands on the shore of a lake of the same name, the largest in a mosaic of lakes radiating from it to the east and southeast. Lake Rotorua, measuring 12 by 10 km, fills a caldera formed some 150 000 years ago and has at its centre a small island, Mokoia, famous because of the legend of the lovers Hinemoa and Tutanekai.

The beautiful Hinemoa lived with her family on the shores of Lake Rotorua and, against the wishes of her parents, fell in love with Tutanekai, a young chief. She planned to take a canoe to join her lover on the island but was discovered and the canoes were beached. Eventually Hinemoa could wait no longer so she swam across, supporting herself with dried gourds.

East of Lake Rotorua is the Okataina volcanic centre, where many volcanic domes and lava flows have built up over the last 200 000 years. It has also been the scene of several large explosive eruptions. One of the biggest, between 40 000 and 50 000 years ago, formed a great sheet of fragmented pumice, called the Rotoiti Breccia, which covered much of the area to the north. Lakes Rotoiti, Rotoehu and Rotoma are at the northern edge of the volcanic centre. Old craters may exist within these three lakes, but the present shores are defined simply by the topography of the surrounding lavas. Lake Rotoma is the highest at 316 m, followed by Lake Rotoehu, 295 m, and Lake Rotoiti, 279 m. There is no surface outlet from either

▲ *Beyond Lake Tarawera rises the volcanic cone of Mt Edgecumbe, in the Bay of Plenty district*

Rotoma or Rotoehu. The water presumably seeps through the volcanic rock and eventually reaches Lake Rotoiti.

There are several hot-spring areas within the lakes, notably at the southeastern corner of Lake Rotoehu and in the deepest part of the floor of Lake Rotoiti. The latter may well be connected to Tikitere thermal area to the south. Tikitere, or Hell's Gate, is a particularly active thermal area with many furiously boiling springs, mud holes full of sulphate-rich water, and craters discharging sulphurous fumes. One of the main attractions is the Kakahi Falls, where visitors may splash in a pleasantly warm cascade.

There is a legend concerning Tikitere. It is said that Rangi-te-ao-rere, a famous warrior, was presented with a beautiful young woman of high rank to marry. For a while Rangi-te-ao-rere and his wife Huritini lived happily, but then he became bored. Huritini, realising she had lost him, plunged into the mud pool which now bears her name. When the sad news was made known to her people they cried '*Taku tiki-i-tere*'—'our greatly loved daughter has floated away'. So Tikitere the place became.

Lake Okataina is a particularly beautiful lake, nestling between steep-sided, bush-covered volcanic domes. There is no road around the lake and the only way to explore it is by launch. There are small secluded beaches and the surrounding bush is full of native birds. The road from Highway 30 to Lake Okataina is delightful, passing through native bush with many tree ferns and a 3.2 km stretch of native fuschia or *kotukutuku*.

◀ *Steaming cliffs are part of the shore of Lake Rotomahana, in the southeastern arm of*   *the Rotorua lake district. The lake was created by the eruption of Mt Tarawera*

▶Mud boils furiously at Tikitere, the most active thermal area in the Rotorua region. It lies between Lakes Rotorua and Rotoiti

Craters at Waimangu

▶ *The larger crater is Echo Crater, also known as Waimangu Cauldron, and the smaller is Southern Crater. Between the two craters, one of the world's largest geysers used to play.*

Waimangu Thermal Valley did not exist as a hydrothermal area before the Tarawera eruption of 1886. There was only a stream flowing down the Haumi valley. During the eruption, explosions formed ten craters along an extension of the Tarawera fissure, southwest of the lake. After the eruption Lake Rotomahana rose, filling and covering the three northeasternmost craters. The remaining craters still exist within the Waimangu thermal area. The two craters nearest to Lake Rotomahana are on the slopes of Te Hape-o-Toroa. They are now partly breached and form part of what is often called the 'Rift Valley'. Next are Black Crater and Fairy Crater, less accessible than the others. Basalt lava, similar to that from Mt Tarawera erupted from Black Crater in 1886. The craters usually visited at Waimangu are the three southwesternmost—Inferno Crater (now generally called Ruaumoko's Throat), Echo Crater and Southern Crater. Inferno Crater is a vertical-walled explosion crater in the side of a hill. It contains a sky-blue lake which fluctuates up to 10 m in level. About every six weeks the level rises above the outflow and a river of hot water flows out and down to the Frying-Pan Stream below. After a few days the lake level recedes below the outflow and the river dries up.

◀ *Deposits of algae and minerals in the water flowing over Warbrick Terrace create this display of colours.*

◄Cathedral Rocks steam on the wall of Echo Crater, which was formed by the explosion of a geyser in 1917. The fearsome crater below holds a hot, bubbling lake

▼Ruaumoko's Throat, or Inferno Crater, holds a lake which fluctuates up to 10 m in level. About every six weeks its hot waters overflow

Echo Crater is a large basin filled by Frying-Pan Lake, or Waimangu Cauldron, which is one of the world's largest 'boiling' lakes. It is over 48 500 m² (4.85 hectares) of hot water (53°C) which constantly bubbles, due to the release of gas, and steams eerily. There have been periodic explosions within the crater too. The most spectacular was that of the Waimangu ('black water') Geyser, which broke out at the northeastern end in late 1900. During its activity the geyser threw muddy water and blocks of debris commonly to heights of 150 m and occasionally as high as 488 m, the highest of any geyser in New Zealand. Its explosions were as unpredictable as they were violent. In August 1903 four persons who were too close to it during a violent outburst were killed. The geyser became extinct in November 1904.

In April 1917, another geyser exploded without warning at Frying-Pan Flat, south-west of the Waimangu Geyser. The main blast lifted the roof off an accommodation house 800 m away and scalded the occupants. Two of them later died. Violent explosions continued for a few days but then subsided and water started to collect in the crater floor, forming Frying-Pan Flat.

The most recent hydrothermal eruption occurred on the southeast shore of Frying-Pan Lake in February 1973, from Trinity Terrace. This was a small eruption, lasting only 15 minutes and causing no damage.

The southwesternmost crater, Southern Crater, has had a quiet history compared with its neighbours. It is now occupied by a cold-water lake and is mainly noted for the colourful algal growth developed within it.

Waimangu is a short drive (26 km) from Rotorua. A well-maintained track starts at the tearoom and passes Southern Crater, Frying-Pan Lake and goes on to Inferno Crater. Visitors can see the most spectacular features within an hour by walking 2–2.5 km. However, those with more time will find a walk along the hot Frying-Pan Stream to Haumi Stream, Warbrick Terrace and Lake Rotomahana is well worth while. From the shores of Lake Rotomahana there is an excellent view of Mt Tarawera, especially the large chasm on the southwestern side. The walk back to the tearoom can be along a high-level track from which there is a good view of the thermal valley.

There is a bus-launch round trip from Rotorua most of the year. It includes a guided tour through Waimangu, a launch trip across Lake Rotomahana, past the steaming cliffs, and a second launch trip across Lake Tarawera to the site of Te Wairoa, a village buried by the eruption of 1886. Extensive excavations have uncovered the site. The tour then continues by bus.

Thermal activities at Waiotapu

►*Crater-like pits, up to 13 m deep, are a feature of the scenic reserve at Waiotapu*

Hot springs and steaming ground occur over an area of about 18 km²; at the Waiotapu thermal area, adjacent to Highway 5, about 25 km southeast of Rotorua. Part of the area is open to the public as a tourist reserve. As at Whakarewarewa, the thermal activity is closely related to fault systems. In the northern part the Ngapouri Fault has provided a channelway through which waters have risen to the surface. In doing so they have chemic-

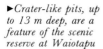

▼*Champagne Pool lies in Primrose Terrace, also known as the Artist's Palette. The* hot pool bubbles with escaping gas and is rimmed with deposits rich in metal ores

ally altered the dacite volcanic rock on the western side of Maungakakaramea to multi-coloured clay. The play of colours has earned the volcano the name of Rainbow Mountain. A number of hydrothermal explosion craters are aligned along the fault. The largest are occupied by Lakes Okaro, Ngahewa and Ngapouri. Explosions from these craters are thought to have occurred about 900 years ago, sending blocks of debris up to 500 m away. Numerous hot springs also occur along this fault and between them there are many areas of steaming ground. The main Waio-

tapu tourist reserve, Waiotapu Wonderland, occupies the southern part of the thermal area. Although the name means 'sacred waters', Waiotapu appears to have attained little prominence until after the Tarawera eruption of 1886. Among the main features of the reserve are numerous crater-like pits, up to 20 m in diameter and 13 m deep, which are in rough north-easterly alignment and may therefore be controlled by a fault. Some of them have boiling pools of muddy water at the base, others contain hot or warm water, but the majority are dry. In many, vapours

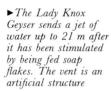

▶The Lady Knox
Geyser sends a jet of
water up to 21 m after
it has been stimulated
by being fed soap
flakes. The vent is an
artificial structure

escaping from cracks have deposited yellow sulphur on the sides.

To the southeast of the pits, within an apron of pastel-coloured sinter known as Primrose Terrace, or the Artist's Palette, lies the spectacular Champagne Pool. The water in this pool, which covers 2000 m², is at temperatures between 70°C and 75°C and bubbles merrily with escaping gas, particularly near the edge. Just inside the pool on a narrow ledge, there is a remarkable orange-red powdery substance. It contains high concentrations of metal sulphides, in particular arsenic (2 per cent), antimony (2 per cent) and mercury (170 parts per million), and the metals gold (80 ppm) and silver (175 ppm). Similar values occur in the underlying sinter. The gold, at 80 ppm (more than 2.7 oz to the ton), would constitute a high-grade ore deposit if there were enough material to mine.

At the south end of Primrose Terrace are the Bridal Veil Falls, where water from the Champagne Pool cascades down a sinter terrace, highlighting the colours. At the base it joins water from Whangioterangi, Echo Lake, to flow eventually into Lake Ngakoro. This lake is cooler (25°C) and is usually coloured green by algae.

Just outside the reserve, beside a loop-road on the northern access road to Waiotapu, are some excellent mud pools. These develop a good deal of gas and make delightful patterns, particularly after rain. During dry spells the pools seem to become even more active and form small mud volcanos which frequently throw mud into the air and build up cones around the vents.

Also outside the reserve is the Lady Knox Geyser, named in 1904 after the daughter of Lord Ranfurly, then Governor-General of New Zealand. This geyser is artificial and was constructed about 1906 by the chief warder of Waiotapu Prison Farm. Apparently it had simply been a vigorously boiling pool, but when prisoners came to wash their clothes in it, it was discovered that it would erupt and form a geyser when soap was added. In order to make it more spectacular the chief warder installed a cast-iron pipe, restricting the orifice and consequently the height of the jet. He then camouflaged the pipe with pumice blocks. These have now been covered by silica from the water and the appearance is natural.

Lake Taupo

Lake Taupo is the biggest lake in New Zealand and it is a volcano. Today it is a peaceful place, but it has not always been so. There were gigantic eruptions from the lake and its surroundings 330 000, 20 000 and 1850 years ago. Such eruptions are fortunately very infrequent, but there is no reason to suppose that there will not be another

Lake Taupo, covering 616 km² is one of four centres of rhyolite volcanic activity in the North Island; the others are Maroa, Rotorua and Okataina. Together they have erupted huge quantities of volcanic material, estimated at 12 000 km³. This is enough to cover the whole of New Zealand to a depth of 45 m, but in fact much of it has accumulated —up to 4000 m deep—within the active Taupo Volcanic Zone, which extends from White Island, in the Bay of Plenty, to Oha-kune, a small town south of Mt Raupehu.

This zone, which lies between faults, is being stretched by forces created by opposing movements along the boundaries of the Pacific and Indian-Australian plates of the Earth's crusts. Measurements show that the zone is widening by more than 5 mm a year. As the zone widens, it subsides into a rift structure, called a graben. The area cracks, forming a pattern of faults and along them basalt, originating from below the crust, is able to rise to the surface periodically.

A particularly violent eruption occurred in the Taupo area about 330 000 years ago.

Molten rock, or magma, formed in the Earth's crust and rose to within 5 km of the surface. Gas pressure built up in the magma until finally the rock overlying the magma chamber gave way, probably along faults or fractures, and the gas-rich magma escaped. The first eruption may have been small and spread a thin covering of ash over the district. Once the fractures became wide enough, however, a great surge of hot pumice, ash and rock debris erupted.

Dense, swirling masses of the material swept across the countryside in fast-moving pyro-clastic flows, in which debris was carried along by trapped hot gases. When the pumice and ash settled from the flow, the fragments were so hot that they welded together to produce a hard rock known as a ignimbrite. The flows first filled river valleys and then spread out over the surrounding district to form the Whakamaru Ignimbrite. This covered 2500 km² on the western side of the Taupo Volcanic Zone to a maximum depth of more than 200 m.

About 150 km³ of ignimbrite was erupted.

The sudden removal of this material from the crust under the source area caused the roof of the magma chamber to collapse and form a great crater, or caldera, which is now filled by the Western Bay of Lake Taupo.

The Whakamaru Ignimbrite is now partly eroded, but it still covers a large area to the west of Lake Taupo. Ignimbrite is thickest in the northwest, where the first flows from the eruption filled a depression. After the eruption the Waikato River cut a course across the horizontal ignimbrite sheets, creating a deep gorge near Whakamaru and Maraetai. Along this section of the river hydro-electric dams have been built.

Pyroclastic flows may have also swept to the north and east, either at the same time or shortly after the Whakamaru eruption and these flows form the Rangitaiki and Wairakei Ignimbrites. After these events, the volcanic centre became much quieter and activity was restricted to two types of eruption. Occasional minor explosive eruptions formed tephra, which mantled the landforms of the surrounding area. The other type of eruption was the extrusion of rhyolite domes, similar to those of the Rotorua caldera. These form large hemispherical hills, often aligned along fault lines. The hills north of Lake Taupo are formed by these domes. Others occur to the southwest, forming Rangitukua, Pukekaiki-ore and Kuharua peaks.

About 20 000 years ago an eruption from the north-eastern part of Lake Taupo, not quite as violent as the ignimbrite eruptions, spread more than 40 km³ of pumice over a wide area to produce the Oruanui Breccia.

The last Taupo eruptions were in 130 AD. They began as a normal explosive eruption from a vent close to Horomatangi reef, on the eastern side of the lake. After a while the explosions became more violent, sending gas, ash and pumice into an enormous cloud which may have reached 40 km or more above the volcano.

The cloud contained so much solid material that it collapsed to spread out as pyroclastic flow over a wide area. The debris formed a sheet now called the Taupo Ignimbrite. At the same time fine ash which had risen to the top of the cloud was carried by winds around the volcano eventually to fall as tephra over much of the North Island.

▶*For the most part the shore of Lake Taupo is curiously inaccessible by road, but the lands surrounding it hold plenty of interest*

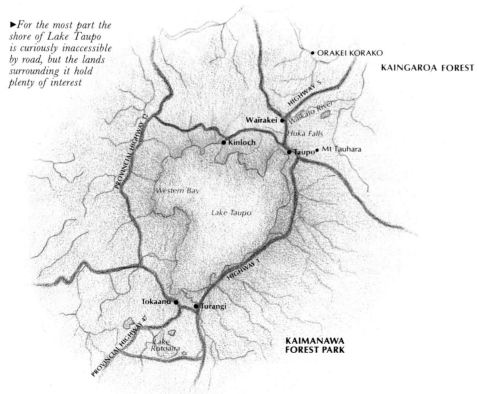

▼ *White pumice beaches lining the eastern shore of Lake Taupo are picturesque testimony to the violent volcanic past*

Around the shores of the lake

►*Mt Tauhara, an extinct volcano east of Taupo town, provides those who climb it with fine views of the lake lying below*

Lake Taupo's volcanic past has left it with an interesting shore, particularly on the northern and western sides. A spectacular feature on the western side is the Karangahape Cliffs, the eroded remains of an old volcano. The lower parts of the cliffs are pink and grey rhyolite lava and form part of a volcanic dome. Some time after the dome formed, basalt lava was erupted, covering the rhyolite. Much of the basalt was oxidised to red scoria. Later, violent eruptions from the lake caused part of the dome and the overlying basalt to collapse, leaving the cliffs. The Maoris used some of the clefts as burial caves and hence the cliffs are now regarded as *tapu*.

High cliffs around Western Bay are composed entirely of ignimbrite and they mark the boundary of a great caldera formed after the Whakamaru eruption about 330 000 years ago. In Waihora Bay, within Western

Bay, the Otupoto Falls plunge over the cliffs into the lake. In other valleys, headward erosion has produced waterfalls some distance upstream from the lake, as at the Tieke Falls on the Wiahaha River.

In the south-eastern part of the lake is Motutaiko Island, said in Maori legend to be the home of Horomatangi, a god brought from Hawaiki who turned into a *taniwha* (legendary serpent). Horomatangi supposedly lives in an underwater cave off the island and for many years was said to upset canoes and devour their occupants.

Lake Taupo is perhaps best known for its trout, and overseas visitors come to the lake purely to hook one of the beautiful fish, many of which weigh over 3 kg. Trout were introduced to New Zealand in 1868 when brown trout eggs were imported from Tasmania, although it was not until 1886 that they were

sent to Lake Taupo. Rainbow trout eggs were imported from California in 1883 and hatcheries were established. Trout have since been liberated in many New Zealand rivers and lakes and they have thrived.

The rainbow trout in New Zealand are all descended from the original shipment and hence the strain has remained pure. Careful conservation has preserved a species which in its native California has interbred and is no longer so pure.

One of the three trout hatcheries operated by the recently formed Department of Conservation is at Turangi, at the southern end of Lake Taupo. It is primarily and 'eyeing' and rearing station for rainbow trout. Eggs are milked from female trout, fertilised and incubated for about 18 days, at which time the 'eyes' are visible. They are then incubated for a further month, when the young fish,

◄ *The eastern shore of Lake Taupo is skirted by Highway 1 for much of its length. Access to the western and northern shores is much more limited*

or fry, hatch out. After this they are reared at Turangi and other places around the region before being released in rivers or lakes.

One of the country's most famous trout streams is the Tongariro River, which meanders into Lake Taupo through a delta north of Turangi. When the Tongariro Power Scheme was established a major consideration in the design was to disturb as little as possible the trout fishing in the river. The scheme diverts the headwaters of many of the rivers flowing off Tongariro National Park into Lake Rotoaira. The water then goes through a tunnel to the Tokaanu power station and into Lake Taupo.

A good overall view of Lake Taupo can be gained by climbing Mt Tauhara ('lonely mountain') east of Taupo. This 1099 m high peak is an extinct dacite volcanic dome. The track up the mountain starts at the end of Mountain Road, off Highway 5. To climb to the top and return takes two or three hours.

It is possible to drive around the lake on a 150 km round trip from Taupo. South of Taupo township, Highway 1 skirts the lake in many places, some with good beaches and camping areas, and crosses many popular fishing streams. The mouth of the Waitahanui River, for example, is well known. When fishing is good anglers form a 'picket fence' across the river mouth. At Turangi, Highway 41 leads to the small settlement of Tokaanu. This is a thermal area and nearby, on the shore of the lake, is the small picturesque village of Waihi.

At Kurutau, Highway 32 turns off Highway 41. It is a good road, some distance back from the lake, but glimpses of the lake may be obtained from it. Many road cuttings expose the Whakamaru Ignimbrite erupted from Lake Taupo 330 000 years ago. Finally, near Tihoi another road leads through the dry pumice country back to Taupo township. A short detour can be made from this road to Kinloch, a small lakeside holiday resort with its own marina.

▲The Whangamata Bluffs separate Whangamata and Whakaipo Bays on the northern edge of Lake Taupo. The high cliffs of Western Bay (in the background at left) were formed after a strong eruption more than 330 000 years ago

▼The Waikato River, which rises on the slopes of Mt Ruapehu, both feeds and drains Lake Taupo. The part of it that meanders into the lake through this delta, north of Turangi, is known as the Tongariro River

Down the Waikato River from Lake Taupo

▶Shortly after leaving Lake Taupo, the Waikato River narrows to surge through this gorge before hurtling over the Huka Falls

The longest river in New Zealand, the Waikato runs 425 km from its source on the eastern slopes of Mt Ruapehu, through Lake Taupo, to the Tasman Sea southwest of Auckland. From Lake Taupo to the mouth is 354 km. Shortly after leaving the lake, the river thunders over the spectacular Huka Falls. It narrows to 15 m wide as it rushes through vertical walls of silicified breccias—probably an old thermal area—and tumbles 11 m into a deep basin. The falls can be seen from a loop road off Highway 1 between Taupo and Wairakei, but they are probably more impressive from a viewpoint immediately beside them.

About 2.5 km farther north the river receives the outflow from the Wairakei geothermal power station. *Wairakei* means 'adorning water', or 'the place where pools were used as mirrors', and many thermal pools once existed there. They were mainly in Geyser Valley, or Wairakei Valley, where numerous geysers played, many of them at regular intervals. Perhaps the most spectacular was the Great Wairakei Geyser, which until the early 1930s sent up a column of water nearly 20 m every 10 minutes. Others included the Black Geyser (so named because it was surrounded by an encrustation of black silica), Dragon's Mouth Geyser, Red Coral Geyser and Eagle's Nest Geyser. Many of them were surrounded by colourful silica terraces and after an eruption the water would cascade down the sides of the terrace. Waiora Valley, nearby, was the site of many bubbling pools and mud pools.

In 1948 investigations began into the possibility of utilising some of the vast energy stored in the thermal areas within the underground reservoirs of hot water. Such reservoirs had already been tapped in Italy, at Lardarello, providing 250 kilowatts of geothermal energy, and it was decided to see whether the same could be done at Wairakei. The presence of a large volume of hot water and steam was confirmed and in 1958 the field was brought into operation. High-pressure steam from the bores was piped to drive the turbines of a power station built on

▶*The Huka Falls are remarkable for neither their height nor their width, but the force and volume of water ejected from the gorge make the sight and sound memorable*

the banks of the Waikato River.

Today the process is more efficient, as 'flashing' units allow some of the hot water, previously wasted, to be converted into steam under pressure and pumped along separate pipelines to the power station. In 1979 the station had a load capacity of 192 megawatts, sufficient to provide about 5 per cent of the country's total power consumption.

The establishment of the Wairakei geothermal scheme has not been without cost. The geysers of Wairakei Valley no longer erupt. The silica terraces remain and there are many areas of steaming ground and some hot-water basins, but the tourist reserve is only a shadow of its former grandeur. Waiora Valley, the main source of water for the geothermal scheme, is closed to tourists.

A new area has recently been established at the 'Craters of the Moon', or Wairakei Tourist Park. This is in the Waipuwerawera valley and includes the Karapiti 'blowhole', which in the 1930s was the most powerful fumarole in the Taupo Volcanic Zone. Today Karapiti has lost much of its power, but it combines with mud pools and areas of steaming ground to provide an interesting

small thermal park, worth an observer's visit.

Wairakei is no longer the wild place it was in 1930. Nevertheless the geothermal scheme shows the awesome power that is locked up in a volcanic area and how it may be harnessed for human benefit.

The Waikato River, too, provides electric power. It widens downstream from the Wairakei outflow to form Lake Aratiatia, the farthest upstream lake formed by damming of the river for hydro-electricity. The power station has a capacity of 90 megawatts.

At Aratiatia the river passes over spectacular rapids and drops 28 m in 800 m. These rapids result from the presence of vertical 'sheets' of rhyolite and obsidian—volcanic glass—which are presumed to be remains of an eroded volcanic dome. There was

▲*The Golden Fleece Terrace, nearly 15 m high, is one of the most remarkable sights at Orakei Korako. Like the nearby Rainbow Terrace, it consists of silica encrustations on an old fault line.*

◄*Silica terraces at Orakei Korako fringe the dammed waters of the Waikato River*

an outcry when the power station was built and the flow of the river was to be diverted through it. As a concession to public opinion, the spillways are opened and water is allowed to flow along its old course each day, from 10–11 a.m. and 2.30–4 p.m. During these times the rapids are worth seeing.

About 50 km downstream from Aratiatia is Orakei Korako, which has long been a well-known thermal area. In the mid-1800s there was a fairly large community there. It first became recognised as a tourist area in the early 1900s but it was not until 1937 that walking tracks were established. The area underwent a major change in January 1961, when Lake Ohakuri was filled behind the new Ohakuri Dam. This caused the water

level in the Waikato River to rise about 20 m at Orakei Korako and flood a number of the lower hot springs and geysers. Those at a higher level seemed to become more active after the flooding, however.

Orakei Korako can now be reached by road from either Taupo (37 km) or Rotorua (68 km). The thermal valley is reached by jet boat across Lake Ohakuri and a walk around the valley takes about an hour. The first feature seen is Diamond Geyser, which plays intermittently to a height of 3 m. Nearby are the boiling Hochstetter Pool and then the Rainbow Terrace, or Cascade Terrace, coloured by algae thriving in the warm waters. Perhaps the most spectacular feature is the Golden Fleece Terrace, a massive buttress of

white silica, nearly 5 m high, cascading down from the Artist's Palette above.

The best known feature at Orakei Korako is probably Ruatapu ('sacred cave') or Aladdin's Cave. In pre-European time this cave was reserved for use by Maori women as a place to adorn themselves, mirrored in pools in the bottom. Tall tree ferns frame the entrance and filter the sunlight by day. At night glowworms in the roof of the cave make a starry spectacle.

Orakei Korako, though changed, has not suffered greatly from the demand for power from the Waikato River. The Ohakuri Dam is the first of eight over a distance of 108 km. The others are at Atiamuri, Whakamaru, Maraetai I and II, Waipapa, Arapuni and Karapiro. Ohakuri Dam has utilised a rock that must once have been a geothermal reservoir like that at Wairakei, but the hot water and steam have long gone, leaving a hard silicified rock which makes a good foundation. The other dams are built on either rhyolite or ignimbrite.

Beyond this section, the river flows through Hamilton and the Waikato district, one of the most productive agricultural regions in the world. It finally enters the sea at Waikato Heads, where ironsand is mined from coastal dunes north of the river mouth. Titano-magnetite is extracted from the sand and sent to steelworks at Glenbrook. The Waikato River is important in New Zealand's economy. It supplies a significant amount of electricity, provides a major recreational facility and over time has contributed some of the sand that is now the basis of the New Zealand steel industry.

Artificial and natural forests of plateau and ranges

To the east of Rotorua and Taupo is the extensive Kaingaroa-Tangitaiki ignimbrite plateau. It extends from the eastern margin of the active Taupo Volcanic Zone to the rugged greywacke ranges which form the 'backbone' of the North Island. In some places the pyroclastic flows which produced the ignimbrites swept up valleys and deposited their loads on the side of the ranges.

After the ignimbrites were formed, widespread tephra deposits formed from explosive eruptions. The last of these was the Taupo eruption of 1850 years ago. The combination of rather dry conditions and frequent volcanic activity did not allow exten-

sive soils to develop and such soils as did exist were deficient in many minerals. At the beginning of the 20th century the area was a desolate wasteland carrying only a thin growth of manuka and bracken on the rolling country, and monoao and tussock on the plateau itself.

In 1889 a small-scale trial of Northern Hemisphere conifers and hardwoods began at Whakarewarewa, near Rotorua. It was successful and as a result about 3200 hectares were planted near Waiotapu between 1901 and 1912. Much of the planting was done by convicts. In the succeeding years substantial blocks were acquired and during the Depres-

▲ *The Kaimanawa Forest Park, which is mainly beech forest, clothes the lower slopes of the Kaimanawa Mountains, greywacke ranges lying to the east of Lake Taupo*

sion years huge numbers of trees were planted. By 1937 some 105 000 hectares were under trees. At that time about 45 per cent of the forest was radiata pine, 19 per cent ponderosa pine and the rest was Corsican pine, Douglas fir and other species.

Today Kaingaroa Forest has become the scene of a major operation. More than 111 000 hectares of exotic forest has been planted, 72 per cent of it in radiata pine, which has proved to be the most economic tree to grow. The operation also involved the building of nearly 2000 km of road and 400 km of firebreaks and the establishing of a nursery with over 10 million trees, and it employs a work force of almost 500. It is the largest man-made forest in New Zealand and among the largest in the world. Current annual wood production is nearly 3 million cubic metres, obtained by clear-felling and extraction thinning.

Little unplanted land remains today and the main redevelopment is in replacing the 4000–5000 hectares that are clear-felled each year. Natural regeneration occurs within these areas but the new growth is very dense, and on reaching a height of 1.5–1.8 m the trees are thinned to 1.5 m apart. Later the remaining trees are further thinned to leave approximately 100 trees to the hectare. Most of this thinning is done after about 10 years, and the small trees removed are used for pulp or fence posts. At the same time the lower branches of the remaining trees, especially radiata pine, are pruned to produce clean, strong main trunks.

Once the trees reach maturity they are felled and taken to one of the large sawmills in the district. Most go to the Tasman Pulp and Paper Company's large integrated sawmill and pulp mill at Kawerau.

The forests have become the home of several introduced animals, most of them pests. Brushtail possums, from Australia, strip bark from the trees, causing malformation, entry of disease and sometimes even death of the plant. In extreme cases up to 50 per cent of the trees are affected. A major eradication programme by poisoning was instituted in the 1970s, but today high prices for possum skins induce private hunters to maintain control without poisoning.

Deer are less of a problem although they do strip the bark from young stems. Red deer, which were liberated in the district at the start of the century, are widespread throughout the forest. Private hunters keep their numbers to reasonable levels. Entry to most of the forest is restricted and requires a permit, but recreational areas for swimming, picnicking and fishing have been established throughout the forest.

Southeastwards from Lake Taupo, the ignimbrite sheets thin rapidly and the

◄*Rimus and king ferns in the Kaimanawa Forest Park. Rimus and other podocarps grow in the lower western sections of the forest*

greywacke ranges are closer to the volcanic region. In 1900, 18 270 hectares of native forest was declared a 'state forest' and in 1939 an additional 32 024 hectares were added. In 1969 the two forests were combined, small areas were added and by March 1978 the Kaimanawa Forest Park had a total area of 75 708 hectares.

The headwaters of four major rivers—the Waipakihi, Mohaka, Ngaruroro and Rangitikei—are in the park, together with a number of smaller rivers which flow into Lake Taupo. This important watershed has therefore become an area where conservation is of key importance and the relationship between animals and plants can be studied.

The southern and central parts of the park are irregular and broken with several high peaks. The vegetation is dominated by snowgrass, although there are occasional areas of mountain toatoa and bog pine. Red tussock is also common. The northern, eastern and western parts are, however, covered by beech forest of two types. In the northeast is an association of red beech and silver beech, while to the south there is almost pure mountain beech. Some stands of matai and miro with scattered rimu, totara and kahikatea occur on the foothills, but most of the forest

on the lower western sections is a mixture of podocarp and beech.

The park contains red deer and sika deer, which were released many years ago, together with wild pigs, possums and rabbits which have filtered in from the surrounding area. The combined activities of all those animals have caused great damage to the trees and to the higher country by accelerating erosion. A pest-destruction programme was established some years ago and was so successful that control can now be maintained by private hunters.

Today the park is being opened up for recreation by the Department of Conservation. Tracks have been established and huts have been built. It is a large area and for people who like tramping in unspoilt country well worth a visit. There is good fishing in the streams, an abundance of bird life and spectacular views from the tops of the ridges.

Access is obtained by a number of minor roads to the east of Highway 1, from Turangi southwards. Access to the northern part of the park is by Clements Mill Road off Highway 5, the Taupo-Napier road. Camping facilities, picnic areas and better huts are being built so that the park may be enjoyed by more people.

Tongariro National Park

Three active volcanos, including the highest mountain in the North Island, form the centrepiece of the oldest national park in New Zealand. The park also holds forest, scrublands and a strange, bare 'desert'

According to Maori legend, it was a *tohunga*—a person with special powers—who created the volcanic activity, geysers and boiling mud-pools of the North Island. The tohunga, Ngatoro-i-rangi, navigator of the canoe *Te Arawa*, is said to have travelled southwards from his home at Maketu in the Bay of Plenty until he reached Lake Taupo, where he and his companions rested. While they were at Taupo, the clouds revealed Mt Tongariro and Ngatoro decided he must climb the beautiful mountain.

He commanded his companions to fast until his return and set off, with his female slave Auruhoe. But after a while his companions became hungry and broke the fast. The gods were angry and sent blizzards to the mountain. Ngatoro and Auruhoe became frozen, so Ngatoro prayed to his own gods in Hawaiki, to send fire to warm them.

Ngatoro's gods heard him and sent the fire underground but the fires rose to the surface too soon at White Island and then at Rotorua, Tarawera, Orakei Korako and Taupo, before finally bursting forth at Tongariro. The fires warmed Ngatoro and he gained strength, but Auruhoe was already dead. He gave praise to his gods and as a gesture of his gratitude, hurled the body of his slave into the crater, which has ever since been known as Ngauruhoe.

Volcanic activity has been going on in the Tongariro volcanic centre much longer than the legend tells—for maybe 500 000 years. It is not certain when it began, but over several hundred thousand years four major andesite massifs, Kakaramea, Pihanga, Tongariro and Ruapehu, together with a number of smaller centres, Maungakatote, Pukeonake, Hauhungatahi and Ohakune, have formed.

In recent years there have been eruptions from Mt Ruapehu and from Mt Ngauruhoe and several other vents on Mt Tongariro. To geologists, Ngauruhoe is a young cone of the Tongariro massif, although it is commonly regarded as a separate volcano. In the original deed establishing the Tongariro National Park, however, it was considered simply as part of Mt Tongariro and the name Ngauruhoe did not even appear.

▶*Tongariro National Park has road access on all sides and it is within a day's easy driving distance of most cities in the North Island*

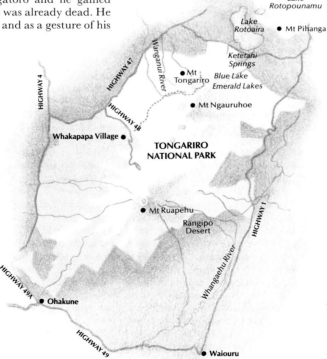

◄*Mt Ngauruhoe, the most vigorously active of the park's volcanos, during an eruption*

▼*The setting sun illuminates two of the volcanos. Cloud lightly veils the multi-cratered summit of Mt Tongariro, at left, and hides the top of Mt Ngauruhoe which geologists see as a part of the former*

New Zealand's first national park

The Maoris always held the Tongariro region in high esteem. It is the focus of legend and for many generations the Ngati Tuwharetoa tribe buried their dead chiefs on the mountainside, which became *tapu*, or sacred ground. In 1886, when the development of New Zealand was being determined largely by the effects of the axe and the match, the tribe's ownership of the mountains came under threat in the Maori Land Court. Rather than see the mountains fall into the hands of despoilers, chief Te Heuheu Tukino gave the mountains to the Government 'for the purposes of a National Park'.

In 1894 an act of Parliament formally constituted the Tongariro National Park, the first national park in New Zealand. At that stage it comprised only 2630 hectares, but more land was added and today it covers 78 651 hectares. It includes the top of Mt Ruapehu, which was excluded from the original gift. The most recent additions to the park include a 4 km wide old lava flow

▲ *The blue mountain duck, usually called whiowhio by the Maoris because of its whistling call*

▶ *A frozen waterfall testifies to the severity of winter in the Tongariro National Park, in the heart of the North Island*

from Mt Ruapehu, now covered by a native forest of red and silver beeches.

The park provides a magnificent outdoor recreation area all year round. In the summer there are many interesting walks and many cliffs suitable for rock-climbing. In winter Mt Ruapehu has three skifields with convenient access roads and chairlifts and ropetows.

An access road to Mangatepopo Valley enables trampers to get on to Mt Tongariro and Mt Ngauruhoe with ease. Well-maintained walking tracks cross Mt Tongariro and circle Mt Ruapehu, punctuated at convenient intervals by comfortable huts.

There is variety in the landscapes, vegetation and wildlife of the park. The tops of the active volcanoes contrast sharply with the lower slopes surrounding them. There is contrast also between the eastern and western lower slopes of Ruapehu. The western side is generally wetter—rainfall averages 2000 mm a year—and the soils developed on young

◀ *Mt Pihanga (on the right), volcanic cone, lies beyond Lake Rotoaira. Water from several rivers flowing out of the Tongariro National Park is stored in Lake Rotoaira before it goes through a tunnel to a power station at Tokaanu and then on to Lake Taupo*

◄The Rangipo Desert, with the cone of Mt Ngauruhoe in the distance. This barren land used to be known as the Onetapu Desert

ashes are fairly rich, so extensive forest developed there. Much of it was destroyed by volcanic eruptions and by humans before the land was included in the park, but some belts of forest remain. Through these quiet secluded areas flow turbulent streams which are the home of the uncommon and secretive blue mountain duck or *whiowhio*.

On the eastern side of Mt Ruapehu is the Rangipo or Onetapu Desert. This is not a true desert—the rainfall is never less than 1000 mm a year—but large areas of ground between tussocks are entirely bare. The lack of vegetation is primarily due to poor gravelly soils and to strong winds in summer, which severely dry the ground. Rabbits have been a great problem too.

To the north of Lake Rotoaira are Mt Pihanga and Kakaramea, the forested lower slopes of Pihanga containing rimu, matai, miro, kahikatea and red beech. Parts of this forest can be seen by driving along the Te Ponanga saddle road. On the north-western side of Mt Pihanga is the Rotopounamu graben, a sunken area between two fault-lines. Within this structure are two small young volcanic cones, Puketopo and Pukemohoao, and three craters. One crater is filled by the beautiful Lake Rotopounamu, which is less than 10 m deep and has several sandy beaches. It can be reached by a short track, 1.6 km through the bush from the Te Ponanga saddle road and is a rewarding detour.

►Dry watercourses in the Rangipo Desert. The bare ground is due less to lack of rainfall than to poor soil and strong, drying winds which cut across the desert in the summer

A steaming crater lake atop a restless mountain

The highest mountain in the North Island, Mt Ruapehu, is the most southerly volcanic massif of Tongariro National Park. The 2797 m high mountain is made up of andesite lava erupted over hundreds of thousands of years.

Early eruptions seem to have been centred slightly to the northwest of the present summit, but over time erosion by ice and water has left only remnants of the old volcano, such as the Pinnacle Ridge, to the northeast of Whakapapa Valley. A dyke—a vertical fissure filled with igneous rock—called Mead's Wall, is considered to have been formed during the same period. The younger structure centred on the present summit is, like the older, built up of alternating layers. These consist of lava flows and thick layers of pyroclastic material—fragmentary blocks and ash from explosive eruptions.

The present summit is broad and has at least two craters, one of which is active and contains a lake. It seems most likely that this broad summit owes its origin to periods of upward growth followed by large explosions and by periods of extensive erosion.

The crater lake has certainly been in existence since the middle of the 19th century. The temperature of the lake's water has varied considerably over the years. In 1926, for example, the surface was reported to have been frozen, but during a period of strong activity in 1968-71, the surface temperature was 60°C.

A few years ago tourist brochures used to suggest swimming in the lake, but this is not safe now because the water is highly acid. Gas often bubbles through the water and occasionally slicks of sulphur appear on the surface.

Mt Ruapehu must have been the site of some very large eruptions in the past, but some of the most devastating events have been lahars, great flows of mud and blocks which spread around the volcano. They formed thick agglomerates of largely volcanic boulders in fine ash and sand. These agglomerates are exposed in many cuttings made for roads in the vicinity of the mountain.

There are several possible explanations for the lahars. They could have been caused by eruption from a crater lake or by the action of heavy rain on the sides of the volcano during

▲ *The sulphurous waters of the crater lake on Mt Ruapehu steam amidst permanent ice and snow on the encircling peaks of the rim. The lake covers an area of 17 hectares. Its waters have sometimes poured down the mountainside, and on one occasion the consequences were tragic for a host of train travellers*

or after an eruption. It is more likely, however, that they formed during periods of more extensive glaciation, when thick snow and ice covered the mountain. A major explosive eruption under these circumstances would melt much of the snow and cause blocks, ash and meltwater to rush down the mountainside as a lahar.

Mt Ruapehu must have been erupted many times in the last few thousand years, from the summit and sometimes from small parasitic cones. Lava from one parasitic cone on the northern slopes flowed almost as far as the Tama Lakes. More eruptions took place in the Whakapapa Valley—the main ski area on the western side of the mountain—and left lava flows which now form the feature known as the 'Staircase' in the main skifield.

Since records began in 1860, all activity has been through the crater lake. Most has been small explosive eruptions, but in March 1945 a dome of steaming lava about 40 m in

diameter appeared in the lake. This was shortlived, but was followed in May by a larger dome, which spread over the floor of the crater. It displaced water, which poured out through an ice cave and into the Whangaehu River.

By 1 July most of the lake had gone and activity began to increase until on 22 August a tremendous cloud of ash-laden steam exploded out of the crater. Ash went as far as Wanganui, 88 km away. Ash eruptions continued in September and October. By January 1946 the eruption was over and water started to fill the crater again. The pools increased in size until by the summer of 1952–53 the lake had returned to its pre-1945 level.

The ice cave had become blocked by ash and the water level continued to rise until by August 1953 it was 8 m above normal. Just before 10 p.m. on 24 December 1953 the ash barrier in the cave broke and the lake dropped 6 m in 15 minutes. A tremendous volume of water rushed down the Whangaehu River, picking up huge quantities of boulders to form a lahar, and this swept down on to the plains. About 10.15 p.m. the lahar hit the railway bridge at Tangiwai sweeping away one of the piers moments before the packed Wellington-Auckland express arrived. The locomotive, tender and five carriages plunged into the torrent, killing 151 people.

Since 1945 explosive eruptions have been common, particularly between 1966 and 1971, when lava was apparently extruded on to the floor of the crater lake. There was a particularly large eruption early on 11 June 1969. Hot ash and blocks melted snow and caused a lahar which rushed down the Whakapapa and Maungaturuturu valleys, demolishing a refreshment kiosk on the Whakapapa skifield. Two thousand skiers are conservatively estimated to have been on the slopes only 12 hours before.

There have been more eruptions in 1971, 1975, 1978 and 1979. The eruption on 24 April 1975 was even larger than that of 1969. The volcano is still in a very active state.

This fact, however, does not prevent Mt Ruapehu from being one of the most popular winter holiday resorts in New Zealand and thousands go there every year.

▲*Pinnacle Ridge, on the Mt Ruapehu massif, is a remnant of a much earlier volcano. Erosion by ice and water has removed all but the resistant lava pinnacles rising there*

▶*Rapids and silica deposits on volcanic rocks can be seen at Silica Springs by taking a half-day walk on a track from Whakapapa Village*

Slopes of Mt Ruapehu

▲ *The mountainside after the eruption of Mt Ruapehu in June 1969, when the snow melted and a lahar of mud and rocks swept down the slope into a skifield. The distant cone is Mt Ngauruhoe*

▲ *The Whakapapaiti stream rushes down the northwestern face of Mt Ruapehu*

▶ *A tracery of water near the upper limit of the scrub zone. Plants growing near waterfalls include mountain buttercups*

The interest of Mt Ruapehu lies in its slopes as well as in its snowy, steaming summit. At one time forest covered the lower slopes, but it is now restricted to remnants on the southern and western flanks.

An almost continuous belt of mountain beech forest extends from Ohakune northwards to Hauhungatahi and east to the park headquarters. Much of this forest is included now in the Hauhungatahi Wilderness Area. Scattered crowns of kaikawaka trees poke through the mountain beech in some places. Mountain beech is replaced on the southern side of the Ohakune mountain road by red beech, growing as tall as 36 m with straight trunks up to 2 m in diameter, and by silver beech. In this area parakeets can sometimes be seen, and occasionally a New Zealand robin feeding on the forest floor or a kaka tearing at the bark of trees for insects.

In a few places on the southern and western sides of the park there are remnant stands of rimu. Some of the trees are 25–30 m high and are probably more than 600 years old. Podocarps, including matai, miro and kahikatea, also grow in this forest. The undergrowth is little disturbed by deer and even the delicate Prince of Wales feathers fern survives. Brushtail possums feed on the upper parts of the trees.

Birds abound in this type of forest. Whiteheads, tuis, bellbirds and New Zealand pigeons are all to be seen in addition to the species found in the beech forests—riflemen, grey warblers, silver eyes, fantails and pied tits. At night in all these forests the hoot of the morepork, known in Australia as the boobook owl, can be heard, and an endemic New Zealander, the shy brown kiwi, occasionally scurries through the undergrowth.

In the beech forest deer have removed so much of the undergrowth that it now grows only close to roads and settlements. For the most part it comprises fivefinger, broadleaf, and haumakaroa. Fivefinger joins mountain toatoa and coprosma in a belt of dense scrub which lies above the forest. Where this scrub has been burnt, it is replaced by scrub of manuka and kanuka, equally difficult to penetrate, but perhaps more rewarding as it hides up to 12 species of orchids. In places the scrub has now been replaced by heather, which was introduced in the early 1900s to provide shelter for

▲The kiwi, seldom seen in its natural
environment, emerges at night to feed on the
floor of the forest on Mt Ruapehu

grouse brought in as game birds. The grouse did not survive, but the heather flourished and in many places it has ousted native shrubs.

At its upper limit the scrub gives way to tussock, dominated by red mountain inaka. A variety of small flowering plants grows between the tussocks and there are many swampy areas within the zone where bog umbrella fern, wire rush and sedge tussock take over. Small lakes and tarns are common too. The most common species of bird is perhaps the New Zealand pipit.

The tussock and scrub zones begin at much lower levels on the eastern side of Mt Ruapehu than on the western side, because of climatic and ground conditions. This type of vegetation can be seen alongside the Desert Road, in between Waiouru and Turangi. Farther up the slopes, the tussock gives way to small flowering alpine plants and shrubs, including the snow totara, the low-growing pygmy pine, mountain gaultheria and whipcord hebe. The woolly moun-

tain daisy *Celmisia incana* is to be found on the western side of Ruapehu.

The alpine zone is delightful in summer, when many plants carry small but beautiful flowers. The flowers of this zone include the mauve-flowered *Parahebe hookeriana*, which gives way higher up to the white-flowered *Parahebe spathulata*. The latter is often associated with clusters of the large gentian *Gentiana bellidifolia*. There are also species of *Ranunculus*, the mountain buttercup.

At higher altitudes flowering plants disappear until there are only an everlasting daisy, which has small silvery leaves and yellow-centred white flowers, and the mountain anisotome, a carrot-like plant with clusters of distinctively aromatic flowers. These two small plants grow among the boulders and gravel up to about 2000 m. Above that altitude the landscape is very barren, and blocky lava or boulders cover the surface. Small glaciers fill the heads of seven valleys. The top is snow-covered, but in unusually hot summers snow remains only in small patches.

◄The Whakapapaiti
Valley becomes
increasingly barren as
it rises to the bluffs at
its head, beneath the
Whakapapa Glacier

▲Alpine shrubs on the
western side of Mt
Ruapehu. Many of the
plants carry beautiful
flowers in summer

Continually active volcano

▶*Mt Ngauruhoe is a composite cone built up by the alternation of eruptions of lava and explosive eruptions of volcanic bombs, blocks, lapilli and ash*

Mt Ngarauhoe has been continually active since the beginning of European settlement in New Zealand. Most of the time it simply erupts gas—mainly steam—but every few years it becomes more active and erupts ash and gas, usually for only a short time, from a few minutes to a few days. But in 1870, 1949 and 1954 the volcano erupted lava and these episodes lasted for months.

Mt Ngauruhoe, a classic conical volcano, lies near the southern edge of the Tongariro massif. The summit is only 900 m above the surrounding Tongariro lavas, but 2291 m above sea level. The outer slopes, much of which are debris, are steep.

Mt Ngauruhoe is thought to have been born about 2500 years ago, and most of the bigger lava flows, such as those flowing into the Makahikatoa valley, were probably formed early. At the same time, explosive eruptions scattered ash over a wide area, killing much of the beech forest and forming the Mangatawai Tephra, which can be seen near the top in road cuttings around the Tongariro National Park. A dark layer near its base is full of charred beech leaves. Since those early eruptions the activity of the volcano has probably been similar to that of the last 40 years, and ashes from Ngauruhoe and Ruapehu have mixed to form the andesitic ash which lies at the top in most road cuttings.

The most recent eruptions in which lava flowed began in May 1954. Red-hot lava had been seen in the vent some months before, but on 13 May explosions scattered ash and blocks of lava over the district. Lava first flowed on 4 June, accompanied by spectacular lava fountaining within the crater. On 30 June a lava flow reached the Mangatepopo Valley. Lava from the crater also flowed down the western side of the cone in July, August and September. Explosions continued until March 1955.

Since 1955 there have been some spectacular explosive eruptions. In January and March 1974 and February 1975 huge columns of ash-laden gas erupted up to 2 km above the summit. Some of the debris swept down the northwestern side into the Mangatepopo Valley as a dry avalanche, leaving blocks and ash on the slopes.

The eruption of 19 February 1975 was particularly spectacular. An eruption column rose nearly 9 km above the summit and

◀*The volcano erupts. Mt Ngauruhoe has sent out enormous columns of gas and ash several times in recent years. In 1975 walking parties were endangered. Mt Ngauruhoe is safer than many volcanos, but anyone walking near the cone should watch for signs of increasing activity and retreat very hastily when any are noticed*

◄Mt Ngauruhoe, in the right foreground, is separated from Mt Ruapehu by a low saddle upon which lie lakes known as Upper and Lower Tama

◄The crater at the top of Mt Ngauruhoe is about 400 m across

spread out into an ash cloud which reached a height of 12 km. Ash rained constantly over the surrounding area and large avalanches of erupted debris, solid but still hot, cascaded down the side of the cone. Walking parties within 2 km of the crater were pelted with scoria and one group was nearly hit by the avalanches which passed close to the Manga-tepopo Track.

During the latter part of the eruption there were loud explosions as large blocks of hot lava, up to 27 m in diameter, were strewn over the cone. Many of these were plastic when they hit the ground. No new lava was visible in the vent, however. The eruption lasted only eight hours, and after a minor explosion on 23 February, the volcano became quiet again.

▼The summit of Mt Ngauruhoe is 2291 m above sea level. The cone rises 900 m above its surroundings and may have grown quickly, like the famous volcano Paracutin, which erupted from a Mexican cornfield in 1943 and grew 325 m above it in the course of a year

The multiple craters of Mt Tongariro

▶ *Central Crater is one of many craters found on Mt Tongariro. Another is the crater of Mt Ngauruhoe (seen in the background here), which has only in this century come to be regarded as separate*

At least 12 composite volcanic cones can be recognised in Mt Tongariro, a volcanic massif built up over hundreds of thousands of years by many eruptions. It is not as high as Mt Ruapehu—2291 m against 2797 m—but it is perhaps the most colourful volcano in the Tongariro National Park, with red scoria, a blue lake, small emerald green lakes and bubbling hot springs.

Much of Tongariro existed before the ice ages, during which small glaciers carved out wide U-shaped valleys, removing much of the softer volcanic debris. The shape of the original cones can therefore no longer be recognised, but lava considered to have originally been inside the volcanic vents can be found in the walls of some of the valleys.

Much of the present skyline of Tongariro was formed by eruptions within the last 20 000 years. The most recently formed cone is that called Mt Ngauruhoe. Some earlier eruptions of Tongariro were explosive and spread hot ash around the district.

One such eruption, probably about 9700 years ago, spread pea-sized volcanic material called lapilli around the north of the volcano. The distribution of these lapilli indicates that they were erupted from a crater on the north-eastern side of Tongariro, most likely that now partly filled by the freshwater Blue Lake. This crater is circular, about 400 m in diameter. On its higher slopes, to the north of the lake, and on Rotopaunga Trig, lava has been plastered over the ground. This lava was probably formed during episodes when high gas pressure sent a fountain of molten lava high above the crater.

Explosive eruptions took place, possibly

►*The weird vertical cavern in the wall of Red Crater was formed as a result of lava pouring out of a vertical dyke. When the flow stopped, the lava left in the dyke drained back into it, leaving the hole*

about the same time, on the southern side of Tongariro, and formed six craters, two of which form the picturesque Tama Lakes.

North Crater is a flat-topped cone near the northwestern side of Tongariro. Originally it must have been a crater similar to the Blue Lake crater, though it is bigger—1100 m in diameter. It was almost completely filled by a lava lake. After the lava lake congealed there must have been an explosive eruption as there is an explosion pit, 300 m in diameter

and 60 m deep, lying in the crater itself.

Perhaps the most spectacular feature on the top of Tongariro is Red Crater, a young cone with red and black scoria. This contrasts markedly with the light grey of the older andesite lavas through which it was erupted. Small ash eruptions from Red Crater were seen in 1855 and 1926.

The Te Mari craters, on the northern slopes of Mt Tongariro, have also been active fairly recently. The Maoris apparently often saw the lower crater erupt and there were eruptions from the upper crater during the 19th century and possibly in 1928. A lava flow erupted from the upper crater some time in the last 1850 years, almost reaching the line of the National Park-Turangi road.

Nearby are the Ketetahi Springs, whose waters were said by the Maoris to cure all types of ailments, particularly rheumatism and skin troubles. This may be why Ketetahi was excluded when Te Heuheu Tukino gave the mountains to the Government. It remains a small enclave of Maori land within the park. There are many boiling pools, mud pools and small steaming craters at Ketetahi.

Ketetahi can be reached by a good track from the National Park-Turangi road. It is a good half-day trip through bush and tussock. At the springs it is important to keep to the marked track and, if caught in a steam cloud, to wait for it to disperse. A wrong step could result in a nasty burn. This track forms part of the Mangetepopo Track.

West of Tongariro massif, a scoria cone called Pukeonake rises about 143 m above the tussock-covered lower slopes of Mt Tongariro. Lava fountaining formed Pukeonake and layers of red, grey and black scoria radiate down from the crater. The scoria must have been very hot when it landed because

much of it has partially welded together.

Many streams flow off Mt Tongariro, including the Wanganui River, the second longest river in the North Island. It flows off the western side of the mountain to Taumarunui, where it turns south to provide some of the most spectacular river scenery in the North Island. In the first 50 km downstream from Taumarunui there are 90 rapids and then the river passes through narrow gorges. The last 32 km of the river are tidal.

◄*Minerals in the water, particularly sulphur, give a cloudy look to the Emerald Lakes, which lie near the Red Crater*

►*South Crater of Mt Tongariro is of glacial, not volcanic origin. It is near the source of the 225 km long Wanganui River*

The Mangatepopo Track provides a marvellous opportunity to see the main features of the Tongariro volcano. It begins at the Whakapapa village just beside the Chateau Tongariro hotel, skirts Mt Ngauruhoe, crosses Mt Tongariro and finishes at Ketetahi Hut. From this hut the Ketetahi Track leads down to the National Park-Turangi road. The combined Mangatepopo-Ketetahi Track can be walked by a fit tramper in nine to ten hours, but those who wish to be more leisurely and enjoy the many interesting features on the way can stay overnight at the Mangatepopo and Ketetahi huts and complete the trip in two and a half days.

Alternatively, it is possible to drive within 1 km of Mangatepopo Hut, from which a reasonably fit person could complete the traverse of Tongariro and the Ketetahi Track in seven to eight hours or, by stopping at the Ketetahi Hut, in a day and a half. In each case it would be necessary to arrange return transport from the end of the Ketetahi Track back to Whakapapa village.

The first section of the Mangatepopo Track is between Whakapapa village and Mangatepopo Hut. It is about 10 km of fairly easy walking and takes up to three hours. At first the track passes through stretches of low bush and beech forest, but most of the route is through open tussock.

The traverse of Mt Tongariro is the longest section—approximately 15 km—and it includes a number of steep climbs. It usually takes five to six hours. The first two kilometres from the hut are along the banks of the Mangatepopo Stream, past a flow of jagged, blocky lava, which was erupted before Europeans settled in New Zealand.

Near the head of the valley the track emerges into a wide amphitheatre from which a magnificent view of Mt Ngauruhoe may be obtained. Dark lava flows on the side of the cone were erupted in 1870, 1949 and 1954, and a small lighter grey flow almost at the head of the valley resulted from an 'avalanche' of blocks and ash ejected in 1974.

On the other side of the valley are the Soda Springs, where spray from a waterfall has provided a moist habitat for many plants, including mountain buttercup, ourisia and mauve-flowered parahebe.

From the head of Mangatepopo Valley the track climbs steeply 250 m up some of the older lava flows from Mt Tongariro to the saddle lying between Tongariro and Mt Ngauruhoe. From this saddle there is a magnificent view down the Mangatepopo Valley to the rugged King Country landscape. The very fit and energetic can detour at this point to ascend Mt Ngauruhoe. (Allow an extra two to three hours, be careful of falling rocks and take care around the crater—it is an active volcano.)

▲ *The first section of the Mangatepopo Track skirts the base of Mt Ngauruhoe and the low cone of Pukekaikiore. This part of the track is fairly level, apart from dips into stream beds and a climb of nearly 100 m up a spur near the Mangatepopo Hut*

The Mangatepopo Track continues across South Crater, a flat amphitheatre which has been formed largely by the action of glaciers, and then climbs about 150 m to Red Crater at 1820 m, the highest and perhaps most spectacular point of the trip. The light grey of the older andesite lava contrasts sharply with the red and black of the younger scoria erupted in 1855. On a good day there is a magnificent panorama from this point.

The track down the north side of Red Crater is steep and particular care has to be taken on the scoria-covered surface. At the base of the slope are the brilliantly coloured Emerald Lakes and from the track beside them there is an excellent view past the sulphur-covered slopes and back into the centre of Red Crater.

The next kilometre is across the flat Central Crater which, like South Crater, is not a volcanic crater but simply a depression between cones which has been filled by ash. A young lava flow from Red Crater now covers part of the floor. On the far side of Central Crater, the track climbs and then skirts the rim of the crater containing Blue Lake before

Track across a volcano

passing through the saddle between Blue Lake and North Crater. From this point there is a sweeping view to the north over Lake Rotoaira, Pihanga, Lake Taupo and the volcanic district. It is only 1.5 km around the northeastern side of North Crater to Ketetahi Hut and the end of the track.

The road is about 6 km further away and the walking time is about two hours. The route goes through the Ketetahi thermal area, where it is essential to keep to the track, and then descends gently through tussock before descending steeply into the Okahukura Bush. This forest contains Hall's totara, and mountain toatoa. Birds are common there, including New Zealand pigeons and bellbirds. Walking along streams through the forest is a pleasant way to end one of the most spectacular walks in the North Island.

◄*Jagged, blocky lava lies about near the Mangatepopo Stream, at the start of the section of the track which traverses Mt Tongariro*

▼*The track crosses South Crater, which has been formed largely by glacier action and has been smoothed by deposits of ash from Mt Ngauruhoe*

Rugged coast and wild hinterland

◀*Enormous quantities of driftwood, swept down from the hills by flooded rivers, are piled on Hawai Beach*

▼*The flowers of countless pohutukawa trees line the East Cape coast in summer*

The inland route from Gisborne to Opotiki, a distance of 148 km, first passes through a broad and fertile plain where ample rainfall and an annual average of 2210 hours of sunshine permit orchards, vineyards and dairy farms to flourish.

In startling contrast to this man-made patchwork of fields, the wild, bush-clad ranges that lie directly ahead, ridge after ridge, often appear sullen and mysterious under a blanket of mist. To the north is the Raukumara Range, to the south the vastness of the Urewera National Park.

At Matawai the Waioeka Gorge road turns left while the road to Motu swings north. Around Motu the land is much broken and heavily bushed; and the fine Motu Falls are just 4 km away. The narrow, rough Motu Hills road, a relic of coaching days, winds alarmingly around the ridges, through impressive stands of native bush and a great variety of ferns, to the coast.

The Waioeka Scenic Highway, part of Highway 2, is sealed and it is one of the most breathtaking main roads in the country as it twists and turns through magnificent native forest. Within the Waioeka Gorge itself there are many attractive rest areas on the banks of the Waioeka River, which rises in rugged highlands between the Bay of Plenty and Hawke's Bay and flows northwards to enter the Bay of Plenty.

Rainfall is heavy in this high country, often reaching 2000–2500 mm a year. Ferns and tree ferns are prolific. The high surrounding ridges that hem in the gorge, lack the open tops so characteristic of other mountain ranges in the country.

Red beech and silver beech predominate on the highest parts, while northern rata, broadleaf and tawa cover the lower slopes. A family of blue mountain ducks swimming with the current, a kingfisher, or a yellow-crested parakeet might be glimpsed. There are fine trout in the streams.

Opotiki, the 'place of children', is often called the 'gateway to the East Cape'. From there to Gisborne around the coast is a slow but deeply rewarding 341 km journey. The best time to travel this often lonely road is shortly before Christmas, when it is lined with brilliant yellow lupins and the ancient twisted pohutukawa trees display their flaming crimson flowers against wonderful seascapes. The coast offers splendid beaches, often unpopulated, where swimming and fishing can be enjoyed. The cleared coastal lands are broken or scrub-ridden, but behind them rear the forest-clad shoulders of the Raukumara Range, where deer and wild pigs

◀*The rugged hills are never far from the northern coast of the East Cape region. Patches of flat land are few and narrow. From Opotiki to Whangaparaoa the road heads inland only to cross the Motu and Raukokore Rivers. There is nowhere else in the North Island where one can travel so far so close to the sea*

lure the mounted Maori hunter and his team of half-wild dogs.

Just before Cape Runaway is Whangaparaoa Bay, the 'bay of whales', where Maori tradition says the first canoes *Arawa* and *Tainui* landed after the voyage from Hawaiki. A stranded whale was seen on the beach and captains of the canoes, determined to claim it, argued over who had landed first. Finally the *Arawa's* captain conceded both land and whale to Hoturoa, captain of the *Tainui*. Hoturoa's wife is credited with introducing the kumara into New Zealand.

Beyond Whangaparaoa Bay lies Cape Runaway, the eastern extremity of the Bay of Plenty. On 31 October 1769, Captain Cook was rounding this point, bound for the Coromandel Peninsula, where he would claim New Zealand for the British Crown. Suddenly the lookout sounded the alarm. Five large canoes, manned by warriors intent on battle, were rapidly approaching HMS *Endeavour*. Unperturbed, Cook gave the order that grapeshot be fired well clear of them. Cannons belched fire and smoke. Terrified, the Maoris turned tail and paddled furiously to the shore. Cape Runaway seemed a fitting name to bestow on this jutting headland.

▲*Many of the pohutukawa trees around the East Cape are of great age and impressive size. On the horizon here lies Cape Runaway, where Captain Cook frightened away some belligerent Maoris*

▶*The steep-sided valley of the Motu River writhes through heavily forested Raukumara Range*

▼*The Motu Falls are near Motu settlement at the end of the road, beside the river. Thereafter the river takes a wild and remote course to the coast*

Golden beaches on a historic coast

▼*Hicks Bay has one of many beautiful beaches on the eastern coast of the East Cape region. Captain Cook named the bay after Lieutenant Zacchary Hicks, the first of his men to spot it*

▶*Captain Cook anchored near these unstable cliffs at Tolaga Bay in 1769 to take on water and foodstuffs. The well from which he drew water was covered by a landslide in 1930*

From Whangaparaoa, near Cape Runaway, Highway 35 heads inland. The countryside is often hilly, frequently manuka-clad, and small creeks and rivers flow down from the ever-present Raukumara Range; it is no longer possible to glimpse the sea. It is possible, though, to take a side road to Lottin Point, 17 km east of Cape Runaway, where pleasant farmlands run down to the edge of the water itself.

Roughly halfway to Hicks Bay is the Oweka Stream bridge. Waikura road, a secondary one, follows the valley of this small river and eventually leads to the Waikura Valley, giving access to the northern parts of the Raukumara Range.

Hicks Bay—named by Cook for one of his lieutenants—sweeps sharply inland under Matakaoa Point. Fine offshore fishing can be enjoyed here, particularly for snapper. Near Horseshoe Bay is a glow-worm cave and close by a 20-minute bush walk leads to some very old puriri trees with girths in excess of 3.5 m. The rearing coastal hill, a short distance away, is a refuge for forest birds.

Only 14 km from Hicks Bay, at the end of a picturesque curving beach of golden sand, is Te Araroa, near which a bloody tribal battle is reputed to have taken place in 1820. A large number of the Ngati-Porou tribe were attacked by a Ngapuhi raiding party from Northland. The East Cape Maoris were armed with traditional weapons. They were overwhelmed by the raiders, who used the firearms of the pakeha to devastating effect. About 3000 Ngati-Porou are said to have

◄Cabbage trees and a shining sea typify the Lottin Point district. The cabbage trees of this part of the East Cape region are large and luxuriant

▼The Waiapu River is formed near Ruatoria by the joining of the Mata River and the Tapuaeroa River, which rises in the distant hills of the Ruakumara Range

been killed or taken prisoner in this battle.

Te Araroa is also famous for its huge, ancient pohutukawa trees. On the foreshore near the airstrip is a huge pohutukawa named *Te Waho o Rerekohu*, 'the mouth of Rerekohu', after a chief who had a *pataka*, or storehouse, near the tree. It is estimated to be over 600 years old and boasts 22 trunks, with a total girth of about 20 m. It is certainly the largest, and possibly the oldest, pohutukawa tree in the land.

About 20 km from Te Araroa lies the East Cape lighthouse, on a coastline which has seen many a wreck. The lighthouse was originally a little offshore, on East Island. It was extremely difficult to land on the island, which lacks a beach, and keepers found life unnerving as the cliffs kept slipping away. But it was only after four men were drowned while attempting to provision the island that it was judged prudent to move the lighthouse to its present mainland site.

Hikurangi, the mountain said to be the first place in New Zealand to be lit by the rays of the rising sun each day, is clearly visible from Ruatoria, and its lower slopes can be reached by road. Its name, meaning 'sky peak', commemorates a peak in Hawaiki, the legendary homeland of the Maoris.

Natural gas, which the Maoris called *Te-Ahi-o-te-Atua*, 'the flame of the gods', often escapes from vents in the ground around Ruatoria and at Te Puia, farther south. When a match is applied to a vent the gas will burn for a considerable time. The natural gas has been used for heating and lighting for many years at Te Puia, where it also issues from hot springs. The springs are used for therapeutic purposes and for pleasure bathing.

From Te Puia, it is only 103 km to Gisborne, past places that will always be linked with Captain Cook—Anaura Bay and Tolaga Bay, with its fascinating Cook's Cove. The land is more closely settled in this part of the region. The range is farther inland, yet it still dominates the background, beckoning to the adventurous.

An active volcano erupting off the coast

▶ *Pohutukawa trees grow in patches on the northern side of the island, and in a belt along the southern side*

When Maui, the legendary Maori hero, first stepped on the North Island, the new land he had just fished out of the sea, he accidentally caught up some of the fire burning on it. This he shook off into the sea, where it remains today as White Island, an active volcano steaming away 50 km offshore in the Bay of Plenty. Captain Cook, who sighted the island after rounding East Cape on 31 October 1769, named it White Island 'because as such it always appeared to us'.

The island is often obscured by large clouds of steam. It sprinkles the Bay of Plenty with fine dust from time to time and on one occasion it pelted some local fishermen with pieces of lava.

The island is small, only 2.7 km long and 1.5 km wide. The highest peak, just west of the centre, is Mt Gisborne, 321 m high. The southeastern side is occupied by a crater which is 1.2 km long, 400 m wide and rarely more than 30 m above sea level.

In calm weather it is possible to land on the island from a boat, provided permission has been obtained from the private owner, but it is a dangerous place. The mud and water are strongly acid, and there are many fumaroles, emitting clouds of gas which eddies of wind often cause to change direction unpredictably. Conditions can be very unpleasant for anyone without a gas mask.

Over thousands of years the eruption of lavas, ash and lapilli, breccias and agglomerates has built the island up into two overlapping cones. The older cone forms the higher western side of the island and the younger cone the eastern and central part. The younger cone has been destroyed, partly by explosion and partly by collapse, to form the present crater.

Some 30 steam and ash eruptions have been recorded since 1826, when the first European landed on White Island. For most of the 19th century there was a lake on the island but it was drained in 1913 in order to provide better access for extraction of sulphur from the crater.

Sulphur was intermittently mined on the island for many years. The first company, formed in 1885, was forced by conditions on the island to abandon its operations in 1900.

◀ *The dangers of White Island have not always deterred those who sought to exploit the island's sulphur. One sulphur-mining venture ended in the deaths of 11 workers. The last operation ended in 1936, leaving behind a factory whose ruins can be seen near the breach in the wall of the crater*

In 1911 another company bought the island. Some sulphur was extracted but before it could be shipped off the island a collapse in the back wall of the crater covered much of the crater and killed all the 11 men who lived and worked there.

This demonstration of the danger of living and working in the crater of an active volcano, which occurred in September 1914, was not enough to deter another company which was set up ten years later. The factory was rebuilt and operations continued sporadically until a combination of conditions on the island and the economic depression caused a shutdown in 1936.

The island today is free of any commercial venture but it remains a hostile environment. In the crater there is no fresh water and the only plants are a few stunted specimens of *Disphyma australe* near the ruins of the factory.

Plant life is more common on the outside of the cone. Pohutukawas, in a belt on the southern side and isolated patches on the northern side, are the most obvious. These trees appeared to grow well during the volcanically quiet 1950s but they have suffered badly from recent ash eruptions.

Australian gannets regularly nest on the outer slopes, especially in the south, although they are fewer during eruptive phases. Many other seabirds and some land birds, including the house sparrow and the chaffinch, are occasionally seen on the island, although they sometimes succumb to the toxic fumes. The only mammal known on the island is the *kiore*, or Polynesian rat, which was probably introduced by Maoris on fishing trips.

Since 1967 the volcanic activity of White Island has been regularly monitored and changes to the crater floor noted. Short-lived

▲ *White Island emits huge clouds of steam which often obscure its form but decisively* *mark its ominous presence in the Bay of Plenty, 50 km offshore from Whakatane*

ash vents were formed in 1969 and 1971. On 26 December 1976, there was a large ash eruption and a new crater, named Christmas Crater, was formed. This continued to erupt and in March 1977, there was the island's first eruption in historic times of andesite lava. The composition of the lava was very similar to that of young cones in the Tongariro Volcanic Centre at the other end of the Taupo Volcanic Zone.

Ash has erupted intermittently since 1977 and the crater has continued to enlarge. By mid-1980 the bottom of the crater was well below sea level and it had become most important to watch the island closely.

Urewera National Park

The rugged ranges and deep valleys known as the Urewera are covered by the largest area of native forest in the North Island, and they make up the largest national park in the island

Within the 212 672 hectares enclosed by the Urewera National Park lie virtually all the landscape and the botanical features that characterise the inland North Island—grassy river flats, peaks, hog-backed ridges, limestone bluffs, podocarp and beech forests and a trout-stocked lake. Native bird life is abundant and varied. Lakeside temperatures soar in summer while in winter the tops are snow-covered. Although the Urewera landscape is young geologically its scenic appeal is complemented by a sense of antiquity.

The drive from the Murupara Plains into the brooding ranges is a journey back to a time when the hand of man had scarcely touched the landscape. Only one road—tortuous and unsealed Highway 38, completed only in 1930—cuts through the centre of the park from Murupara to Wairoa. It takes visitors to Lake Waikaremoana. There is limited access by road from the Bay of Plenty and from walking tracks.

The Urewera Maoris—the Tuhoe tribe—remained aloof from the rest of the country until the second decade of this century, and even after that made few concessions to pakeha life. One aspect of the park's uniqueness is that the descendants of the Tuhoe people who named its features still live there. These Tuhoe, the 'children of the mist', colonised the valley of the Huiarau Range. Their life was spartan and harsh but after a dispute with the neighbouring Ngati Ruapani tribe, they crossed the Huiarau and began to settle on the shores of Waikaremoana. By the 1860s they had made the lake their own.

In the 1840s the first Europeans penetrated the Ureweras. They were missionaries but none of the churches made many conversions. In 1868 the Maori fighter Te Kooti took refuge in the Ureweras and the Tuhoe revered him as a prophet and fought under his command. Government troops tried to starve the rebels out and pursued a scorched earth policy until Te Kooti left the area in 1872. He was pardoned in 1883. The Ringatu Church, which he established, remains strong among the Tuhoe to this day.

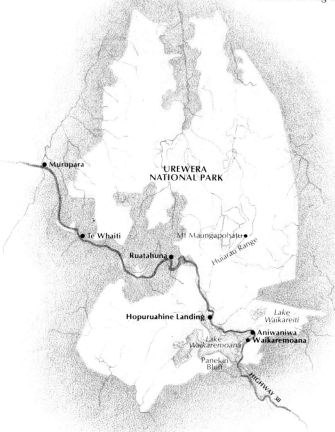

◄*The Urewera National Park lies across the Huiarau Range, which forms a watershed between the catchments of the rivers that drain into the Bay of Plenty or drain into Hawke Bay*

►*The Papakorito Falls, one of several splendid waterfalls on streams that run into Lake Waikaremoana, in the heart of the national park*

Rippling waters at the gateway to the forest

In the Urewera National Park native forest is the setting and Lake Waikaremoana is its gemstone. Regarded as the most beautiful lake in the North Island, Waikaremoana lies 585 m above sea level and is bordered by dozens of bush-clad inlets. The Huiarau Range provides a backdrop to its northern aspect, and Panekiri Bluff rises 610 m sheer from the south shore.

The lake's name means 'lake of rippling water'. In legend, it was formed by the threshings of Haumapuhia, a *taniwha*, or water monster, which created arms and valleys in a desperate but unsuccessful attempt to reach the sea. Geologists identify the lake's origin in a rockfall 2000 years ago which dammed what is now the head of the Waikaretaheke River and flooded the valley-system behind it.

Some of the best known features of the park can be seen from the Waikaremoana track, which skirts 62 km of the western side of the lake, from Onepoto to Hopuruahine. Six huts en route offer accommodation.

From the old Armed Constabulary redoubt at Onepoto the track climbs Panekiri Bluff to over 1100 m above sea level. This is the only really strenuous section. Past Pukenui trig the views of the lake to the north and the cutover hills of Hawke's Bay to the south

are unsurpassed. Beyond the Panekiri Hut the track drops steeply to the Wairaumoana arm of Waikaremoana. From the shore the walker can look back on the profile of Panekiri Ridge and through the Straits of Manaia to the eastern side of the lake. The birdlife—herons, shags, ducks—is plentiful here. Three huts stand around the rim of Wairaumoana and the fifth on the track, Whanganui, is named after the northern inlet. From there it is an easy stroll of two hours and a quarter back to Highway 38 alongside the Hopuruahine Stream.

The park headquarters lie halfway round the lake on the eastern side at Aniwaniwa, a place whose name, meaning 'rainbow', may be due to the presence of the nearby Papakorito Falls, a three-tiered cascade of exceptional beauty. Farther round the lake the Mokau Falls descend over curving rock into the Mokau Inlet. And slightly farther north again the Hopuruahine Cascades emerge close to the end of the Waikaremoana track.

Five kilometres and an easy walk northeast of Aniwaniwa is the park's second and smaller lake, Waikareiti, 'little rippling water'. It is 274 m higher than Lake Waikaremoana and its Mangapuwerawera and Aniwaniwa Streams feed the larger lake. Waikareiti is studded with seven small is-

▲Maraunui Bay is on the western shore of Lake Waikaremoana. Rising up behind it is Panekiri Bluff, which looms 610 m high above the water on the southern shore

lands, one of which itself contains a tiny lake.

Ruatahuna, 47.5 km from Murupara, lies in a wide, grassy valley formed by the upper reaches of the Whakatane River and is the traditional centre for the Tuhoe tribe. In addition to a general store and a motel, it has half-a-dozen meeting houses within a radius of three kilometres.

The remnants of Maungapohatu Pa lie east of Ruatahuna and 19 km along a logging road suitable for four-wheel drive vehicles only. The 1366 m mountain from which it takes its name is a vast fortress of limestone cliffs and columns which the Tuhoe have always regarded as a symbol of their identity. At its base lies a meeting house, and a cluster of derelict homes—all that remains of a thriving settlement of more than 2000 people established in 1907 by the prophet Rua Kenana. These followers of the Wairua Tapu cult were the last Maoris who tried to achieve complete political, social and economic independence from pakeha New Zealand. The experiment came to an end in 1916 in a shootout with police, who arrested Rua on charges of sedition and liquor offences.

◄Korokoro Falls are on a stream which runs into the Wairau arm of Lake Waikaremoana

►The distant water is the Wairau arm, or Wairaumoana. Here it is seen from Panekiri Bluff, looking across the Whareama Range

◄Tapuaenui Bay in Whanganui Inlet, on the northern side of Lake Waikaremoana. In the south the lake shore coincides with the southern boundary of the Urewera National Park at Onepoto, where Highway 38 enters

◀Rainforest near Lake
Waikaremoana. As in
all rainforest, the dense
foliage of the canopy
allows little light to
penetrate to the floor.
In many places the
density of the Urewera
forest has been reduced
by possums and five
species of deer

Rich and varied forests where birds abound

◄*Thick, stringy bark distinguishes the trunk of the towering and long-lived totara*

A popular Tuhoe saying advises people to 'go to the mountains that you may be cleansed by the winds of Tawhirimatea' (god of storms). It is a call to return to roots, to achieve self-knowledge and confidence before confronting the wider world. But it is also an expression of the primitive and profound satisfaction humans have always felt in the primaeval forests of the Ureweras.

From river flats and lake-shore to mountain tops, the Urewera National Park contains a greater variety of native plant life than any other area in the country. Altitude mainly determines what grows there. On the northern side kohekohe spreads luxuriantly in the mild Bay of Plenty climate. Generally, rimu, northern rata and tawa are dominant below 800 m and beech and rimu above. Higher up, the rimu is replaced entirely by hard beech and even higher by red and silver beech. And with the exception of Maungapohatu, there are no uncovered peaks.

Within this pattern are variations in different sectors of the park. The Murupara side is drier than the rest. Matai and totara grow there with rata and rimu. Gullies are crammed with tree-ferns and hardwood scrub: five-finger, fuchsia, mahoe and wineberry. In the northern sector puketea and mangeao are prolific, many of them trailing epiphytes such as kiekie. Nikau palms and tree-ferns grow below the kohekohe and break the regularity of the bush line. The forest floor is often carpeted with ferns.

On the Huiarau Range, silver beech predominates at altitudes above 1200 m, and these trees indicate a higher rainfall than elsewhere. In many places they develop twisted trunks draped with mosses and epiphytes—contributing to the Tuhoe conviction that these parts of the forest are inhabited by goblins and fairies. The broad-leafed cabbage tree *toii* is also a feature of the Huiarau. Ferns grow more prolifically in New Zealand than in any other temperate country. They are to be found in all sorts of habitats, from salt-sprayed coastal cliffs to mountain rocks at high altitudes, sunbaked at some times and deep in snow at others. But they are best seen in the humid forests, and nowhere better than in the Urewera. They range in size from tall tree-ferns and high-climbing creepers to minute filmy ferns with fronds barely a centimetre high.

The piupiu, or crown fern, can appear as a creeper or a miniature tree-fern. Its upright, elongated fronds often form a crown a metre tall, and it is a handsome species. However, its ability to form extensive colonies on the forest floor and at higher altitudes gives it dominance over the seedlings of regenerating trees and threatens the future of the forest.

Few New Zealand plants have brightly coloured flowers. This is thought to be due to the absence of long-tongued bees in prehistoric times when the distinctive plants of New Zealand were evolving. Two red flowers are to be seen in the Urewera forests, however. One is the kaka beak, or *koehai-ngutu-kaka*, a familiar plant in gardens. It still grows naturally in only two areas, one of which is Waikaremoana. The only other red-flowering plant is the red mistletoe. A parasite like its European counterpart, it can usually find a home on the branches of a beech.

The forests of the Urewera National Park teem with birds, though they are more likely to be seen from walking tracks than from the highway. At daybreak the dawn chorus is dominated by the clear notes of the honey-eaters, the tui and the bellbirds. At night in summer the harsh shriek of the long-tailed cuckoos suggests the tropical jungles from which they migrate. Native pigeons frequently allow walkers to come close. Kakas, on the other hand, are more often heard squawking than seen. There is a proliferation of smaller birds: whiteheads, riflemen, grey warblers, tomtits, silvereyes and fantails. Wekas have been reintroduced and their numbers are increasing steadily.

◄*Beech forest. Three species of beech grow in the Urewera National Park, each in its own altitude range*

Egmont National Park

Mt Egmont, an isolated volcanic cone standing 2518 m high, is New Zealand's most climbed mountain. The national park that encompasses its snowy summit and forested slopes offers easy access and many walks.

Mt Egmont, 2518 m high, stands in isolation from any main range. The Maoris, who call Mt Egmont *Taranaki*, 'barren mountain', have a legend to explain its isolation. Taranaki once lived in the centre of the North Island with Tongariro, Ruapehu, Putuaki, Tauhara and Pihanga. All were male except the lovely Pihanga. They all loved her but she loved only Tongariro. Great battles ensued and the sky was dark with smoke and streaked a fiery red as the volcanoes hurled their devastating weapons at one another.

Tongariro was the victor and the defeated had to leave. Tauhara, the most reluctant to go, reached only Taupo. Putuaki went north and is now called Mt Edgecumbe. Taranaki dejectedly travelled westward, gouging out the huge channel of the Wanganui River. While he rested overnight, the Pouakai Ranges—which rise to 1399 m and extend west to east across the northern flanks of Mt Egmont—thrust out a spur and trapped the volcano in the place where it now stands.

In clear weather Mt Egmont can be seen from as far away as the northern tip of the South Island, but mist or heavy cloud often hide it. It must have been so hidden when Abel Tasman, the European discoverer of New Zealand, sailed along the Taranaki coast in December 1642. He recorded the headland now called Cape Egmont but made no mention of the majestic mountain.

It was on the evening of 10 January 1770 that the mountain was first revealed to Europeans. Captain Cook and the company of his ship were justly impressed by its splendour. It was recorded in the ship's log as '. . . a very high mountain and in appearance resembling the Peak of Teneriffey. . .'. Cook named it in honour of the Earl of Egmont, once First Lord of the Admiralty.

For the Taranaki tribes the mountain possessed a *mana* all its own. They climbed its slopes in search of red ochre to use as pigment, or to bury their dead chiefs and *tohunga* in secret caves. But the higher reaches of the mountain were *tapu*, the haunt of the mythical reptiles called *ngarara*.

In 1839 Ernst Dieffenbach, a young German geologist of the New Zealand Company, and James Heberly, a whaler, set out with Maori guides to climb Mt Egmont. After an arduous trek they reached the snowline. The superstitious guides would go no farther, but the pakehas pressed on. The final ascent was dangerous, over ice, but they reached the summit and triumphantly looked into the snow-filled crater.

During the 1860s and 1870s a route to the lower slopes of Mt Egmont was formed. It started at New Plymouth, wound a tortuous path through the Pouakai Ranges and eventually came within striking distance of the peak. Many who went there were enthralled by the wonderful forest clothing the mountain's lower slopes.

In July 1881 it was decreed that all land within 9.6 km around the summit of Mt Egmont be fully protected and in 1900, the Egmont National Park Board took control. More land was gradually added to the park until today it covers 33 543 hectares. There are three mountain houses on Mt Egmont— all about 900 m above sea level.

◄*Highways encircle Mt Egmont and roads lead from them to three mountain houses about 900 m above sea level*

▶*From some viewpoints Fanthams Peak, a secondary volcanic cone, breaks the symmetrical outline of Mt Egmont*

Devastating eruptions of a now-dormant volcano

►*The forested slopes of Mt Egmont contrast with the gentle green Taranaki farmlands. Little of the Egmont forest remains outside the national park*

▼*The crater wall on the western side of Mt Egmont was breached by one of the last eruptions*

Mt Egmont is the largest and latest of a chain of volcanos which have erupted in Taranaki. The oldest can be seen off the coast near New Plymouth, where there is a cluster of small islands called the Sugar Loaves, eroded stumps of a volcano that was active about a million years ago.

The undulating Kaitake Range, rising to 683 m, is all that remains of the Kaitake volcano, which during its active period about 500 000 years ago was probably as high as Mt Egmont is now—some 2500 m. Pouakai, which was active about 250 000 years ago, was perhaps as high as 2000 m before erosion began to grind it down.

While Pouakai was slowly dying out, about 70 000 years ago Mt Egmont was born. By the beginning of the last ice age, some 20 000 years ago, its height approached 2700 m. A thick ice-cap covered much of the mountain, and each major eruption produced searing stony mud-flows called lahars, which scoured away its flanks and higher slopes. Explosions and natural structural collapse combined to reduce the height of the volcano to less than 1200 m.

In glacial times and later, rivers and creeks were diverted when massive lahars rampaged down the mountain's flanks. The Waitara River probably followed a south-westward course across a gently sloping plain to the sea until Mt Egmont's base grew in size and diverted it to the north.

The present upper half of the mountain's andesite cone has been formed since about 12 000 years ago by frequent eruptions of ash and lava. Much of Mt Egmont's earlier geology has been obscured by the eruptions of the last 500 years, but it is likely that a cone similar to the present one had been formed some 35 000 years ago.

On the southwestern slopes of Mt Egmont is a large, subsidiary cone, rather like a shoulder. This is Fanthams Peak, named after Fanny Fantham, who in March 1887, at the age of 19, became the first woman to climb it. It was apparently formed in the early stages of the rebuilding of Mt Egmont. Debris that had not been ejected with sufficient force to fall farther afield fell back into the crater and eventually plugged it. The forces inside the mountain were not at that stage powerful

◀Erosion has deeply scarred the slopes of Mt Egmont and over the last few hundred years there have been some great flows of debris down its sides

▼The remains of a lava dome formed by the eruption of 1655 occupy much of the crater of Mt Egmont. The sharp point at right is known as the Shark's Tooth

enough to blow out the plug but they formed the secondary cone.

Geologists estimate the most devastating of recent eruptions of Mt Egmont took place about the year 1500. During this gigantic upheaval a plug of stiff viscous lava was pushed up into the crater and thick ash was dumped over the mountain. Pumice, gravel and stones in enormous quantities were heaped upon the smouldering landscape, eventually covering 260 km^2 to the northwest of the mountain itself, and a layer of ash spread as far as the coast.

These eruptions destroyed much of the forest of the middle slopes of Mt Egmont. The devastation was greatly increased when fire raged round the mountain's face, spreading northwards 3 km across the bush-covered slopes of the Pouakai Range. Torrential rain created more havoc on the unstable slopes. Massive landslides thundered unchecked down to the forest, creating fans reaching from Okauha Stream, in the southwest, to the Ahukawakawa Swamp, between the mountain and the Pouakai Range.

With Mt Egmont quiet again, the forest regenerated. Then about 1665, the mountain became violent once more. This date is confirmed by the kaikawaka trees which survived on the steep slopes at a level of 900-1100 m. These gnarled, wind-blasted relics are estimated at 350-400 years old. By removing a core of wood from one of these trees, and counting its annual rings back to the first one which reveals a reduction of growth-rate, scientists estimate the date of this last great eruption of Egmont.

The latest eruption, however, is believed to have taken place in 1775. It seems to have been a minor affair, with perhaps 5-12 cm of ash being cast on the higher slopes. Today Mt Egmont is dormant rather than extinct, but a volcano can still erupt after thousands, even millions of years of inactivity.

◀On the horizon, far beyond the Shark's Tooth, rise Mt Ruapehu and the other volcanos of Tongariro National Park

◄Egmont National Park was originally declared a circle 9.6 km in radius from the peak, and its shape is striking from the air. Additions have broken the symmetry in places. The Kaitake Range is a separate part of the park

Standing on Mt Egmont's summit on a clear, sunny day is like standing on the roof of the world. The air is pure and the scenery unforgettable. To the east rises Mt Ruapehu, capped with dazzling white. Seaward, a long stretch of black sand is in startling contrast to the white-flecked deep blue of the Tasman Sea. Far below is the forest, a dark green-brown carpet flecked with lighter tones.

Mt Egmont's vegetation forms several different zones. On the lower slopes, from about 490 m to 900 m, is a typical mixed broadleaf-podocarp rainforest where the mighty rimu often reaches a height of 50 m. The massively-trunked northern rata grows there too, tall enough at 30 m to reveal itself above the canopy. From afar rimu and rata appear to dominate growth in the forest, yet they cover only one-eighth of the lower zone. The smaller trees—kamahi, mahoe, broadleaf and tree fuchsia—provide the greater cover. Beneath the canopy the undergrowth is prolific. Creepers and ferns choke hidden watercourses. Bush lawyer and supplejack abound. Many trees are garbed in a profusion of mosses and lichens.

On the steeper slopes between 900 and 1100 m, the yellowish-green totara intermingles with the darker-foliaged kaikawaka. They rise above a scattering of small, lighter-coloured trees such as fuchsia, broadleaf, and mountain five-finger. Kaikawaka reaches its southerly limit in the North Island at Taranaki, but it also occurs in the South Island. Its interrupted distribution appears to be a relic of an ancient time when the two strongholds of kaikawaka were joined by dry land, because birds do not carry its seeds.

The rainforest gradually peters out and dense, almost impenetrable scrub takes full control. At least 2 m high, it mainly consists of a tough shrub called leatherwood.

Beyond this grey-green scrub barrier the tussock waves in the wind up to about

◄Moss mantles many of the trees in the Egmont rainforest. The rainfall is high—at 900 m up on the north side it averages 7500 mm a year

▶One of the oldest and most simple plants in the world, Tmesipteris elongata grows in spectacularly unusual profusion on Mt Egmont

▲*Dawson Falls,*
18 m high, are on the
Kapuni Stream, near
one of the tourist
centres within the park

▶*Wilkies Pools, on*
the Kapuni Stream
above the Dawson
Falls Tourist Lodge,
are reached by track

1400 m. Within this zone there are many small herbaceous plants, some of them unique to Mt Egmont, and two species of mountain daisies that differ slightly from other New Zealand species. A rare fern, *Polystichum cystostegia*, which can be found only on Mt Egmont, flourishes in rock-strewn gullies at this altitude. On the other hand, mountain beech and more than 100 other common species of plants are absent from these alpine slopes. Evolution has taken place over thousands of years on Mt Egmont in isolation from other alpine habitats.

Rearing dramatically above the tussock up to the 1980 m level, are the alpine fellfields and screes, savagely dissected with many rock slides and beyond this point Mt Egmont is usually under snow and ice.

Waterfalls cascade over marble-smooth rocks in the park. Prominent amongst them are the Dawson, Bells, and Curtis Falls. A staggering number of cut tracks—totally more than 300 km in length—put viewing these splendid natural attractions within easy reach of a moderately fit person.

The climb to the top of Mt Egmont is easy enough, given kindly weather, and hundreds of people admire the view from the summit every summer. Yet it must never be forgotten that the mountain is ruled by the elements. Temperatures can drop alarmingly, whatever the season. Mist insidiously blots out landmarks and the rainfall is often torrential. Mt Egmont's graceful slopes have been the scene of many search-and-rescue operations. The mountain that the Maoris had regarded with such awe and had declared to be *tapu*, has claimed its share of the unwary and the ill-prepared, and demands caution.

Hawke's Bay and Wairarapa coast

This long stretch of the North Island lacks a handy, comprehensive name but there is nothing anonymous about its coastal scenery. The coast, fringing hills cleared for sheep, is a wild place of rocks, great cliffs and fine sandy beaches

The striking, often dangerous coast from Cape Kidnappers in Hawke's Bay to Turakirae Head on the western side of Palliser Bay is a region of great natural beauty, where white-capped surf breaks on golden sand; where fast-flowing rivers, rising in the inland high country, wind across fertile plains once the site of native forests, before finally losing their identity in the broad Pacific.

According to legend, Kupe explored this coast in the 10th century and is said to have lived with his wife and five children in Palliser Bay and he may have bestowed names on many places there. Below the lighthouse at Cape Palliser is Matakitaki-a-Kupe, a Maori reserve, which contains Kupe's sacred pool and from which he is said to have stood and gazed across the sea to the snow-capped Inland Kaikoura Range. Nearby there are also large rock formations called Nga-Ra-o-Kupe—the 'sails of Kupe'. By tradition he hung out his sails to dry there and an impression of sails appears in the remarkable forms of these large rock masses.

The Maoris considered Palliser Bay, with its pleasant east coast climate, a perfect place to live. Dense virgin forests swept right down to the coast and were full of birds to hunt. The shore and rocky reefs contained many types of shellfish, and the sea was alive with fish. The Maoris cleared the ground and planted kumara, and supplemented their diets with wild fruits. There were many rivers and streams rising in the nearby Aorangi Mountains and the South Island was within easy reach by canoe.

Captain Cook sailed round this coast too and he is responsible for the naming of many prominent headlands.

Heading south from Cape Kidnappers, which harbours the only known mainland colony of Australasian gannets, the true southeast coast of the North Island is reached. This region, which some would call East-

land, is bounded on the west by the Tararua Range and extends from Palliser Bay in the south to a line extending eastwards from the Manawatu Gorge in the north. Between the ranges and the sea, the country is mostly hilly. Very little of the vast forests remain, the result of early land-clearing fires which spread at times much farther than intended.

Often the coast is inaccessible. The raging sea hurls itself at sheer cliffs yet there are many fine beaches, among them Ocean Beach and Waimarama Beach, both close to Cape Kidnappers. Farther south there are others at Porangahau, Herbertville, Castlepoint, and Riversdale. Fishing along this coast can be dangerous. Unexpected swells of enormous power and height often sweep unwary fishermen off the rocks.

North of Cape Palliser there is a long, flat coastal shelf. Colenso, Thomas and Harrison and other early travellers took full advantage of it when trekking south from Hawke's Bay.

It is only in the southeast corner of the region that the land becomes mountainous, with the Aorangi Mountains—once called the Haurangi Mountains—trending northwards from Cape Palliser.

▼The highways are inland and travellers who would visit the coast must make side trips. Much of the coast cannot be reached by road at all

◄Cape Kidnappers, where gannets breed on the few flat places, is the northern extremity of this region

113

High headland where gannets make their nests

▲*The sandstone cliffs of Cape Kidnappers rise 60-90 m above the* *sea. Captain Cook named the cape after an attempted abduction*

At the southern extremity of Hawke's Bay there is a distinct, weathered headland of battleship-grey sandstone. Its Maori name is *Te-Matau-a-Maui*, meaning 'the fish-hook of Maui'. Indeed the very formation of this promontory as it plunges down from the lighthouse in a succession of jagged swoops resembles some wickedly-spiked Polynesian fish-hook and to the Maoris the crescent shape of the bay itself reminded them of how Maui had pulled up the huge fish—the North Island—out of the sea.

In October 1769, Captain Cook anchored off this headland. Maoris seized a young Tahitian boy from his ship and attempted to carry him off in a canoe. But when Cook's men opened fire and created confusion, the boy dived into the sea and swam back to *Endeavour*. Cook therefore named the promontory Cape Kidnappers.

Cook recorded the presence of gannets in local waters, but made no mention of them at Cape Kidnappers. When a naturalist, Henry Hill, trekked to the cape over 100 years later, he discovered a gannetry of about 50 birds which, it was considered, would have been established some 20 years previously. Hill's find was both significant and exciting: this was—and still is—the only known mainland nesting site of the Australasian gannet.

The cape having no predators, the gannets quickly increased their numbers. The main nesting site is a promontory known as the Saddle—a large, scooped-out hollow, favoured by the sun. This nesting site was given to the Crown in 1914 as a reserve for the protection of gannets. At that time an estimated 2300 birds were nesting there.

The concentration of gannets nesting on the Saddle became so heavy that the birds colonised other sites in the 1930s. One is the Plateau, 110 m above sea level; another is on

◄*Cape Kidnappers is reached on foot by walking along the beach from Clifton at low tide. The walk should not be started earlier than three hours after high tide at Clifton. The return walk should begin not later than an hour and a half after low tide at Cape Kidnappers*

Black Reef, 2 km distant from the cape itself.

In 1933 Cape Kidnappers became a bird sanctuary. When, in 1960, Black Reef was also included the total land area came to 12.95 hectares. Today about 4500 birds nest at the three main sites.

By early May the Cape Kidnappers gannetry is strangely deserted. The male birds return first, about mid-July. Fiercely they claim possession of nesting sites they may have occupied for years; their lifelong mates join them later. About mid-August the building of nests commences. In October the younger birds—which have not as yet established fixed nesting sites—arrive on the noisy scene. The last to arrive are the youngest birds, which return from Australia in December and January. They have little choice but to make the best of any unoccupied ground.

From 1 July through to the Wednesday before Labour Day the sanctuary is closed to all visitors. This is a vital period in the life of a gannet, when mating, nesting, and egg-laying are at their peak. They need to be as little disturbed as possible.

November and December are undoubtedly the best time to visit the gannets. A permit is not necessary to observe the birds at the

▲*Australasian gannets began breeding at Cape Kidnappers in the mid-19th century and now about 4500 birds* *nest at three mainland sanctuaries. Elsewhere in New Zealand the birds breed on small offshore islands*

Plateau colony which, at that time, is dotted with countless pairs of gannets and their chicks. Permits are required for visits to the Black Reef or Saddle colonies, however.

A visit to the cape on foot involves a walk of about 8 km along mostly yellow beaches, below towering cliffs. It starts at Clifton Domain, 21 km southeast of Napier. At least two hours must be allowed for the walk each way.

Cliffs, rocks and beaches of a dangerous shore

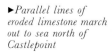
▶White Rock is a reef near Te Kaukau Point, at the end of a road which reaches down from Martinborough towards the eastern side of Cape Palliser

▲Cliffs on the southern Hawke's Bay coast

▶Parallel lines of eroded limestone march out to sea north of Castlepoint

The coastline south of Cape Kidnappers has its own distinctive features. It combines a number of fine beaches with rocky headlands and a shore at times both dangerous and in-hospitable. And even at one or two beaches there are hidden depths and surges.

Ocean Beach, a superb stretch of golden sand flung up against steep cliffs, has no such risks. Lying not far from Cape Kidnappers, it attracts both swimmers and fishermen. Beyond it is Waimarama Beach, just as beautiful, and from its sands the bleak, grey cliffs of Bare Island can be seen offshore.

Farther south along this rugged coast the Porangahau River sweeps into a bay about 12 km long. At its northern end is Blackhead where the skeletonic remains of the scow *Maroro* lie. Low tide reveals it on this rather exposed beach where the prized shellfish, toheroa, buries itself deep in the sands.

Cape Turnagain, 100 km south of Cape Kidnappers, is a headland roughly halfway between the mouths of the Porangahau River to the north and the Akitio River to the south. When Cook sailed down this coast in the February of 1769, he turned around in sight of this point and sailed back the way he had come.

A further link with Cook is to be found at

◄*Heavy seas, not uncommon on this coast, provide spectacle where they meet reefs*

Castlepoint, where he observed a rearing tower of rock and was struck by its similarity to the battlements of a castle. But since then earthquakes and severe storms have gradually eaten away its castellated formation and today the 160 m rock bears very little resemblance to the landmark Cook saw.

The beach there is a popular summer retreat and is said to have been first discovered by Kupe. Maori legend says that he started his long pursuit of a huge *wheke*, or octopus, just off this beach, finally killing it at Whekenui in the South Island.

At the southern end of Castlepoint beach a rocky promontory protrudes into the waters of the Pacific joined to the coast by a narrow causeway of rock and clay. Beyond the lighthouse on this headland, a curving reef encloses a tidal lagoon where the swimming and the crayfish are delights.

But on the journey south the coast becomes quite impenetrable until yet another fine beach is reached at Riversdale, north of Uriti Point; but it is a short relief on what is an otherwise rugged coastline where three little-known rivers—the Oterei, the Awhea, and the Opouawe—rising southeast of Martinborough in the Aorangi Mountains, enter the sea at deserted, windswept beaches.

But at last the coastline chooses another direction, and becomes more rounded. This is the southernmost tip of the North Island, where the Aorangi Mountains end. Cook completed the first circumnavigation of the North Island here on 7 February 1770 and named it Cape Palliser in honour of the first captain under whom he had served. This storm-lashed coastline was for many years the scene of numerous shipwrecks.

▼*On the southern Wairarapa coast, high hills rise steeply above the beaches. This scene is at Tora, south of Martinborough*

Remote southeastern corner of the island

▶ *Off the rocky coast of Cape Palliser, seals frolic in waters which are often stormy*

East of the rich Wairarapa Plains is a coastal chain of hills which rises to 450 m for much of its length. But suddenly the land climbs to 750–900 m and then plunges sharply into Cook Strait. This is the Aorangi Mountains, steep U-shaped valleys, broken spurs, and sharp ridge crests.

Two blocks of Department of Conservation land form the 19 382 hectares of Haurangi Forest Park. The northern and southern blocks are separated by the reverting grasslands of the Turanganui River catchment. Streams rising in the southern block flow directly to the sea or join forces with the Opouawe River. Regular vehicle access is from Martinborough, although an unformed road suitable only for four-wheel-drive vehicles follows the southern boundary of the park from White Rock to Cape Palliser.

These mountains are the home of many birds, among them the grey warbler, whitehead, morepork and native pigeon. But the wildlife was once even more extensive, and several species of moas, the North Island takahe, Finch's flightless duck and the huia, all now extinct, flourished on the forested slopes.

On the more stable slopes of the forest up to an altitude of 520–580 m the predominant trees are mahoe, hinau, and rewarewa. Below 490 m, on the more exposed and drier ridges, black beech reaches a height of 27 m. In the southern parts, silver beech is much in evidence. The vegetation has been drastically modified by fire, and introduced animals caused extensive damage to the canopy and understorey before they were controlled. Scrub and tussock terrain in the Turanganui River catchment and on the Mt Barton tops, is a result of early land-clearing fires.

The principal river of the Wairarapa district is the Raumahanga, which rises on the north-west slopes of the Tararua Range. In its journey to the sea the river enters the southern part of Lake Wairarapa, an extensive sheet of water, 18 km long, 6 km wide, and 79 km² in area. The lake is so shallow that in summer it is possible in some places to walk from one side to the other. *Wairarapa* means 'glistening waters'. Eels are particularly plentiful in the lake and during their migration season in February and March, large numbers of Maoris come to exercise traditional fishing rights.

Close to the southern part of the lake are lagoons and marshes which provide an excellent habitat for many water birds. The lower part of the lake is also the outlet to tiny Lake

▲ *The white-faced heron is a common inhabitant of the marshes, lake shores and of the southern Wairarapa*

▶ *The Turakirae Head terraces are old beaches, successively raised above sea level. The present beach dates from 1855*

▼ *The Putangirua Pinnacles, inland from Palliser Bay, have been formed by erosion. Detail at right shows the basic material*

▲ *Tiny figures at lower left give scale to organpipe-like cliffs which are part of the Putangirua Pinnacles*

Onoke. The outlet is so small and shallow that when southerly storms sweep in from Cook Strait it is often blocked by sand and shingle. Only by opening this outlet can severe flooding of the surrounding alluvial plains be avoided.

With its marshy surrounds and extensive mudflats and a 3 km long shingle bar separating it from the ocean, the environs of Lake Onoke provide a rewarding spot from which to observe wintering black-backed gulls and black-fronted terns on the mudflats. Nesting colonies of gulls, Caspian terns and banded dotterels may also be observed in the spring.

On the eastern shore of Lake Onoke is Lake Ferry, a popular seaside resort. The ocean beach shelves too sharply for safe swimming, however, and the waters of Palliser Bay are notorious for dangerous rips. The bay is bounded on the southeast by the snub-nosed headland of Cape Palliser and on the west by Turakirae Head.

This head has five distinct terraces, marking successive uptilting of the land over the last few thousand years. The most recent upheaval was in 1855 and was accompanied by a severe earthquake. The highest and oldest terrace was uplifted some 6500 years ago. At each uplift the sea retreated to form a new beach on the exposed bed.

Inland from Palliser Bay is another natural wonder. To reach it one must leave the road 17 km from Lake Ferry and walk for about 50 minutes to the head of the winding Putangirau Stream. There, in an enclosed valley, are the Putangirau Pinnacles, massive grey vertical pillars created by uneven erosion. Behind them are sheer, fluted cliffs.

Marlborough Sounds

Interlocking labyrinths of land and water constitute the Marlborough Sounds. In some places long tentacles of land reach into the sea; in others the water snakes into the hills. And everywhere there seem to be islands, but the insularity is often an illusion

Drowning of a continuation of the Richmond Ranges, a landscape of closely spaced, many-branched valleys and sharp-crested ridges, has formed the Marlborough Sounds. Crests of plunging spurs have become islands. The tops of smaller spurs have been trimmed by wave action to become dangerous rocky shoals, and those that are barely submerged are now razorback reefs. The sea has filled valleys, making deep bays. The drowning was partly due to the rise in sea level after the ice ages, but the whole Sounds block appears also to be tilting increasingly down into Cook Strait.

The Maoris, however, believed that certain gods came down from the heavens in a great canoe, but so far from their source of power that they were unable to return. The canoe ultimately capsized, and the Marlborough Sounds are really the intricate carving of its shattered prow.

Captain Cook was probably the first European to sail into the Sounds. Coming down the turbulent Tasman Sea, his ship sluggish and foul from many months' growth of marine excrescences beneath her waterline, he needed to careen and clean her. He was delighted to discover what he described as a 'snug cove' and named it after Queen Charlotte, wife of King George III. He dropped anchor in a broad, bush-lined bay now called Ship Cove, and was immediately surrounded by Maori canoes. The Maoris seemed hostile until Cook invited some of them aboard and gave them presents. On the crest of the island of Motuara he hoisted the Union Jack and claimed the entire mainland for the King. Parliament in London subsequently repudiated his claim to the land. He later crossed to Arapawa Island, from whose height he saw the 'eastern sea', the Pacific, and was fascinated to note that a broad strait connected it with the 'western sea', the Tasman.

Queen Charlotte Sound is one of the two main inlets of the Marlborough Sounds. On the far side of the lofty peninsula which rises from Ship Cove is the twisting, many-branched Pelorus Sound; and between Pelorus Sound and Queen Charlotte Sound are three major 'blind' sounds and a bewildering number of minor waterways.

The entire region is steep, in places heavily forested. Pelorus Sound receives the waters of the Pelorus River, which runs through a sort of rocky grotto at Pelorus Bridge, clear and deep and beautiful.

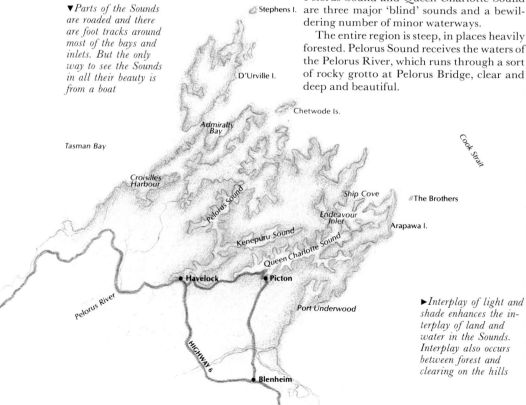

▼*Parts of the Sounds are roaded and there are foot tracks around most of the bays and inlets. But the only way to see the Sounds in all their beauty is from a boat*

Stephens I.

D'Urville I.

Chetwode Is.

Admiralty Bay

Tasman Bay

Croisilles Harbour

Pelorus Sound

Ship Cove

The Brothers

Endeavour Inlet

Arapawa I.

Cook Strait

Kenepuru Sound

Queen Charlotte Sound

● Havelock

● Picton

Pelorus River

Port Underwood

HIGHWAY 6

● Blenheim

HIGHWAY 1

▶*Interplay of light and shade enhances the interplay of land and water in the Sounds. Interplay also occurs between forest and clearing on the hills*

120

Sound where Captain Cook had his base

▶ *The interlocking of land and water in the Marlborough Sounds presents vistas that change with every turn of the path*

Queen Charlotte Sound has two entrances. Captain Cook found one of them—a 12 km stretch of suddenly calm water between Cape Jackson, with its long, scrubby ridge, and Cape Koamaru, northern tip of the angular, 26 km long Arapawa Island. The other entrance was not even suspected by Cook—the 21 km Tory Channel, a 1.5 km wide slot between Arapawa Island and the mainland. It is the principal entrance to Cook Strait for ferries between Picton and Wellington.

The whole sound, notched and scalloped with innumerable bays and coves, and dotted with islands, is a small-boat sailor's dream. There are delightful beaches beneath soaring, often forested peaks—beaches like the delightful Ship Cove, where Cook careened his vessel and established an exploration base. Largest of its inlets are the northward-curving Endeavour Inlet and East Bay, directly opposite each other. Endeavour Inlet is an 8.5 km sweep of deep blue, sheltered water, walled by 600 m high ridges with almost perpendicular faces up which dark beech forest climbs.

On the ocean coast, sweeping southward in a clean curve, is Cloudy Bay, its northern end poking up into Port Underwood, a long inlet formed in the same way as the rest of the Marlborough Sounds. It once shared with Kororareka in Northland the reputation and name of 'hell-hole of the Pacific'. It was a whaling port, without the steadying influence, such as it was, of the Bay of Islands mission station at Paihia.

Indeed, when a Wesleyan mission superintendent came to do something about the bestial way of life that prevailed, he was told bluntly to 'keep his bloody Sundays out of Port Underwood'. But his successor, Samuel Ironside, and the equally redoubtable Mrs Ironside, managed to gather about them five couples who had been cohabiting and reproducing with some fervour, marry them and baptise their broods. He got a permanent church built, and celebrated its consecration with a mass wedding and baptism of 40 couples, along with the baptism of 160 more and their children, and he overcame their final objections that they neither had nor could get wedding rings by producing a box of brass curtain rings.

In the bay, there is a small islet, Horahora-Kakahu, 'the spreading of the cloak', which is linked to the mainland by a reef. There, on 17 June 1840, the chieftain Nohuroa signed the Treaty of Waitangi. Bluejackets from HMS *Herald* erected a flagstaff, hoisted the Union Jack and fired a 21-gun salute, which was probably the last loud sound heard in Port Underwood before it went off into the pleasant dream from which it has never awakened. The whaling industry can still be traced around the shores. Perhaps the whales will some day return to its deep, clear waters.

Arapawa Island is a long and bending ridge of land, partly farmed, badly eroded in places, and partly forested. Its name means 'misty path', said to have been bestowed by Maoris who looked across Cook Strait to see it rising up, mist-covered and mysterious, lying across the 'canoe path' to the south. In 1777 Captain Cook put ashore some goats and sheep, a future store of meat, milk and hides if the animals thrived. They and their descendents—interbred with other breeds of sheep and goats—did thrive, to such an extent that they caused a great deal of environmental damage to the island. When it was decided that the animals would have to be destroyed there was an immediate protest from people living on Arapawa Island and from other interested groups who claimed that the goats were the Old English milk goat, which is now extinct in Britain. Most of the animals were destroyed but a hundred goats were kept to be studied on a Lands and Survey Department farm near Nelson.

◀*Long points and islands snake out in many parts of Queen Charlotte Sound. Most of the smaller islands are reserves within the Marlborough Sounds Maritime Park*

▶*Heavy forest covered the valleys and hills of the Marlborough Sounds before settlers arrived with their axes and saws. Much has been cleared, but much is still there*

Islands of Cook Strait

▼ *The tuatara, a relic of the dinosaur era, survives on several islands in Cook Strait*

► *Underwater cooling formed knobbly rock called pillow lava, on D'Urville Island*

The last of the chains of mountain peaks still holding their heads above the sea, the outer islands of the Marlborough Sounds have a fascination all their own. From D'Urville Island, the largest of them, to some of the tiny lumps of rock which are dignified with the title 'island' largely because they belong to some group such as the Chetwodes, they nearly all possess some unique feature that makes them worthy of notice.

The sea about them is seldom calm. Cook Strait is defined as that area lying between a line drawn from Kapiti Island to Stephens Island, and a line between Cape Palliser and Cape Campbell, some 50 km south of Port Underwood. It lies in the wind belt known as the Roaring Forties. Winds of up to 240 km/h are not uncommon, and powerful currents flow between the Tasman sea and the Pacific Ocean.

D'Urville Island, with an area of 4090 hectares, is the largest of the outer islands of the Marlborough Sounds by a considerable margin. The Maoris called it Rangitoto. Captain Cook probably believed it to be a part of the mainland, but Jules Sebastien César Dumont d'Urville suspected otherwise and in 1827 set out to prove his theory. He sailed into what he called the Basin of Currents, and there discovered French Pass. This narrow strip of water rushes between a knob of scrub-covered mainland and the reef which stretches out from Reef Point, half buried in a constant swirl of white water. The whole strait is only about 500 m wide, and actual navigable passage is about 110 m wide.

Dumont d'Urville made two attempts to sail his corvette, *Astrolabe*, through the pass, and literally managed to scrape through on the second attempt. *Astrolabe* struck the rocks twice and its false keel was smashed. Dumont d'Urville named the passage *Passe des Français*, but recommended that it be used only in an emergency, and then with 'a strong breeze well established, and that nearly aft'.

Many years later, French Pass was used by screw-propelled vessels on the direct route between Wellington and Nelson. For 24 years, between 1888 and 1912, a Risso's dolphin named Pelorus Jack met every ship and 'piloted' it through the pass—actually enjoying a free ride on the pressure wave before the bow—and became a tourist attraction in its own right.

Three kilometres north of Cape Stephens, on the northern end of D'Urville Island, is Stephens Island. The island is a long, steep ridge, rising at its highest point to 283 m. The slopes are largely tussock-covered, though there is a patch of typical Cook Strait coastal forest, consisting largely of kawakawa, mahoe, supplejack, kohekohe and ngaio, mostly fairly stunted, with the odd struggling nikau palm. There is a lighthouse and a small cluster of keepers' cottages and outbuildings. There is no landing place, but people and stores are brought in by launch, which sails in with great skill and holds station beneath a winch while a large box is lowered. The box is caught, held on the vessel's foredeck and

◄ *When the tide rips through French Pass it reaches speeds as high as 3.6 m a second*

▲ *Forest on D'Urville Island, stunted by the powerful winds that often lash Cook Strait*

◀Remnant forest on Stephens Island, a wildlife sanctuary

▼The Stephens Island frog is found only on the tiny island

loaded with goods and sometimes people. As it is hauled up, the vessel circles away, returning to reposition itself for subsequent loads.

Stephens Island is just over 2000 m long and about 1400 m wide. It is riddled with the burrows made by small petrels, particularly the dove petrel, or fairy prion. These birds share their burrows with the tuatara, a creature that looks like a lizard but belongs to a quite separate order called the Rhynchocephalia, or beakheads. These reptiles co-existed with the dinosaurs 135 million years ago, but they have been extinct everywhere but New Zealand for about 60 million years. Tuataras hatch out of leathery eggs after 12-14 months incubation. They grow up to 600 mm long and take about 20 years to reach breeding age. Nowadays they are found only on 20-30 islands from Cook Strait up the east coast to near North Cape. They are strictly protected and the species is not close to extinction.

The Chetwode Islands, off the entrance to Pelorus Sound, consist of Nukuwaiata, about 300 hectares in area, and Te Kakaho, 100 hectares, and three smaller islets. The two main islands rise with characteristic steepness from the sea and are covered with native grasses and unspoiled native bush. They are wildlife reserves, and the bird population is wide and varied, with native and introduced birds living happily together.

The Brothers Islands lie near Arapawa Island and were strictly *tapu* to the Maori. The legendary Kupe killed a giant octopus near here, and placed its eyes on top of the Brothers islets. The first canoe travellers had to keep their eyes covered, for fear of breaking the *tapu* and being drowned.

◀The steep coast of Stephens Island offers no landing place

▲The Brothers lie near the entrance to Queen Charlotte Sound

Golden Bay

In the east a pitted mountain of marble stands between Golden Bay and the rest of the world. In the west, behind the comfortable farmlands fringing the placid bay, is one of the largest areas still unmarked by roads in New Zealand—the wild Nelson hinterland

The only road into Golden Bay writhes up and down that part of the Pikikiruna Range known as Takaka Hill or 'Marble Mountain'. Some motorists find the tortuous road so tiresome that they stay away from Golden Bay. To others who will drive over the hill that is in itself one of the quiet attractions of a region which lacks the readily merchandised scenic splendours that draw tourists to southern mountain centres.

Beyond the hill, Golden Bay curves away to the northwest. Settlement is largely confined to the rim of the bay and two short valleys which open onto it. Rugged mountains rise just behind the farmlands. These rugged ranges extend from far south of the Buller Gorge.

The interest and appeal of Golden Bay's wild places is wonderfully enhanced by a richness and diversity of plant and animal life which can be observed everywhere—from the tidal flats of Farewell Spit to the tops of the mountains and the depths of the great marble caverns. This richness of natural life is probably the region's most outstanding characteristic. It finds its origins in unique circumstances during the geological past which have made the bay area a showcase of natural adaptation and evolution.

An important influence is the region's geology, which is wrought in a fascinating complexity of granite, schist, sandstone, conglomerate limestone, marble and volcanic rocks. A diversity of rock types exposed at the surface over a wide range of altitudes provides the raw material for an equal diversity of soils, vegetation and wildlife. Nowhere is this more dramatically illustrated than in the areas of limestone and marble, where species of plants and small animals that are found nowhere else have evolved special adaptations. The presence of limestone soils at both high and low altitudes has contributed greatly to the variety of life forms in the whole region.

More than once in the more recent geological past, Golden Bay has been connected with the North Island by a dry-land bridge which allowed two-way migrations of plants and animals. In addition, the bay region acted as a refuge for southern species during a series of ice ages which temporarily displaced both plant and animal populations from some areas and eliminated the less hardy species from other areas of inhospitable cold. Thus was formed the mixture of northern and southern species that now inhabits the Golden Bay region.

Alternations of climate successively warmed and chilled this mixture, inducing the plants and animals to migrate to different levels on the region's slopes. Thereby they encountered an unusually wide variety of rocks and soils. From this stimulating flux of habitats has emerged Golden Bay's remarkable profusion of species, evolving life forms and ecological communities.

About 800 years ago, the Maoris came to Golden Bay, but little is known about this long period of human occupation. Tribal fighting decimated the population after European muskets reached the area. European settlers then purchased almost all the land and a short-lived boom followed while the region's accessible natural resources of gold, coal and timber were exploited and removed. Single-purpose farming rapidly and uniformly subdued the lowlands, leaving little trace of the original vegetation. Excessive forest clearance proceeded up the fringing slopes of the high country, from which settlement was later forced to retreat. Most of the mountainous back country has remained untouched.

▲*Abel Tasman National Park, New Zealand's smallest national park, just 22 541 hectares, lies more in Tasman Bay than Golden Bay, but the only road access is from Takaka, on the Golden Bay side*

▶*The Heaphy River runs through part of the vast Northwest Nelson Forest Park, from the Tasman Mountains to the Tasman Sea. The Heaphy Track follows the course of the river as it nears the coast*

Abel Tasman National Park

▲*Frenchman Bay was the site of a boatbuilding operation in the 1870s. Many of the park's bays and inlets were settled for quarrying, milling, fishing, farming and boatbuilding, but these operations all declined*

▼*Bizarre outcrops of marble cover large areas on the top of Takaka Hill, which is also known as 'Marble Mountain'*

►*Awaroa Inlet, in the distance, was the site of a thriving settlement in earlier times, and farming continues there, outside the park*

Steep, broken granite country, rent with rivers, drops into an azure sea on the eastern side of Abel Tasman National Park. Between water and forest is a flashing line of sand. That is the essence of the park. In summer it is the most attractive holiday coast in the South Island. Yet the park is perhaps at its best in autumn and winter. Indian summers are the rule and autumn is an ideal time to make the two-or-three-day coastal walk from Totaranui to Marahau.

There are coves, headlands, submerged reefs, offshore islands, low-tide caves, and long golden beaches enclosing languid lagoons. The composition of the park's soft golden granite holds the key to all these characteristic landforms. They have developed as results of water working at the weaker joints of the composite rock. It splits the mica from the feldspar and the feldspar

from the quartz to leave the sparkling saffron faces of crystalline rocks reflecting amongst the seaweed.

The park was established in 1942, the tricentenary of Abel Tasman's discovery of New Zealand. Totaranui, once the estate of a Nelson entrepreneur and politician who made a fortune selling land in the 1857 gold rush, was added in 1948. It is now a centre for camping, boating, swimming and walking. The transition from private ownership to public access has been complemented by natural forest regeneration across a landscape frequently despoiled by milling, farming and quarrying.

The grandeur of the original native forest will eventually be restored along the whole coast. Beneath a dense, developing understorey of native plants, fire-induced stands of bracken, gorse, manuka and radiata pine ultimately fail to reproduce themselves. This

▶ *Waterfall at Bark Bay. In pioneer times bark was gathered from trees at the bay and was used in the tanning of hides.*

can be seen on the Tinline Walk.

On the western edge of the park is an area of mountainous, infertile marble and schist terrace called Canaan. It is a steep-sided broken spine virtually devoid of people. The road from the top of the Takaka Hill to Canaan Downs traverses an awesome landscape where bush abuts onto open spaces of fluted grey marble and tussock. Through the centuries steady drops of acid water have hollowed out a marble mountain, 100 million years old, into a honeycomb of caves and tunnels.

At the end of the 11 km road, a short track leads to Harwoods Hole, which drops a clear 360 m into the centre of Takaka Hill. It is the deepest sinkhole known in New Zealand. Intrepid cavers have abseiled down into this extraordinary abyss, to walk and crawl through a cave system that bursts out into sunlight and bush at the bottom of the hill.

▼ *The Cobb River flows from the Tasman Mountains to join the Takaka River. There is a power station at the junction of the rivers and the Cobb has been dammed upstream to provide a suitable reservoir*

The remote northwest

The recreational opportunities that Golden Bay and its hinterland offer to a visitor are of three kinds. First, those demanding some special skills, experience or stamina. White water canoeing, wilderness travel and cave exploration are examples. Second are visits to those scenic or interesting places available to the casual visitor and accessible by car or a short walk. Falling somewhere between these two is a third: the deeper experience of natural country available to any reasonably fit person willing to plan and carry a few necessities on the back.

The number of people seeking this kind of experience has suddenly and dramatically increased in the last decade, and Golden Bay offers them good opportunities. Such people are the 'new recreationists'—families and small groups of all ages who are taking to the back country in far greater numbers than were ever attracted to the traditional pursuits of the mountaineers, hunters or trampers. The new recreationists seek an intimate communion with wild nature through botany, birdwatching, photography and unhurried walking. In the Golden Bay hinterland, they are particularly attracted to the Heaphy Track and the Mt Arthur Tableland.

The Heaphy Track, a much easier trip than most New Zealand back-country trails, is a three-or-four-day journey of 70 km, with comfortable huts no more than five walking hours apart. Safe bridges cross all the major rivers. Facilities are virtually as good on the Mt Arthur Tableland, which can be

▲ *The entrance to Whanganui Inlet. The large inlet runs parallel to the west coast near the tip of the South Island*

◄ *Oystercatchers, in black-and-white plumage, and godwits are among the wading birds that find their food on the tidal shores of Golden Bay*

▲ *Farewell Spit reaches out to enclose Golden Bay. The long sandspit* *can be visited by taking a bus trip to a lighthouse near the end of the spit*

traversed in a pleasant two-day ramble from Flora Saddle on the Motueka side to the Cobb Road on the Golden Bay side.

There are interesting sights accessible by car in Golden Bay, including the Pupu Springs near Takaka, the Te Anaroa Caves near Rockville, the Whanganui Inlet, or Westhaven, on the western coast and near it, the Kaihoka Lakes Scenic Reserve. This reserve is a good place to watch for one of Golden Bay's most remarkable creatures—a huge carnivorous native bush snail. In Westhaven at high tide an excursion by boat or canoe up the winding, forested canyon of the Wairoa estuary is a special experience.

By far the most outstanding and important natural area in Golden Bay is the wildlife sanctuary on Farewell Spit. The road goes to where the sand dunes begin. The Spit, 26 km long, attracts many species of migratory wading birds. As many as 109 different species have been noted. The largest numbers are of the eastern bar-tailed godwit and eastern knot, both Arctic waders which migrate halfway around the world to their breeding grounds in the Siberian tundra and adjoining areas every year.

To watch a cloud of 2000 birds rise like a single, living body, climb to a great altitude and then wheel northward to begin that

brave and exhausting journey, is to witness one of the most momentous events in nature's annual cycle. It can be observed during March and April, when successive waves of restless birds take to the sky.

In anticipation of their departure for the northern breeding grounds, much of the undistinguished summer plumage of adult male godwits and knots changes to a rich nuptial red, a dramatic transition which normally occurs about six weeks before their departure. The birds return in September for the southern summer.

The Spit itself consists of a curving tongue of sand, partly vegetated and partly of drifting dunes. Its origin is remarkable. Hundreds of kilometres to the south, rock ground off the Southern Alps by the erosive force of glacier ice is swept into the sea as sand by Westland's turbulent and powerful rivers. The northward drift to the Westland Current pushes this sand relentlessly up the coast until it gradually loses its momentum in a giant eddy around Golden Bay. There the sand eventually settles onto the Spit and tidal flats at the rate of more than 3 million cubic metres a year. The shallow banks on the landward side of the Spit form the enormous and extremely productive intertidal habitat where the wading birds feed.

◄New Zealand's only native palm, the nikau thrives in the mild climate of the northwest Nelson area

▲Looking along the Peel Range to Aorere Peak, second highest point in the Tasman mountains at 1708 m

▼Boulder Lake nestles in the Haupiri Range, between the Taka and Aorere Valleys. The peak behind it is Brown Cow (1402 m), and it has a sister peak called Black Cow which lies to the north

From Golden Bay to the West Coast on foot

►*Nikau palms along the Heaphy Track, towards the west coast*

▲*Footbridges cross all the rivers and major streams on the Heaphy Track, eliminating the flood danger which used to beset walkers*

◄*Luxuriant rainforest grows on the steep slopes of the coast between the Heaphy River and Karamea*

Charles Heaphy, renowned as explorer, artist and soldier, travelled by a coastal route from Golden Bay to Westland in 1846 in one of the most arduous feats of New Zealand exploration. His journey included what is now the coastal section of the Heaphy Track, but he never ventured inland over the major part of the route named after him.

For hundreds of years the Maoris had traced an inland route from Golden Bay to the West Coast, climbing up from the Aorere River onto a forest-encircled plateau where they feasted on wekas, and then departed westward down the Heaphy River. In 1860 the government agent James Mackay, returning from the trip on which he purchased almost the whole of the West Coast from the Maoris for £300, led his party over this inland route. Later, he cut the first 'Heaphy Track' from the upper Aorere River to the mouth of the Heaphy in 1862.

Most trampers begin their journey from the east, taking the 35 km drive from Collingwood or flying in to the Bainham airstrip. From the road end, the Heaphy Track rises gradually but steadily through cool beech forest, following a route cut for packhorses to carry heavy loads over the mountains.

The heart of the Heaphy Track is the open, rolling plain of the Gouland Downs. In the half light of dawn and dusk and clearing storms, the red tussocked hills and stepped landscape evoke a strange mood. The track is well-marked and it is comfortable walking, but not everyone feels at ease here. Trampers

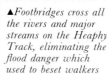

◄*Approaching Kohaihai Bluff, a walker nears the southern end of the Heaphy Track. This last section along the beach can be dangerous at high tide because of freak waves. Lives have been lost here*

▲*Native plants such as the native genetian flower profusely in the herbfields of the Gouland Downs*

◄*Frosted beech trees at the Perry Saddle, which marks the end of the long climb up from Brown River at the Collingwood end of the 78 km long track*

have called it the 'Queer Country'. Some find it full of foreboding and unknown threats. A guide to the track describes the Gouland Downs as 'barren and lifeless'.

The Gouland Downs is a 30 km² fellfield of red tussock, interspersed with luxuriant herbfields and limestone outcrops harbouring pockets of silver beech. Although it is at a comparatively low altitude, the Gouland Downs is essentially naked of forest because most of the soil is thin and impoverished. No doubt this is why some feel the area to be barren. In fact, it is an extraordinarily rich

garden of herbs and flowers. Twenty-six species of orchids and an array of native lilies, gentians and daisies burst into a profusion of colour every summer. An astonishing 448 species of native plants have been identified here, some of them rare or endemic.

The journey from the open downs to the warm west coast is down ridges and valley flats through a forest that becomes more and more tropical with every step. Tall trees surround the track in a singing, luscious world of green, where light glitters through emerald shades. Vines and epiphytes, in their

upward search for light, clasp the giant trunks of native podocarps.

Finally, the track bursts from the cool green of the forest onto a long sweep of ocean coastline. And the last day's walk along the sand to the roar of the pounding West Coast surf deafens memories of the silent highland downs and prepares those who have visited this wild place for rejoining the road, 11.5 km north of Karamea.

▼*The Gouland Downs inspires unease in some trampers, perhaps justly because some have become lost after leaving the track here*

Nelson Lakes National Park

Beautiful placid lakes and mountain tarns contrast with rugged ranges, dark beech forests and turbulent rivers in this national park

Crumpled as a carelessly dropped bedsheet, the Nelson Lakes National Park region is a tangle of high ranges and deep, narrow, forested valleys, products of the often counteracting influences of prehistoric glaciation and continual block-faulting.

Through it runs the mighty Alpine Fault, the western boundary of the Southern Alps. It is plainly discernible even from the valley floors, for the ranges to the northeast of it soar to heights in places greater than 2000 m, whereas to the northwest there are no peaks higher than 1000 m. Along the line of the Alpine Fault a remarkably straight series of saddles and cols separate the higher mountains on the eastern side from lower ranges which lie to the west.

Nelson Lakes National Park itself comprises 101 753 hectares of mountainous country. The associated areas are almost as great. The region is walled to the east by the lofty St Arnaud Range.

Along the mountain wall of the Alpine Fault are scarred and denuded slopes, alternating with heavy forest of great beauty. This is magnificent country, wild even where it has been harnessed to human use. Massive peaks, snow-crowned in winter, bare and scarred with scree-slides in summer, rise above river valleys where the red and silver beech of the higher slopes give way to podocarps, flax, rata and golden kowhai on the floors. The spectrum of plant life is vast, from subalpine to rainforest species.

In this region, as practically nowhere else, it is possible to drive amongst the forested mountains without having to climb over them. Highway 6, a winding but good road from Nelson, runs southwestward to Westport through the Upper and Lower Buller Gorges. Highway 63, less tortuous but often steep, runs westward from Blenheim, up the wide, straight, Wairau Valley and travels on past the Nelson lakes to join the Nelson-Westport road.

Sheltered by high eastern and southern ranges but open to weather from the west and north, the Nelson Lakes National Park is prone to heavy rainfall on the western side. Snow can fall to low levels when low-pressure centres pass to the north and the air is cold. Snowstorms can last for several days, and thick coatings of snow lie on the tops, with heavy rain and often snow in the valleys. Storms are most likely in spring and early summer, usually brought on by disturbance from the west. Settled weather is most common from late January to April.

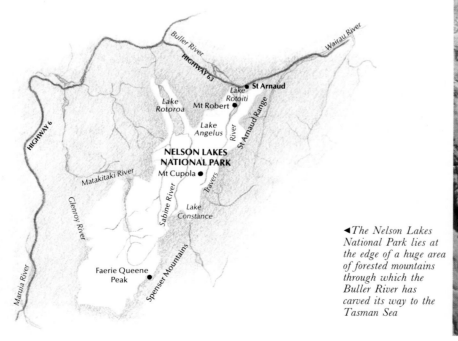

◀*The Nelson Lakes National Park lies at the edge of a huge area of forested mountains through which the Buller River has carved its way to the Tasman Sea*

▼*Lake Rotoroa, the larger of the two main Nelson lakes, seen from high in the Spenser Mountains at its southern end*

A lake trapped between forested ranges

In the last phase of the ice ages, a glacier carved its way down from the region of the Travers Saddle and flowed a short distance across the lower land beyond the western face of the alpine ranges, as far as the base of a mass of ancient lava now known as Black Hill. There it was forced to fork. It piled before it a towering wall of terminal moraine, and failed to get very much farther. Tem-

peratures rose and the ice melted, leaving a deep trench. The run-off from the ranges gradually filled the gouged-out valley, and where once the glacier lay, the Travers River ran down from the saddle between the St Arnaud and Spenser Ranges. Swelled by the torrents from the mountainsides, it filled the hollow until it reached the lip of the terminal moraine, where some spilled out into the valley beyond as the Buller River. The Buller, broad, deep and swift right from its source, found its way between the spurs of interlocking ranges in a headlong race to the Tasman Sea. From the northern fork of the glacier,

water at other times flowed down the Wairau Valley and out into Cook Strait.

Today, Lake Rotoiti's glacial origins are immediately apparent The short, forested spurs of the St Arnaud Range drop steeply into the lake's waters. Mt Robert's friendlier broad height, with its skifield and its small remaining lakeside fringes of native bush, drops down suddenly on its eastern side to slide deeply into the still water. Only Black Hill stands back from it, a black basalt formation spewed from an ancient volcano when this crumpled landscape was a flat, smooth seabed. Black Hill was surrounded

▼ *The Buller River rushes from the northern end of Lake Rotoiti to begin its journey to the Tasman* *Sea, about 170 km distant. The St Arnaud Range walls in the lake along its eastern shore*

completely by glacial ice 22 000 years ago. The ice receded during a warm period and advanced again some 16 000 years ago, when it built up the moraine that now slopes away to form the peninsula and the morainic ridge near the township of St Arnaud.

In 1846 the surveyor William Fox suggested that Lake Rotoiti would make an excellent summer resort for British invalids from India. They 'could find among the lakes everything calculated to restore health, and might soon surround themselves with many of the amusements and resources of a watering place', he said. The invalids never came. Many people extolled the beauty of the lake but it never became a fashionable watering place. Nelson citizens eventually discovered the lake and many of them spend their holidays on its northern shore.

Lake Rotoiti lies at an altitude of some 610 m, surrounded by steep, high country which demands that those who explore it are robust and equipped for tramping in rough country. There are two reasonably easy rambles, however. A two-hour walk from St Arnaud wanders along the shore of the peninsula to West Bay. A branching path runs up to Rotoiti Lodge, a youth hostel, and from there, a track goes back to the village through the beech trees. The lakeside track continues around the shore to the point where the Buller River rushes from the lake.

There is also an easy day's walk from St Arnaud to the lake head. The track wanders along the eastern shore of the lake, here and there toiling up and over the ends of forest-clad spurs, pausing in glades and on open spreads of grass with beaches that are appealing invitations to picnic. The bush on the steep lakeside slopes rings with the song of

▲*Snow on beech forest on Mt Robert, near St Arnaud. The township is thronged with skiers in winter and holiday-makers in summer, but has few permanent residents*

bellbirds, and the tui is often to be seen. The New Zealand falcon is a likely sight.

Behind St Arnaud, a steep pathway scrambles up the side of Black Hill, through the beech forest. It takes about an hour to reach the top, 737 m above the lake, where there is a glorious panorama.

Mt Robert, separated from the peninsula by West Bay, offers another view. The geologist Julius von Haast, the first European to climb it, named it after his son, whom he had left in Europe.

An all-weather road skirts the lake and runs up to the Robert Lookout, from which there is a fine view up West Bay to the Buller River and Black Hill.

In the ranges above the Nelson lakes

►*Forested slopes of the St Arnaud Range. Beyond its bare peaks, range after range, it stretches away to the Inland Kaikouras*

▼*The young Travers River near the limit of trees in the upper Travers basin*

Forming the eastern wall of Lake Rotoiti, the St Arnaud Range rises from a 610 m saddle which runs between a 1436 m forested eminence named Beeby's Knob and the 1681 m St Arnaud Peak. It starts southward in a gentle curve until, at a point level with the southern end of the lake, it begins to zig-zag and twist, trending gradually southwestward and terminating in a scatter of peaks of which the highest are Mt Travers, 2338 m, and Mt Franklin, 2327 m.

Out of this broken collection of heights and ridges runs an organisation of sinuously bending razor-backed ridges, connecting a series of handsome peaks known as the Spenser Mountains—named after the poet, Edmund Spenser. Their two most beautiful heights are the 2237 m Faerie Queene and its lesser companion, Gloriana Peak, 2214 m. Snow-crowned for much of the year, they gaze down Right Branch Valley of the Maruia River's source complex, toward Lewis Pass, the northern route across the Main Divide. Mount Una, where four steep spurs lift up to a pyramidal peak, is some 64 m higher than the Faerie Queene.

Branching from the northern end of this range are the Travers, Mahanga and Ella Ranges, their northern ends chopped off as though by some giant blade, where the Alpine Fault runs in an almost straight line from the outlet end of Lake Rotoiti, past the head of Lake Rotoroa.

The crests of these ranges are bare and inhospitable, often swept by strong winds, massively scarred by erosion and snow-covered to a considerable depth in winter. Their glacial origins are betrayed by deep, still tarns cradled in the arms of the mountains. These tarns are ice-eroded hollows filled with meltwater and run-off from the surrounding ridges.

The lower slopes are forested, mainly with beeches, but with stands also of miro, kamahi, matai and rimu. In the lower and more

sheltered localities, kowhai grows strongly, and rata patches large areas. There is a scattering of flax in the broader creek valleys, and plumes of toitoi are fairly common.

Between the Travers Range and St Arnaud Ranges, a deep and densely wooded valley runs down to the head of Lake Rotoiti. At its southern end, where it climbs out of the forest and up between scree-scarred slopes to the Travers Saddle, the Travers River is born, growing rapidly and leaping and ruffling its boisterous way down through the woods, to feed the lake. Eventually it will fill it with sediment, for it carries much gravel from the crumbling young mountains.

Foot tracks lead up the valley, one along each bank of the river. The right-bank track crosses the stream some 5 km from its mouth, to join the left-bank track. Other paths branch from the left-bank track, climbing up into the mountains. The first track follows the Hukere Stream where it rattles down through the beech forest from its sources—the still and coldly beautiful Lake Angelus,

the neighbouring Hinapouri Tarn and the smaller tarns nestling close to Sunset Saddle, beneath the 2084 m Angelus Peak. There is a trampers' hut at Lake Angelus.

The track along the Travers River terminates at a hut below the Travers Saddle, but experienced trampers, properly equipped, can go over the saddle to link with another track which runs up the Sabine River valley from Lake Rotoroa.

Climatic conditions on these harsh slopes range from searing heat to blasting cold and preclude the growth of most species of plants. Yet specialised plants have developed, especially on the shingle slides, that can cope with these inhospitable extremes. One of the most beautiful, though difficult to find, is a little blue-grey forget-me-not, *Myosotis traversii*, with white and cream flowers.

At their southern end, the Spenser Mountains fall away somewhat into the short, curving Freyberg Range, which is generally some 300 m lower. About its forested feet, the Maruia River spreads across its gravelly bed,

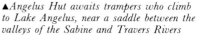

▲*Angelus Hut awaits trampers who climb to Lake Angelus, near a saddle between the valleys of the Sabine and Travers Rivers*

curling northward up the Shenandoah Valley, to join the Buller.

High above the young Maruia River, at 911 m, is the Lewis Pass. The Lewis Pass road runs easily up from the eastern side, so that the summit of the pass seems not particularly high, and only the verges of snowgrass at the edge of the beech woods betray its altitude. The forest falls away from the pass, down almost perpendicular slopes to the Maruia River. There are gaps where the roadside trees part like theatre curtains to frame a breath-taking vista of lofty spurs, dark with bush and crowned by white, shining peaks dominated by the Faerie Queene.

This is merely the high point of the pass proper. A little farther up the Maruia River is a dark and sinister sunless gorge, called *Kopi-o-kaitangata*, ('the gorge of the feasting on man-flesh'), by the ancient Maoris. It was there that east coast Maoris used to kill and eat slaves who had carried greenstone from the west coast to the top of the pass. It is now called Cannibal Gorge—and looks the part.

In these river valleys, the beech forest is enriched by hebes, olearias with their white flowers and musky scent, astelias of the sword-like leaves and panicles of flowers, coprosmas, horopito or pepper tree, weeping matipo and mountain ribbonwood. Beech saplings and mossy fallen timber make penetration difficult.

Where the Maruia River runs northward, the country is generally lower than the Spenser Mountains locality, but rugged with dense forest right over the tops.

◄*Bad weather approaching Sunset Saddle. Hinapouri Tarn is in the background and Angelus Peak top left*

Lake Rotoroa and its beautiful satellites

◄*The Blue Lake is a small tarn, sheltered by beech forest, on the west branch of the Sabine River*

At Gowanbridge an all-weather but rough and narrow road branches off Highway 6 and slips southward up the Gowan River to Lake Rotoroa. Like Lake Rotoiti, Rotoroa lies in the trench scooped out by a glacier. Its European discoverer was Charles Heaphy, who called it Lake Howick. Rotoroa is a long lake—15 km against Rotoiti's 8 km—broader at its head than at its outlet.

The D'Urville and Sabine Rivers, flowing out from the northern slopes of the Spenser Mountains, and from Lake Constance, around either side of the pyramidal bulk of Mount Misery, feed Lake Rotoroa.

While Rotoiti in summer buzzes with power boats, Rotoroa drowses peacefully, disturbed by nothing more noisy than the soft plop of rising trout. While Rotoiti is dramatised by lofty, snow-clad walls, Rotoroa lies snug and hidden in the midst of hills that are completely forested. It lies at an altitude some 149 m lower than Rotoiti. Rotoroa is the deeper—145 m compared to 70 m.

Rotoroa is favoured by people who value peace and quiet and by trout fishermen. It is accounted one of the best trout waters in the land—immeasurably better than Rotoiti.

Rotoroa's coves and bays are apt to be reedy. The forest clings no closer to its shores than that at Lake Rotoiti; but it seems to, because it is thick with the familiar shrubs of lowland forest—the sunny gold of kowhai and the red of rata. Flax and toitoi are abundant, and so are matai, rimu and rata, their trunks rough with lichens in colours ranging from yellow to grey-green.

Even more than Lake Rotoiti, Lake Rotoroa is favoured by the New Zealand scaup, a strictly protected diving duck, recognisable by its habit, when rising from the water, of pattering across the surface on quick feet, wings beating rapidly. The female is dark brown with a brown eye and the male almost black with a yellow eye.

There are walking tracks about Rotoroa. The easiest and shortest is the Porika Track from the outlet end of the lake, leading over the ridge between the 918 m Rotoroa Peak and the 992 m Hodgson Peak. Where the track runs out of the forest, a vista opens up of the entire lake, with 1600 m Mount Misery towering above its head, and the D'Urville and Sabine river mouths on either side of it. This walk takes about half a day.

A full day is required for the lakeside Rotoroa Track, which is rough, and scrambles along the eastern shore through dense forest, to the Sabine Hut near the mouth of the Sabine River. The Sabine has two principal sources. The east branch rises high on the slopes of the 2108 m Belvedere Peak, at the southern end of the St Arnaud Range. The west branch flows out of Lake Constance and through Blue Lake.

Lake Constance, 2 km long, is an exquisite, bush-fringed water lying sheltered and

◄*Beech forest in the valley of the west branch of the Sabine*

◄Lake Rotoroa from Mt Cupola, in the Travers Range. It is the longer and deeper of the two main Nelson Lakes

mirror-smooth in a ring of peaks and ridges which include 2327 m Mt Franklin, 2192 m Mt Mahanga and a 2205 m peak which is unnamed, perhaps because it is a mere knob on a high ridge. The reflection of these peaks, when at their snow-mantled best, placed Lake Constance amongst the most beautiful waters in the country. Blue Lake is a small tarn of gem-like loveliness, sheltered by beech forest, reflecting the clear, slightly dark blue of the alpine skies.

A two-day to three-day tramp begins at the end of the Howard River Road, in the valley east of Lake Rotoroa, and follows a scrub-patched river flat to where the Tier Stream emerges from the beech forest. From there the track follows the Tier through mossy woods, where the elusive kiwi has often been seen and the bird life is rich and varied, to a hut in a glade of beech beside that lovely stream. The way from there leads over a for-

ested saddle, where a number of tinkling, fern-bearded streams run, and it dips down to join the Rotoroa track a kilometre from the Sabine Hut.

From the Sabine Hut, a track goes around the lake-head bays and crosses the D'Urville River to a couple of huts beneath the 1400 m Mount Hutton. From there it goes on for about 2 km along the left bank of the D'Urville before climbing through the forest over the Tiraumea Saddle and making its way down to the Tiraumea River. There is a hut in a forest clearing 4 km below the saddle on the north-western side and from there the track follows the river down between the interlocking spurs of high, bush-clad ranges, to the Tutaki Valley road and the Mangles River, a major tributary of the Buller.

Throughout these ranges, red deer were formerly plentiful; but a policy of severe culling and the great increase in the numbers of

casual hunters with precision rifles has brought them to the verge of extinction. The chamois, too, used to be seen on the high, bare tops and vertical faces, small herds of the graceful creatures, leaping from ledge to vertiginous ledge on sheer, wet rock faces high above the forests; but these, too, are now rare. Nevertheless, a fair number of wild pigs roam the high hills.

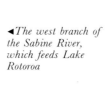

▲Beeches dominate the forests of the Nelson Lakes National Park. Red beech, silver beech, black beech, mountain beech and hard beech are all found within the park, usually in association with one another or with kamahi

◄The west branch of the Sabine River, which feeds Lake Rotoroa

Through the Buller Gorges

◄*This ridge is called the Old Man of the Buller because of its distinctive profile when seen from the junction of the Maruia and Buller rivers*

From its outset, the Buller is an impressive waterway. It was called Buller by the explorers Brunner, Heaphy and Fox, though not before some discussion had taken place. Heaphy and Brunner both owed their appointments as New Zealand Company surveyors to Charles Buller, MP, a director of the company. Fox favoured his own benefactor, but the majority won. Many people have suggested that it would have been better to retain the descriptive Maori name, *Kawatiri*, which means 'swift and deep'—for that is exactly what the river is, almost from start to finish.

The Buller heads in a north-westerly direction from Lake Rotoiti, on a course between the two Nelson lakes which is almost at right angles to the line of the Alpine Fault. The river flats along this stretch are scrub-patched, with bare, eroded hillsides rising up on either side. The vast Howard Forest, of 72 814 hectares, which meets the Buller River at its junction with the Hope River, is a tangled wilderness of beech, undergrown with shrubs and small trees, including the striking tree-daisy *Senecio hectorii* and various species of ferns.

At Gowanbridge, the Buller is joined by the turbulent Gowan River—all white, raging water—which drains Lake Rotoroa. From Gowanbridge, the Buller loops and writhes through splendid gorge scenery for some 75 km, emerging into the coastal terrace uplands 14 km from its mouth.

Blue Cliffs Ridge, a 16 km long, darkly wooded wall rising to over 1000 m, blocks the river's passage, turning it southward until it rounds Beeres Rock, near Murchison. There it becomes briefly benevolent and clatters westward across the town's pleasant valley, over broad gravel flats and through tamed and barbered meadows.

Murchison sits on flat land in the angle formed by the Buller and Matakitaki Rivers. The lower slopes of the surrounding ranges are bare, grazed over by sheep, though the tops are heavily forested.

The Matakitaki was repeatedly dredged for gold until 1940, and the dredge-tailings are seen here and there, now much overgrown with bracken, blackberry and scrub.

Murchison is in an area of active faults, where blocks of the earth's crust are still moving with timeless slowness, except for an occasional impatient quiver—such as happened one day in 1929, when an earthquake of devastating intensity, with its epicentre close to the township, tore the land apart. The scars are still visible where the shattered landscape thrust upward in some areas, and subsided in others. The Matakitaki River was displaced from its bed by a huge landslide and spilled across the countryside, gouging out a new channel to form the Matakitaki Falls.

From Murchison, the Buller River follows a sinuous course, its banks and flats and terraces lined with old goldmining localities and faint echoes of a boisterous past. Eight kilometres from Murchison, in a magnificently forested area and leaned over by tall cliffs, the river sweeps through the Upper Buller Gorge, swinging in a tight loop about the

◄*The Buller River winds through two heavily forested gorges, separated by flats at Inangahua Junction*

▲*Swirling currents in the Buller River catch the light near Little Hawks Crag*

▶*Near the start of its course from the outlet of Lake Rotoiti the Buller River is swift and turbulent*

▼*Beyond the farmed flats near Inangahua Junction the Buller River plunges between the hills to enter its lower gorge*

northernmost spur of the Brunner Range. Then it races westward again, past Inangahua Junction and its confluence with the Inangahua River. *Inanga* is the whitebait *Galaxius maculatus*, a tiny infant fish which grows to an adult length up to 15 cm. The larvae hatch in swamps and backwaters and go down to the sea in vast shoals. The tiny fish, a few centimetres long and translucent, are caught in their return migration to the rivers and are a New Zealand delicacy. Inangahua township was severely damaged by an earthquake in 1968.

Westward, beyond the farmed flats, the forest comes down to the riverbank again—silver beech, red beech growing in places 25–30 m high, and some podocarps, with a rich understorey of shrubs and tree ferns.

This is the beginning of the Lower Buller Gorge, if anything, more spectacular than the upper. The river sweeps irresistibly through it, deep and green and broad, its fast-flowing surface almost smooth, troubled only by intermittent outbreaks of eddies and whirlpools which hint at the rocky bed and the fierceness of the current. The gorge proper begins at Berlins, a one-time goldmining settlement which is now little more than a pub and a few scattered farmsteads. The valley opens out about 16 km to the west, where the confining hills stand back and *pakihi* (claypan) terrace country rolls down to the cliff-bound coast.

The gorge, though wide open to the sky, seems closed in, so closely do the craggy hills lean over the valley, with massive rocks overhanging the road. At Hawks Crag the road was carved into a vertical face.

The river enters the Tasman Sea at Westport. Ten kilometres west of the Buller River mouth is Cape Foulwind, a rocky point with tall cliffs and, trailing away from it into the depths of the sea, a series of pinnacles and reefs—the Giants Tooth, the Three Steeples and Black Reef. A lighthouse on the point warns shipping of the dangerous clusters of rock. This cape was named in 1642 by Abel Tasman, who called it *Clyppegen Hoek*, which means 'rocky point'. The present name was given 128 years later by Captain Cook as he sailed away in appalling weather.

The Kaikouras

*The rockbound Kaikoura coast, at the foot of towering snowy
mountains, is a place of magnificent moodiness—sparkling
and friendly in calm, sunny weather; lowering and bleak
when clouds hide the mountaintops; and wild and boisterous
when the easterly winds lash the sea into fury*

▼*Seen across the bay from the Kaikoura Peninsula, the Seaward Kaikouras seem to rise straight from the sea, but in fact a low plain reaches inland first. To the north and south of the peninsula, bush-clad hills crowd down to a rocky shore*

South of Cape Campbell, the southern portal of Cook Strait, the land rises dramatically, forming into two parallel mountain ranges—the Seaward Kaikouras and the Inland Kaikouras. The former are splintered at their northern end into jagged peaks around the Totara Saddle. The Clarence River, rising on the Spenser Mountains in the west, runs northeast for 70 km along a great fault separating the Inland and Seaward Kaikoura blocks, dividing a tangle of bush-filled valleys. It has cut a deep gorge across the northern end of the Seaward Kaikouras.

The Inland Kaikoura Range, a mighty pressure-fold ridge with peaks rising to more than 2700 m, butts onto the Blue Mountain Range in the north. Its western slopes go down in long parallel ridges to the Awatere Fault, a possible continuation of the Wellington Fault in the North Island. Running parallel to the Awatere, 36 km to the northwest, is yet another fault-rift, along which flows the lower course of the many-channelled Wairau River, whose name means 'many waters'.

Seen from the air, the whole area of nearly 500 000 hectares is an impressively crumpled land of strong parallel ridges, chains of lofty peaks, scarred prodigiously by erosion, and split by three great parallel faults in the earth's crust. It is forested on sheltered slopes and in vast hollows, and watered by innumerable rivers and mountain torrents. Its coastline is a ripple of minor indentations and long, curving sweeps of sandy beach which run between Cape Campbell's rocky promontory and the great sea-stain about the mouth of the Clarence River. From there to the Kaikoura Peninsula, it is a rock-bound coast where the giant kelp swirls in slow motion, like brown oil-slicks, and the breakers are white and dazzling on the cruel reefs.

From the ground, there is a vista after vista of snow-capped peaks, interspersed with stretches where bush-clad slopes rise so abruptly from the roadside that there is no question of seeing the tops. The eye then turns naturally to the rocky coast, a succession of little bays fronting a sparsely-settled, inhospitable landscape. Above all, it is a fisherman's coast. It is the fishermen, mostly, who have named the turbulent and rocky little bays—Halfmoon Bay, Irongate, Riley's Lookout and Goose Bay. Their boatsheds stand on rocks, barely out of the sea's reach,

particularly near the Kaikoura Peninsula, which sticks out from the land like a jaunty thumb, providing shelter for the calm, gently-shelving sandy beaches of South Bay and Gooch Bay.

Inland, the Clarence River winds its often turbulent way between the high ranges in a chill valley which in winter the sun reaches late and leaves early. To the north-west of the Inland Kaikouras, broad upland valleys, troubled with lumpy upthrusts of bare peaks, lie through much of the winter under snow 2 m deep on the valley floors and up to 5 m deep on the tops. At the height of summer they are bare, eroded and burnt khaki-brown. There are lonely farmsteads huddled at the foot of high fells, amidst close clumps of exotic trees. Inland from the Awatere River, strong parallel ridges run at a tangent from the Kaikoura Ranges, trending due north towards the Wairau River.

▼*From near Goose Bay to the Waima River, the highway clings to the sparsely-peopled coast of the Kaikouras*

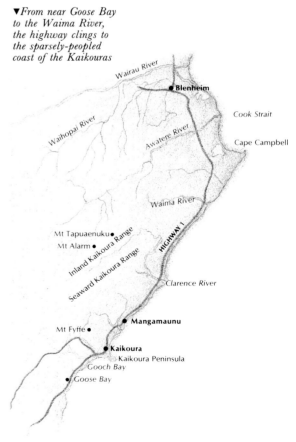

◄*Vegetable sheep live
in rocky subalpine and
alpine regions. Plants
of three genera form
these cushions. Small,
white, woolly leaves
cover the tips of
densely crowded short
branches spreading
from a woody anchor
root. The final
branchlets send roots
into water-storing peat
inside the dense, hard
outer mass*

▼*The Awatere River
wriggles within the
confines of a long,
straight fault-rift. The
side streams in this
bare country can rise
during rainstorms to
flood proportions
within an hour and
fall again as quickly*

The Inland and Seaward Kaikoura Mountains were named 'Snowey Mountains' by
Captain Cook. He lay becalmed off the coast
on 15 February 1770 and 57 Maoris in four
double-hulled canoes put off from the Kaikoura Peninsula and paddled out to within
speaking range. They said nothing, even
when Cook's interpreter spoke to them. Perhaps unsettled by their steady, expressionless
stares, Cook named the peninsula 'The Look-
ers On', but a later navigator transferred the
name to the mountains. It is quite apt, for
they do have prominent peaks—Manakau,
2610 m, and Te Ao Whekere, 2596 m, on the
Seaward Kaikouras, and the mighty Tapuaenuku, 2886 m, on the Inland Kaikouras—
which seem to gaze impassively down at the
neighbouring sea.

The Inland Kaikouras, longer than the
Seaward Kaikouras by nearly 19 km, form
the watershed between the Clarence and
Awatere Valleys. Sizeable streams rush and
tumble down steep northwestern slopes to
the Awatere River as it runs its sinuous
course within the confines of a long, straight
fault-rift from the Barefell Pass slopes to its
outlet at the northern end of Clifford Bay.
On the southeastern side, shorter, fiercer
brooks rush down to swell the equally tortuous Clarence River.

The mountains are generally bare windswept slopes scarred with scree-slides. They
are snow-covered from their crests down to
the river valleys in winter, and often snow-
capped on their highest peaks through all but
the hottest summers. Wind-stunted manuka
scrub covers some of the lower slopes, and
shrub forests fill a few sheltered valleys.

In the labyrinth of valleys where the Clarence River begins to carve a way out to the
sea, there is some bush, especially between
Peninsula Peak and The Pikes. But mostly
the slopes are bare.

At the southern end of the Inland Kaikoura Range, the ridge divides to form a
steep-walled pocket containing the still,
landslip-dammed, deep-green Lake McRae.
It is fed by snow-melt and the little burns that
tumble down from the mountainside springs,
and is drained by underground seepage.

◄A lonely homestead crouches beneath Mt Tapuaenuku, the highest peak in the Kaikoura Mountains. In winter the inland valley floors are covered by snow up to 2 m deep, often from late April to early October. It is hard, dangerous country, where a snowstorm can trap a hunter, tramper or stockman. If he is lucky he will find shelter in one of many huts but he will need firing and food if he is to survive, and there is little or no firewood to be found. Rescue may be deferred for weeks if bad weather settles in

At this southern end of the range, around Lake McRae, Turks Head (1859 m) and Barefell Pass, is Molesworth country. Molesworth, last of the immense 19th century sheep runs, covered more than 181 000 hectares, spreading from the Clarence River, over the Inland Kaikouras to the Saxton Saddle, more than 35 km to the north-west; and from the confluence of the Molesworth Stream with the Awatere River, to where the Clarence comes down around the southern end of the Kaikoura Ranges. Sheep, deer and rabbits ate the heart out of Molesworth and its surrounding runs, but careful pasture management and a change to cattle have largely restored the land.

A road runs through, now, where once only cattle and horses could go but it is not for the novice or the smart saloon car. Another road penetrates the vast area of rumpled landscape—all bare slopes and broad, grassy valleys—between the Awatere and Wairau Rivers. It forks near the banks of the Waihopai River, the Wairau's most important tributary, and ends beneath high peaks. Walking tracks go on over high and bleak windy spurs to the Awatere Valley.

◄It is between bare, nearly vertical slopes like these that the Clarence River makes its northwards journey. Among the rocky outcrops lives the chukor, a small partridge introduced from the Himalayas

◄*When the snows have gone in summer, the work of erosion is revealed and some peaks look like great mounds of shingle*

▼*The Hodder River rises on the slopes of Mt Tapuaenuku, the highest peak in the Inland Kaikouras*

Tapuaenuku is higher, at 2886 m, than any peak in the North Island, and higher than most South Island peaks outside the group in the Mount Cook massif of the Southern Alps. It lifts up a clean, snow-covered, symmetrical head to a height that seems to tower above the Kaikoura Ranges, both of which stand high enough to be plainly visible from Wellington, 150 km across Cook Strait.

Tapuaenuku has a companion peak, Mt Alarm, connected to it by a 2684 m saddle. Mt Alarm stands at 2865 m, a mere 21 m shorter than its consort; but Tapuaenuku is the peak that is seen by travellers on the coast road, as it swings inland at the mouth of the Clarence. The mighty peak stands dead ahead, framed between the lofty walls of the George Spur and Black Hill. Clustered about the two are Mitre Peak, 2620 m, in shape almost the mirror-image of Tapuaenuku, Pinnacle, 2697 m, and Crows Nest, 2453 m.

On the north-western side of this cluster two major spurs run down to the Awatere Valley and between them running almost northwards from Mitre Peak, is a boisterous mountain stream which becomes the Hodder River. Like the adjacent Cam, Isis and McRae Rivers, it is a spectacularly savage mountain torrent, especially when snow is melting or rain is heavy. These streams are more wildly dramatic because they are not softened by forest trees or mossy banks. They bash their way down to the Awatere Valley over boulders and rapids, between dripping walls of granite.

The valleys are lonely, forsaken places. Dotterels, black-fronted terns, black-billed and black-backed gulls inhabit their small flats and soggy hollows. In the small patches of bush, introduced birds live side-by-side with native bellbirds and tomtits, fantails and warblers, which are slowly returning to regenerated areas.

In the higher valleys, where the Awatere rises below Barefell, the lordly moa once roamed, apparently unmolested by Polynesian hunters. They found enough on the coastal flatlands and seaward downs.

The Clarence River writhes between the two Kaikoura Ranges, heading northeast. At the bare wall of Pikes Peak, it turns south around the northern end of the Seaward Kaikouras, and heads eastward again, out through a rugged gorge to the sea.

Southwards to Kaikoura

►*At Mangamaunu
Beach the sea foams
furiously as it claws
up the shingle beach*

The Seaward Kaikouras loom over the rugged coast from Peninsula Peak, 1249 m, down to the maze of peaks and ridges dominated by the 1747 m crown of Mt Tinline. The range bulges slightly coastwards between Mt Manakau—at 2610 m its highest peak—and Te Ao Whekere ('the dark cloud'), second loftiest at 2596 m. Its lower slopes and foothills carry heavy growth, with tall forest trees and a dense coastward cover of shrubs. Streams descend on the inland faces to feed the Clarence River. In one valley, below Te Ao Whekere and the inverted fan-tracery of Fidget Spur, in the end of Fidget Stream, a hot spring serves as a reminder that the rift between the Inland and Seaward Kaikouras is indeed a mighty split in the earth's crust.

The streams on the seaward side are short mountain torrents which tend to combine into three sizeable rivers—the Hapuku, just north of Kaikoura; the Kowhai, spilling into Gooch Bay on the southern side of the peninsula; and the Kahutara River, at the southern end of the gently-curving bay.

From Cape Campbell southwards, the beaches are generally narrow, steeply shelving and shingle-strewn, with tussock-covered dunes and great shingle banks rising behind.

The Waima River flows out from the Inland Kaikouras, between Blue Mountain

▼*The Clarence River rushes toward
the sea after leaving its gorge. It runs between
the Kaikoura Ranges for most of its course*

◀Kaikoura means
'meal of crayfish' to
modern travellers as it
did to old-time Maoris

▼Cape Campbell marks
the entry to Cook
Strait and the end of
the Kaikoura coast

and Ben More, and the Kekerengu River, little more than a creek, tumbles out from Blue Mountain's southern face, over a brown landscape planted with pine and macrocarpa for stability and shelter. Between Waima and Kekerengu, continually creeping earth flows keep pushing the railway and road out of alignment towards the sea.

Highway 1 creeps southward around the feet of the high hills, at last reaching a narrow, flat shingle-fan which spreads about the mouth of the Clarence River, from the Clarence Gorge, an impressive, high-walled notch in the mountains through which, blue with distance and soft haze, the flanks of Tapuaenuku rise up to the shining peak.

South of the Clarence, the open, shingle-and-dunes coastline changes, and becomes a succession of shallow bays and coves, rock-bound and romantic, where the giant kelp swirls in the inrushing swell, and jagged rocks fend off the sea in clouds of spray; and fishermen bring their launches ashore, running them through the occasional clear gut, winching them up rails and slipways to corrugated iron boatsheds amongst pinnacles of rock high above the water. At Mangamaunu Beach, the reefs part, clearing a wide enough gap for the surf which charges into shore and ends its mad rush in foam-fringed sheets of water clawing their way up the beach.

Along this coast, the bush hangs from greywacke sandstone escarpments above the road, which cuts through massive outcrops at the top of high promontories. The railway keeps the road close company, roofed over by concrete against the slips and minor avalanches of rock which heavy, driving rains loosen and temporary torrents tear free even from the bindings of shrub and tree roots on the almost perpendicular slopes. Here the mad ocean winds lash the coast, whipping gravel off the embankments and flinging it across the road. In or immediately after wet weather, the road calls for extra caution, because slips from roadside banks not infrequently slide out across it in an axle-deep sea of mud; or boulders roll out into the roadway.

From the Hapuku River, the brief triangular plain reaches back to where the pretty Kowhai River emerges from behind the long Mt Fyffe ridge, and from it the Kaikoura Peninsula pokes out into the sea.

The crayfish coast

The Kaikoura Peninsula was once an island. It is basically limestone, a reef which was built up over aeons by an accumulation of the shells and skeletons of small marine creatures, bonded together on some primaeval ocean floor. Silt and stones washed down from the ranges form a triangular plain, which has gradually reclaimed the base of the peninsula from the sea.

Like Banks Peninsula, it was a good place for the Maoris, with seafood in great abundance, the forest birds and, in earliest times, moas. The soil was fertile and the area was easily defended. The Maoris settled and lived there for generations, and they gradually wove legends about the place. The North Island was *Te-Ika-a-Maui*, 'Maui's fish', and the South Island was *Te-Waka-a-Maui*, 'Maui's canoe', from which he hauled up the monstrous catch. The Kaikoura Peninsula was the projecting end of the oarsman's thwart, *Taumanu-o-te-waka-a-Maui*, against which Maui braced his foot while he struggled to pull in the fish.

The peninsula was named by the legendary explorer, Tamatea-Pokai-Whenua, who came in pursuit of runaway wives. The *koura* is the crayfish, and the full name of the peninsula is *Te-Ahi-Kai-Koura-a-Tamatea-Pokai-Whenua*, 'the fire at which crayfish were cooked for Tamatea-Pokai-Whenua'.

▲*Kaikoura Peninsula displays a variety of fascinating rock forms. The vertical leaves of these rocks have edges that are knife-sharp*

▶*A large seal colony lives on the Kaikoura Peninsula. Seals can be seen basking on the rocks at low tide and sometimes they may be watched as they swim*

▲*Stalactites in Maori Leap Caves on the shores of Gooch Bay* — *where a warrior leaped from the bluff above the caves and lived*

▲*Vertical rock strata on the Kaikoura Peninsula. A few* — *metres away the rocks take on different but equally curious forms*

It is still a good place for crayfishing, though much unbridled commercialism has depleted even Kaikoura's bountiful reefs. The crayfish caught there are the common spiny crayfish. At the New Wharf—more than 70 years old—crayfish are packed for export. At the Old Wharf, built in 1882, all stores for the settlement used to be landed in the days before road and railway linked Kaikoura with Blenheim and Christchurch. From the New Wharf may be seen the matchless panorama of the heaving ocean, the white-fringed coast and the towering, snow-mantled Seaward Kaikouras almost on the coast.

The land rises up to a lighthouse, beneath which is a reef where seals bask. Great rocks provide an ideal and undisturbed chain of basking-places, and seals are often seen swimming and diving amongst the fishing boats too. Early in the 19th century, sealers almost exterminated them, but the population has recovered well.

On the sandy beaches between the reefs, and on the reefs themselves at low tide, white-faced herons, both variable and South Island pied oystercatchers, pied stilts, godwits and turnstones are seen in considerable numbers. And in a small lagoon, paradise shelducks, mallard, pied stilts and banded dotterels feed. Red-billed gulls nest on a tall reef beyond the coastal rocks. White-fronted tern colonies nest along the cliffs near East Head, and skuas, sooty shearwaters and giant petrels fish the abundant offshore waters.

From Gooch Bay, south to Oaro, the smooth, sheltered, sandy beaches of the southern side of the Kaikoura Peninsula give way once more to jagged reefs and kelp-choked channels.

Some 2 km along the main highway are Maori Leap Caves, limestone caverns hollowed by underground streams out of cliffs against which the sea was beating no more than a few thousand years ago. They contain delicate, almost translucent, honey-coloured stalactites and stalagmites, and fossilised bones of seals and penguins.

An old story explains the name of the caves. When Ngai-Tahu invaders captured a pa on the bluff above the caves, a Ngati-Mamoe warrior, preferring death to slavery, leaped from the 30 m high cliff. He landed shaken and bruised, but with no bones broken, to escape and fight another day.

Goose Bay is a locality dotted with fishermen's cottages, and known for its nesting populations of pied shags and little shags. At Oaro, where the road at last leaves the coast and climbs into the scrub-covered, unkempt folds of the Hundalee Hills, there is a pleasant beach, with reef herons feeding among the wave-washed rocks. Bellbirds call from the bush-clad hills which stand back a little from the sea. The small Oaro River spills across the sand into the ocean.

▶*Southwards from the Kaikoura Peninsula the coast is wild and* — *rocky. The road runs below steep bluffs and even through tunnels*

Arthur's Pass National Park

Differences in climate and altitude cause ecological contrast in this national park—dense rainforest to the west of the Main Divide and beech forest on the drier eastern mountains

In the mid-1800s, sheepmen searching for grazing land beyond the Canterbury Plains were the first Europeans to explore the mountain wilderness now called Arthur's Pass National Park. But it was the lure of gold that shaped the region's destiny.

Gold was first found on the West Coast in 1863. The newly arrived English settlers of Canterbury were prepared to leave their homes and trek for hundreds of kilometres on the merest chance of making their fortune, but the awesome barrier of the Southern Alps lay between them and the alluring goldfields.

The first European explorers, like the Maoris, preferred to cross the Southern Alps by the Harper Pass route, but an endless train of gold-seekers, packhorses, cattle and sheep had reduced the bridle path to a boulder-strewn morass by 1863. An alternative route was imperative.

In February 1864, two young men, Arthur Dobson, a surveyor, and his brother Edward, rode horses up the Waimakariri and Mingha Rivers. Then they came to the long Bealey Valley. At its head they walked over a moraine left by a huge glacier which had once filled the entire basin.

Arthur Dobson, however, pronounced the route extremely difficult, if not impossible, because of the precipitous descent on the western side. There was enough width for a zigzag cutting to be made into the head of the gorge, but a good deal of heavy rock cutting would be required beyond, he wrote. The search continued, but no better route was found and in 1865 Arthur's father, Edward Dobson senior, the Canterbury provincial engineer, decided a road would be cut through Arthur's Pass.

Within months a horse track had been forged and work begun on a metalled road. About 1000 men toiled through the bitter alpine winter and completed the road in less than a year, using only hand tools, rudimentary rock drills and explosives.

Arthur's Pass is the highest and most spectacular highway across the Southern Alps. Nature is elemental in this mountain vastness, where glaciers carved out deep gashes between the mountains. Erosion, earthquakes and avalanches have added their imprints, bringing down millions of tonnes of rubble and fashioning vast scree slopes and sprawling shingle riverbeds.

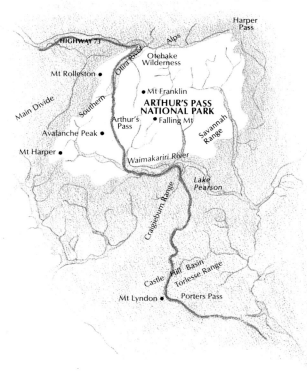

◀*The highway over Arthur's Pass is the highest road over the Southern Alps, crossing the Main Divide at 920 m. It passes, tortuously in places, through mountain scenery of elemental grandeur*

▶*Lacy beech forest and slender waterfalls are among the charms of the eastern approach to Arthur's Pass. Above the tree line, however, the scenery is bold and severe in aspect*

A high pass just beyond the edge of the plains

▲ *The last light of a winter afternoon catches peaks of the Torlesse Range, named after Charles*

Obins Torlesse, an early surveyor and a nephew of the great coloniser Edward Gibbon Wakefield

▼ *The Craigieburn Range encloses the Castle Hill basin in the west. Only vestiges*

of beech forest cling to the eroded slopes, but the forest survives farther to the north

The Arthur's Pass road runs 160 km from the little farming community of Springfield in Canterbury to the old gold town of Kumara in Westland. The highest point, strangely, is not the summit of Arthur's Pass, but a crossing of the foothills only 20 km from the eastern access at Springfield.

Porters Pass, at 945.5 m, is 14 m higher than the pass across the Main Divide. Named

after three brothers who pioneered the nearby Castle Hill sheep station, the pass and its steep ascent were the first taste of the harsh terrain which lay ahead for the early goldseekers. For those returning, often emptyhanded and dispirited, the prospect of the rich Canterbury plains, rolling out before them like a patchwork, signalled relief.

Today Porters Pass is a winter mecca for tobogganists, who drive from as far away as Christchurch for a day in the snow. Lake Lyndon, a couple of kilometres farther along the road, is also popular in the winter, since it is one of the few lakes in the region which sometimes freezes right over and becomes a giant skating rink during frosty weather between June and August.

Birdwatchers at the lake may catch a glimpse of the black and white plumage and flashing red bill of the sturdy South Island pied oystercatcher. The oystercatcher thrives on the northern and eastern coasts but is not at all averse to breeding inland on riverbeds and lake shores. Nor is its companion the banded dotterel, the small plover the Maoris call *tuturiwhatu* because of the frantic trilling calls of the male at mating time.

From May to January, the banded dotterel lives up to its name, with two distinctive bands, one black, the other chestnut, on its

◄Castle Hill Peak, at 1996 m, the highest in the Torlesse Range, rises beyond the course of the Porter River

neck and breast. It is a great rover. Some take off across the Tasman in autumn and winter for the warmer Australian coasts, from Western Australia to Queensland, and some have been seen as far afield as Fiji.

Above the lake rises Mt Lyndon, 148 m high, and to the northeast the stark Torlesse range, named for the Canterbury surveyor who scaled one of its high peaks in 1849. The first known description of the region belongs to Charles Torlesse, who said that the view towards the Waimakariri basin was 'a romantic and chaotic mass of mountains'.

On the way back after his feat Torlesse and his Maori guide exhausted their food supplies and were faced with the need to kill either their dog or their donkey for the next meal. A coin was tossed and the hapless dog lost, but had the good luck to catch a weka which took his place in the pot.

The big, flightless weka, or native woodhen, was a common sight in those days and Maoris crossing the mountains would often catch them by using snares. But by the mid-1920s the buff weka—so called because it lacks the grey under-feathers of its North Island counterpart—had completely disappeared. In 1962 it was reintroduced into the park from the distant Chatham Islands, where some had been taken and established last century.

Inquisitive and not at all fastidious about what it eats, the weka is a notorious scavenger, particularly well-disposed towards bright, shiny objects. An expert at speedy escape, it can run away rapidly or swim across many bodies of water that obstruct it.

As the highway runs north from Porters Pass there opens an extraordinary vista of smooth, rounded hills and oddly shaped rock formations. This is Castle Hill, which takes its name from these limestone outcrops, sculptured by centuries of erosion.

There, as on many other limestone outcrops in the South Island, the Maoris drew pictures on the smooth, weatherworn overhangs—probably, it is conjectured, while taking shelter from heavy storms. The material used was charcoal, sometimes dry, sometimes mixed with fat or oil. Few of the drawings have been dated but charcoal in the soil suggests that those at Castle Hill were made by hunting parties about 500 years ago.

Four centuries later, Castle Hill had a new role as one of the staging posts on the long coach journey from Christchurch to Hokitika. Cobb and Co started the service as soon as the road was opened. By the time it ended, 57 years later, it had become one of the longest running in the country. For £8 passengers had the privilege of being jogged and jolted over some breathtakingly infelicitous terrain. Rivers bursting their banks, snow blocking the way, sections of the road simply disappearing without warning, grades so steep that passengers had to get out and walk, and sometimes a drunken driver all made the journeys hazardous.

Horses were changed every 25 km or so, drivers less often. In good weather the journey lasted 36 hours; in bad weather it could seem interminable. As the railway was extended from both east and west, the connecting coach service became shorter and shorter, until it ended altogether with the opening of the Otira rail tunnel in 1923.

◄Limestone crops out from smooth, rounded hills at several places in the surprising Castle Hill basin

▼Many centuries of erosion has produced a variety of fantastic shapes at Castle Hill

Trout lakes among bare, eroded hills

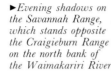

►*Evening shadows on the Savannah Range, which stands opposite the Craigieburn Range on the north bank of the Waimakariri River*

The Craigieburn Range, to the west of Castle Hill, is skiing country in winter. The ski basin, high up in the range a few kilometres west of the highway, has the distinction of being the coldest weather recording station in New Zealand, with a mean annual temperature of 3.6°C.

The beech-and-tussock-clad northern reaches of the range are a forest park. As in almost all the forest cover east of the Main Divide—except where there are scattered stands of red beech and silver beech—the trees are small-leaved mountain beech. At higher altitudes within the eastern ranges, the trees become progressively more stunted, and in exposed places may be only 2–4 m tall. Around 1100 m, the forest merges with the sub-alpine scrub.

Beyond the Craigieburn Forest Park, there is little plant cover on many of the hillsides. Early runholders in the Canterbury high country took to large-scale burning of tussock in an endeavour to clear ever more land for grazing. The legacy of this wholesale destruction of the native plant cover has been the erosion of hilltops and deluges of shingle sliding down into the valleys below.

Nowhere is this devastation seen more clearly than on Purple Hill, a 1679 m high cone whose slopes are scarred by long shingle slides. Much of the shingle slips into Lake Pearson, a narrow-waisted lake 3.5 km long and 12 m deep, which was named for Joseph Pearson, an Englishman who was the first European explorer of the upper reaches of the Waimakariri River. Pearson later took up a sheep run on the edge of the Canterbury Plain which he called Burnt Hill— doubtless a reference to devastation wrought in clearing the way for his sheep.

Up in the high country that Pearson explored, the Department of Conservation is now attempting to repair the ecological damage. At the Flock Hill run, south of Lake Pearson, special nurseries have been set up to grow selected shrubs, grasses and clovers with which it is intended to revegetate the stricken hills.

Lake Pearson is famous for its fishing, and it teems with brown and rainbow trout. It also harbours the crested grebe, a sleek, tailless waterbird which is sometimes mistaken for a duck. It has a long slender neck and a sharp pointed bill. In summer its satin brown and white plumage changes and is jauntily set off by red-brown tufts on its head which have

◄*Matagouri, spiky and impenetrable, is one of the few deciduous native plants in New Zealand. Its name is a European corruption of the Maori* tumatakuru

►*Beech forest in the Craigieburn State Forest Park. In winter, skifields in the area can be reached quickly from Christchurch, some 120 km distant*

led to it also being called the topknot shag.

A few kilometres along the road is another lake where trout thrive, tiny Grasmere, lying like a jewel amongst expanses of brown tussock and hills streaked with shingle slides.

The road passes around the northern end of the Craigieburn Range and follows the great Waimakariri River to its confluence with the Bealey River at the entrance to the Arthur's Pass National Park. Rising in the perpetual snows of the Southern Alps, the Waimakariri courses 150 km through alpine valleys and deep canyons and across lowland flats to its distant outlet in the Pacific Ocean. Its name means 'cold water'.

On the shingle flats close by the junction of the Waimakariri and Bealey Rivers is the site of a once-thriving but short-lived town. As the road was built, followed rapidly by the installation of a telegraph line, settlements mushroomed along the route.

The first attempt to build a town was made on the north bank, at a place named Klondyke Corner because it was so cold—it receives no sunshine in winter—and was reminiscent of the Alaskan gold rush settlement after which it was named. It began as a single hut across the river, used as a refuge when the river was impassable. In 1865, with about 100 people already encamped, 208 sections were surveyed and an ambitious street plan mapped out, with names like Albion, Cal-

▲*Erosion-ravaged mountainsides surround Lake Pearson. They are a legacy of reckless burning-off by the pioneer runholders*

edonia and St Andrews. Eighteen months later everyone except a telegraph operator and a police sergeant had moved to the sunnier site, which also had the advantage of being on the Christchurch side of the Waimakariri River.

Tourism began early in the area. One of the pioneers was a man named O'Malley, proprietor of the then illustrious Bealey Glacier Hotel from 1882 to 1901. He personally guided his guests to the head of the Waimakariri Valley to gaze at the glaciers.

◄*Lake Pearson, so narrow-waisted that it is almost two lakes, reflects the stark peaks and rocky outcrops of the Craigieburn Range*

▲*The buff weka has been reintroduced into the Arthur's Pass National Park, where it became extinct by the 1920s*

Sources of the great Waimakariri River

◄Mt Rolleston, one of the higher peaks of the Arthur's Pass National Park, carries the Crow Glacier

The snow-topped mountains of the Main Divide rise above the tawny floor of the upper Waimakariri Valley. The raw and austere features of the valley demonstrate the tremendous power of glaciers to carve and mould the land.

The park has had four major periods of glaciation, spanning half a million years. The effects of the last are the most obvious. During the last advances, ending only about 10 000 years ago, the upper valleys were filled with solid masses of ice. An earlier Waimakariri Glacier, at its extreme, had stretched as far as Springfield, 55 km to the east. From the same snowfields, westward-flowing ice streams reached Kumara, 9 km from the west coast. As they receded with each warming of the earth, the glaciers left a legacy of cavernous valleys, deep lakes and jagged rock faces that give the region its grandeur.

Since then, raging water, rain, earthquakes and avalanches have added their marks. So too have people. In their haste to clear land for grazing, the early farmers became avid arsonists, setting fire to large tracts of scrub and completely devastating parts of the valley. The result was the steady incursion of manuka, a tough indigenous shrub so adept at reclaiming the land that it is commonly treated as a weed.

The upper Waimakariri is a tramper's paradise. In a matter of hours Crow Hut, Carrington Hut, Klondyke Corner or Avalanche Peak can be reached. And four or five days' steady trekking across three alpine passes to Westland, offers the reward of superb views and the sensation of passing from one distinct climatic zone to another, with dramatically different plant life in evidence.

Part of the route follows a wide trail cut over a century ago by miners determined to forge a way over the mountain wall. The valley offers mountaineers the real challenge of many unclimbed ridges and rock faces.

Although most of the glaciers finally melted between 15 000 and 10 000 years ago, not all have disappeared. High in the Waimakariri watershed, at the headwaters of its tributary, the White River, three glaciers—the White, Marmaduke Dixon and Cahill—splay their ice-blue tongues out across the mountain face. And to the northeast, at an altitude of 2211 m, the Crow Glacier straddles the southernmost face of Mt Rolleston.

From this glacier the Waimakariri's other tributary, the Crow River, flows southward through a long valley webbed with streams. In fine weather, trampers reach the Crow Valley from the Bealey Valley by way of the Avalanche Peak track, which crosses a mountain ridge before descending a long scree of loose rocks and boulders to the valley floor. At the head of the valley, in a clearing in the bush, is a New Zealand Alpine Club hut.

It is in country like this that many New Zealand climbers have first tested their skill, learning the basic techniques, gauging their stamina and ability before going on to more testing terrain. Loose rock offers a constant challenge. Most of it is greywacke, weakened by the cycle of frost and thaw and ready to cascade down the hillside at the merest provocation. Its companion, the black, shaley argillite, is also notoriously unstable. Both reflect the huge pressures which eventually heaved the rocks up out of the sea, bringing

◄The Crow River runs down a long valley from the Crow Glacier to the Waimakariri

▲The kea, unique to the mountain regions of the South Island, is always on the alert for mischief. When it flies, its drab olive-green plumage is enlivened by flashes of vermillion underwing

with them telltale fossils of shell and fishbone.

One of the first to test himself against these deceptively tranquil mountains was Arthur Peal Harper, whose most notable conquests included Mt Philistine in 1891 and Mt Davie in 1912. He gave his name to Mt Harper, a peak at the northern tip of the Birdwood Range first climbed in 1913. At 2240 m, Mt Harper is fifth highest of the park's 16 mountains over 2000 m and still one of the most popular with mountaineers.

The park's rivers and valleys play host to dozens of different birds, but virtually the only species to brave it out in the alpine

reaches are the little brown-and-white New Zealand pipit and its unlikely companion, the large, raucous kea. This parrot nests high up—in rock crevices, in holes in the ground or in trees—but it will swoop down hundreds of metres into the forest, or even to the open river flats, in search of food. The kea has a well-deserved reputation as a clown-cum-vandal and is incurably curious, but has gained an undeserved reputation as a sheep killer. It will feed on carcases, but instances of it attacking live sheep are extremely rare. It is also extremely noisy making mainly tuneless sounds and cries.

▲The Waimakariri River swings from side to side of a broad valley in its upper reaches. It passes through a narrow gorge as it leaves the high country for the Canterbury Plains.

▼Mt Harper stands on the western boundary of the park. It was named after Arthur Peal Harper, co-founder of the New Zealand Alpine Club

Through the seasons in the heart of the park

Throughout the Arthur's Pass region, chains of mountains radiate from the towering peaks, enclosing labyrinths of deep-cut valleys and swift, rock-strewn rivers. The long Edwards Valley branch of the Mingha River, east of Arthur's Pass township, stretches northwards towards the Southern Alps. At its head is the Taruahuna Pass, one of a string of easy passes bridging east and west.

This is earthquake country. Major faults are still active. Taruahuna Pass spectacularly shows how an earthquake can devastate the landscape in a few hours. A strong shock in March 1929 caused a large segment of nearby Falling Mountain to collapse, showering hundreds of thousands of tonnes of rocks onto the pass, up the slopes of Mt Franklin on the other side and 5 km down into the Otehake Valley. Everything in the way was obliterated, and even today there is barely a trace of vegetation on the giant slip. Taruahuna Pass is a vast pile of debris. Beyond, in the Otehake Wilderness, hot springs bubble to the surface, an eerie reminder of the forces in the earth's crust.

The Edwards Valley, with its well-defined bush tracks and upland tussock, is ideal tramping territory, and the trip over the Taruahuna Pass to the Otehake Wilderness, can be comfortably accomplished in four days. But the heart of the park is the great Bealey Valley, where the tiny township of Arthur's Pass lies on flats between sprawling beech forests and the winding river.

The plants and birds in the Bealey are typical of the eastern valleys. Orange lichen and moss cling to the grey shingle of the river-bed. Summer-flowering daisies, coprosmas, harebells and other small plants mingle with the tussock grasslands beyond. There are large populations of paradise shelducks and pipits. Banded dotterels, pied oyster-catchers, hawks, Canada geese and black-backed gulls, also live on the valley floor.

Higher up, the dark forests ring with the song of the bellbird and, in summer, the piercing screech of the visiting long-tailed cuckoo. There are other small birds as well — silvereye, fantail, tomtit, grey warbler and,

◄ *The Edwards River flows down from the Tarauahana Pass. It joins the Mingha and Bealey Rivers near the broad valley of the Waimakariri River*

◄Mountain beech trees, small-leaved and graceful, dominate the blue-green forests on the eastern side of the Main Divide

►Seasonal contrasts of light and colour in the Arthur's Pass National Park are revealed by photographs taken from almost the same spot above the Bealey Valley. A beauty of the 99 270-hectare park is that this alpine world is only a short walk away from the road, railway station and park headquarters. Many of the walks in the park are safe at any time, but some are best not attempted in winter months, when snow lies deep and cold winds whistle across the passes. Ice, snow and the threat of avalanches block many of the higher routes until the thaw

smallest of all, the rifleman. And the harsh call of the kiwi is often heard echoing during the night.

Up the valley towards the Main Divide, the forest becomes denser, carpeted thickly with subalpine shrubs like coprosma, lancewood, three-finger and hebe. There are patches of ferns and clumps of bush lilies. But above the forest line the true glory of the park is found—in summer a quilt of alpine flowers, clinging to the rocky ledges, standing tall amongst the tussock and scrub, and even appearing miraculously on the bare stony slopes of the screes. There are delicate gentians, violets, snowberries and foxgloves; tall mountain daisies, with soft white flowers, and black daisies poke through the shingle. The pride of the mountains, the Mount Cook lily splashes the grasslands with shimmering white flowers.

Avalanche Peak, directly east of the township, is aptly named. Extreme changes in temperature between the seasons loosen the soft, brittle rock of these mountains and the weight of snow can be severe. Below neighbouring Mt Rolleston, a bare 1.5 km long swathe through the forest is the dramatic imprint of a huge avalanche centuries ago.

Above the forest stretch bands of subalpine scrub, a rich profusion of low creeping plants and tall, hardy shrubs, perfectly adapted to catch the heavy rains and prevent erosion. Hebes are prevalent on both sides of the divide, dozens of different varieties gracing not only scrublands but also bogs, tussock lands and outcrops of rock. Their leaves are thick, leathery and often concave. All are prolific bloomers, sometimes smothered in flowers from October to April. Like all subalpine plants, they are suited to withstand the intermittent snow cover and chill winds of winter, and hot, dry spells in summer.

East-west contrasts on a mountain crossing

►*Mosses grow thickly in the forests of the Arthur's Pass National Park, softening the contours of fallen tree trunks*

▼*The Goldney Glacier, high on the eastern face of Mt Rolleston, is the source of the Bealey River*

Mt Rolleston, at 2270 m, is not the highest peak in the Arthur's Pass National Park—Mts Murchison, Davie and Wakeman surpass it—but its central position has made it the most striking, the most photographed, and the most climbed.

During the final phase of the last ice age, about 11 000 years ago, a short glacier reached from Mt Rolleston to the head of the Otira Gorge but all that remains today are low, rocky moraines straddling the 920 m high Arthur's Pass. Despite the ravages of fires, the pass has a splendid array of sub-alpine plants. This is an area rich in alpine bogs, fascinating miniature ecosystems where tiny flowers cluster on dense green mounds of alpine cushion and strange plants like the sundew and bladderwort trap microscopic insects to survive.

Some of the park's most stirring sights lie near the township. Less than a kilometre away, the Devil's Punchbowl Falls plunge over the lip of a long-vanished glacier 150 m to the valley below. The falling water is a glistening thread against the dark cliff and forest. Another of the region's many waterfalls, the Bridal Veil descends nearby.

It is not hard to see why Arthur Dobson and his brother gazed down on the Otira Gorge with such dismay. One of the most hair-raising drives to be encountered anywhere on the road cut through this wild, scree-scarred terrain before it was improved to a standard suitable for tourist buses. Its maintenance is expensive. The heavy western rainfall can cause huge sections of hillside, sometimes carrying forest cover, to fall onto the road or segments of the road to fall into the gorge. For all this, the crossing of Arthur's Pass, with its abrupt transition from the uniform beech forest and open shingle riverbeds of the east to the tall podocarps and yellow gorse and broom in the riverbeds of the west, is an experience not to be missed.

The most startling demonstration of how great a barrier the Main Divide presents to climate and vegetation is found in the gorge itself. There the southern rata, one of New Zealand's most beautiful flowering trees, grows thickly, painting the hills all summer with its vivid scarlet blossoms. On the eastern side, just a few kilometres away, there is not a single rata to be found.

◄ *The Devil's Punchbowl is the name that the discoverer of Arthur's Pass gave to the basin into which this high waterfall plunges. It can be visited on a walk from the Arthur's Pass village*

Banks Peninsula

The remnants of colossal twin volcanos, attached to the mainland by a great plain of gravel, form Banks Peninsula. It has long been cleared of most of its forest but its craggy heights, rocky bays and quiet valleys make a memorable landscape

To Captain Cook Banks Peninsula was an island, and he named it after Sir Joseph Banks, the botanist who accompanied him on his 1769–70 voyage of discovery. Cook was mistaken, but it was a pardonable error, because when viewed from the sea, Banks Peninsula looks like an island. On its northern side lies a broad stretch of water, the estuary of the Avon and Heathcote Rivers, while in the south a long, low shingle-spit is all that separates the sea from Lake Ellesmere, a great expanse of water reaching inland.

Indeed, it was an island not long ago in geological time, built up by violent volcanic action on the bed of a shallow sea. But the Canterbury Plains, a vast bed of gravel washed down from the crumbling young mountains, gradually reached out and ensnared it. Geologists say that this happened before man appeared in New Zealand, yet at the time of the first organised European settlement, in 1850, a 15 km wide band of swampy bogs and reedy waterways fringed the peninsula.

But Banks Peninsula is certainly a peninsula, though its craggy peaks and deeply indented coastline, its winding and secretive valleys, implant in the mind a subtle suggestion of 'island'. The peninsula is formed of the truncated cones of two immense volcanos and some lesser eruptions, from which valley-riven ridges fan out and become confusingly entangled. The height of the peninsula—its peaks are around 700 m—is accentuated by the pool-table flatness of the surrounding Canterbury Plains, so beautifully laid out.

The twin volcanos that built the peninsula were much higher. The Akaroa volcano is estimated to have stood 1370 m high, a few metres above the Lyttelton dome, which it eventually overwhelmed on its eastern flank. The latest known eruptions sent a stream of lava from the Akaroa dome down into the Lyttelton crater. The outer valleys and cores of both volcanos had been deeply eroded before this. During the ice ages, when the sea level was lower than now, valleys deepened further and when the sea rose to near its present level 10 000–5000 years ago they became drowned. Basalt pillars—plugs of lava from the long-eroded throats of lesser volcanos—still stand like fantastic castles on the peninsula's skylines, and some ancient lava flows can still be traced to where they poured out and were cooled and solidified, eventually being broken up by the sea, or buried by the accumulating plain.

Today, delightful bays and coves lie between the lava flows. Remnants of the peninsula's forests are preserved. Pleasant little townships nestle about its landward feet and at the heads of its two crater-harbours.

It is a land for summer, for it has its own weather patterns, and in winter its rugged tops are bleak, windswept and often snow-covered. But, winter or summer, it remains cheerfully unkempt, not quite tamed, an endearingly rugged 'island', still keeping to itself wild areas that might never have known man and his machines.

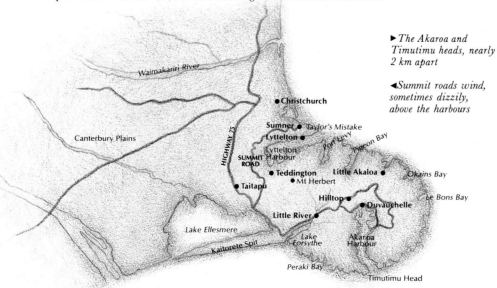

▶ *The Akaroa and Timutimu heads, nearly 2 km apart*

◀ *Summit roads wind, sometimes dizzily, above the harbours*

Rim of an ancient crater

►*Godley Head, here seen from Taylors Mistake, is the northern portal of Lyttelton Harbour*

The part of Banks Peninsula most familiar to the first European settlers was the Port Hills, which separate Christchurch from Lyttelton, its port. They rise abruptly from the sea at Godley Head and sprawl in a more or less westerly direction over three rounded humps which rise in steps to the tawny mass of Mt Pleasant. From 507 m high Mt Pleasant, the crater rim curves southwards, leaping upwards again at the Tors to 449 m. It then climbs in brisk crazy steps for about 6.5 km to the 544 m Cass Peak, and on still higher for another 2.5 km to the lofty Coopers Knob, 573 m above the waters of the harbour, until it drops away finally to Gebbies Pass.

From harbourside or plains, the Port Hills look exactly as their volcanic origin would suggest. Though the contours have been softened and rounded by erosion and earth-

▼*Lyttelton Harbour from the heights above Governors Bay. The Port Hills, of volcanic origin, are at left*

cover, the harsh basalt skeleton of the hills is visible in ridges and cliffs. Grotesque plugs of lava stand jagged against the sky, with fissured faces and threatening overhangs.

On the city side, the slopes have been criss-crossed by streets and dotted with houses; and in the remaining open spaces are sheltering rows of blue gums or pines; but on the northern side, along the estuary of the Heathcote and Avon Rivers, the massive volcanic rubble and lava flows have been cut

▶Inside the crater of the old Lyttelton volcano the slopes are steep and craggy

back by the erosive power of the ocean to form high cliffs pierced with caves. Shag Rock rises up on the side of the estuary, a monolith of basalt which marks the beginning of a magnificent sweep of beach, fronting the little township of Sumner. Midway along this beach is Cave Rock, a lump of lava in which trapped gases left caves.

On the face of rugged Scarborough Head, a slight promontory of Sumner Head, a nesting colony of spotted shags provides a focus of interest for ornithologists. Sumner Head shelters Taylors Mistake, a bay from which a track climbs 3 km to Godley Head, where disused gun emplacements stare at the approaches to Lyttelton Harbour.

The Summit Road begins at Godley Head, though it has to be reached by car at Evans Pass, the 193 m high summit of the Sumner-Lyttelton road. The Summit Road winds around the rim of the ancient crater, offering breathtaking views, now over one side, now over the other. To the west there are vistas of the tidy patchwork of the plains, dotted with little towns, spreading for 60 km to be lost in a soft haze where the foothills begin their climb to the Southern Alps. And on the eastern side is a panorama of Lyttelton Harbour, with its two islands, Ripa and Quail, and its bays and eastern rim dominated by 919 m Mt Herbert, often snowy in winter.

The Summit Road, originally planned to curve in a graceful S-bend from Godley Head to the crater rim above Akaroa Harbour, with four roadhouses along its way, has never been completed. The first roadhouse, the Sign of the Takahe, at the top of the Christchurch hillside suburb of Cashmere, is a Gothic fantasy with magnificent views of city, plains and Southern Alps.

The Sign of the Kiwi stands above the Summit Road where it crosses Dyers Pass Road at 327 m, the highest gap in the hills. The Sign of the Bellbird is a picnic shelter at Kennedy's Bush, a remnant of the forest that once clothed Banks Peninsula.

The Sign of the Packhorse, beneath Mt Herbert, can only be reached by foot track, but that is beyond the Port Hills, which end where the Summit Road dips down into Gebbies Pass and forks either to the flat, salt-marshy ground at Teddington at the head of the harbour, or right, through the pass and down Highway 75, which leads to Akaroa.

Waters that link hills and plain

Highway 75 shuns the hills for some 6 km from Halswell, on the southern outskirts of Christchurch, and runs straight across the eastern edge of the Canterbury Plains to Taitapu through farmland criss-crossed with drainage ditches and dotted with willows and poplars. Taitapu is at the mouth of a pretty, bush-filled valley below Coopers Knob and dominated by Gibraltar Rock. The main highway then begins to hug the outline of Banks Peninsula's western hills, keeping to the higher ground, and following an old bullock-waggon trail.

Between Motukarara and the area known as Kaituna, 'feasts of eels', on the northern shore of Lake Ellesmere, the rocky ribs of the peninsula—remains of lava flows—begin to show through the brown grass more frequently, and the steep slopes change from the rounded pasture-slopes of the Port Hills to a dusty and slightly parched series of steep, parallel spurs.

A good road runs up from Kaituna into the hills through a deep valley, to the very heart of the peninsula. It terminates beneath the towering Mt Herbert, and walking tracks climb from it to the southern rim of the Lyttleton crater.

Beneath Mt Herbert is the largest of the peninsula's forest reserves, a steep 2.4 km climb from the road. The bush fills most of the Kaituna Valley's upper basin. Kahikatea, mountain and lowland totara, matai, broadleaf, and vines and ferns thrive beneath the high canopy of the tall trees, and various species of subalpine plants maintain a precarious foothold in the spectacular rocky bluffs. The bird life is rich and varied, with pigeons, tomtits, noisily chorusing brown creepers, bellbirds and, high in the tops, tuis.

Lake Ellesmere is a broad, shallow coastal lake with a frequently blocked outlet to the sea which is highly regarded for its flounder fishing and, between January and April, for its migrating eels. The Maoris called the lake *Waihora*, meaning 'spreading waters', which is apt, for it spreads over 278 km².

◀*Straight roads and fences dominate the Canterbury Plains, but patterns change when* *the rugged slopes of Banks Peninsula intrude upon the calm geometry*

◄*Many waterfowl and sea birds live in and around Lake Elles-mere. Among them are the Canada goose (right) and the black swan (centre). The curious wrybill (left) feeds among the stones of Kaitorete Spit*

Lake Ellesmere was long famous for its black swans. These introduced Australian birds thrived. Until a few years ago there were at one time perhaps 80 000, the biggest concentration in the world. But a violent storm killed thousands of them in the late 1960s, and the population is now much smaller. Canada geese are also there in considerable numbers, together with various species of duck, including the shoveler, the mallard and the grey duck. Marsh crakes are fairly common, thrush-sized waders, brown, spotted with black and streaked with white, with ash-grey breast and an underside barred with brown and white. Australian cattle egrets occasionally feed amongst the dairy and beef herds in the lake's vicinity, the majestic white

heron, or kotuku, is not unknown, and the welcome swallow, another Australian bird, has been breeding there since about 1960. The pukeko, midnight blue with red bill and legs, is often to be seen stalking along the roadside, or in the fields bordering the lake.

Lake Ellesmere is separated from the sea by Kaitorete Spit, a long, desolate shingle bank swept by every wind that blows and constantly pounded by the waves which roll in from the Pacific. The spit is a late development in the seaward advance of the Canter-

▼*Long, narrow Lake Forsyth is locked between bare, steep hillsides. It is an inlet of the sea shut off by* *the mounting shingle of Kaitorete Spit, which also encloses the shallow expanse of Lake Ellesmere*

bury coast since sea level settled at its present position sbout 4500 years ago. Gravels from South Canterbury rivers, carried northward by the drift of the sea, have built up into parallel storm-wave beach ridges, completely enclosing Lake Ellesmere.

The build-up of gravel also shut off an inlet of the sea at the head of the spit against all but a trickle of escaping water, except in flood times, when it runs out ferociously. This inlet is now Lake Forsyth. About 7.5 km long and a mere 1 km wide, it lies between the flanks of two steep hills, High Bare Peak and Te Oka. Agricultural chemicals washed down the hillsides have nearly killed the lake, and the bulk of its once-extensive waterfowl population has gone away.

Dreamy harbour where New Zealand had its only French colony

◄*Flowering gorse clothes Banks Peninsula hillsides in gold in spring. Farmers detest the plant because it colonises cleared land*

►*The western hills of Akaroa Harbour seen from the Summit Road*

At the township of Little River, about 2 km from the head of Lake Forsyth, a road branches off to skim across a marshy flat at the head of the lake and into the Okuti Valley, where there are small examples of the mixed podocarp and hardwood forest that once clothed Banks Peninsula.

It is possible on this part of the peninsula to climb from the Okuti Valley on roads between the dove-tailing spurs, on a difficult and winding course to the Te Oka Saddle and Bossu Road. It is a narrow way which writhes along the western rim of the Akaroa Crater, takes a sharp double bend around a jug-like lip and becomes Lands End Road, terminating in the saddle below Lucas Peak. The entire length of Akaroa Harbour can be viewed from this 380 m high peak, beneath which the tall cliffs of Jacobs Ladder and Timutimu Head hold out against the pounding of the ocean.

Other roads run down the lateral spurs to the sea, but these hill roads are narrow gravel roads at best, and can be dangerous. There are interesting views to be obtained, but none comparable to the glorious panoramas from the eastern rim of the harbour.

Highway 75 from Little River makes a moderately tortuous climb up to Hill Top, above Akaroa Harbour. From there a slightly less sinuous road descends to Barry's Bay, separated from Duvauchelle by the Onawe Peninsula at the head of the harbour.

Onawe Peninsula is almost an island, a hump of grassy hill rising out of the harbour. Long ago the peninsula was the site of a virtually impregnable Maori *pa*, ditched and pallisaded against attack. But to it came the northern chief, Te Rauparaha, with his Ngati-Toa and his war canoes. They were severely mauled by the Ngai-Tahu defenders until Te Rauparaha's muskets conquered

valour. The Ngai-Tahu were slaughtered, in wanton butchery. The name Onawe is appropriate: it means 'the place of the scar'.

A branch road, leading off to the right, skirts the harbour, running over the folds of ridge and spur which line the crater, through French Farm Bay, Petit Carenage Bay, Tikao Bay and Wainui, where the paved surface gives way to Lands End Road.

The main highway meanders through Duvauchelle at the head of the harbour, a name giving the first hint of the area's Gallic past, but it is when the road drops down from the eastern rim, and runs down into Akaroa itself, that the first concrete evidence is seen of early French settlement. Quaint little French colonial buildings with delicate wrought-iron balconies and shuttered windows, on

streets with French names—Rue Viard, Rue Balguerie, Rue Lavaud, Rue Croix. Its first settlers came from France to found a colony in 1840, only to discover that Britain had laid formal claim to the entire country.

Today, Akaroa dreams serenely in French Bay. Its streets retire into valleys shaded by the whispering bush; and remnants of French vineyards can still be found in the vicinity. Astonishingly venerable fruit trees flourish, and even bananas mature in sheltered places. Green Point, where the Union Jack was flown to remind the newly-arrived Frenchmen that New Zealand was all British, is a pleasant place to sit on a sunny day. And the summit of the old Akaroa crater does not frown forbiddingly down as the Lyttelton summit does.

►*Onawe Peninsula, the scene of a massacre by Te Rauparaha in 1830, reaches into Akaroa Harbour near Duvauchelle*

Yellow hills and a ragged coast

A rewarding and spectacular route above Akaroa Harbour is along the southern Summit Road, which branches off from Hill Top. The crater rim is prominent, even in the tangle of peaks and ridges forming the crater's northern wall. The rim and the road swing southward about 2 km past the Little Akaloa turnoff. Another 2 km farther on is the fine bush reserve of Otepatotu, 37 hectares of forest, divided by a walking track leading up to the 755 m Lavericks Peak.

The Summit Road wriggles on, following the crater rim, through an intersection of five roads—including one to Akaroa—known locally as the Cabstand, and on past it to end in a saddle between Stony Bay Peak, rising to 806 m, and Purple Peak, a great bluff of richly purple rock.

This is high and rugged country, wilder than the landscape about the northern Summit Road around Lyttelton Harbour. Great crags burst from the tops and flanks of the hills, and impressive basalt escarpments leap from clusters of dark bush. The views are superb—alternating vistas of the ragged coast and, on the western side, the beautiful harbour. In the distance, between the peaks of the opposite rim, there are glimpses of the vast Canterbury Plains, a different world from these mountains, though they lie less than 40 km distant.

The eastern bays are especially beautiful. Le Bons Bay is an oblong of deep water with a shelving beach at its head and a tidal creek sidling out past the terraced hillside. Okains Bay, curving inland from the north-east, has a similar beach and an even broader, farm-filled valley. In these bays and numerous smaller indentations in the coast the pioneers cut out the forests, save for carefully preserved stands of timber to keep the hillsides together under the often torrential rains that drench the peninsula. On the still warm ashes of the burnt-off undergrowth, they sowed grasses and created farms.

A small museum at Okains Bay displays the relics of the pioneers and of the Maoris who lived there before them. There are also walking tracks leading through valleys where narrow streams maintain bands of green, pleasant to the eye amid the dry yellow ochre hillsides of the hot summer.

At Little Akaloa—a slight corruption of 'Akaroa', there being no 'L' in the Maori language—the bay is open to nor'easters. The long Pacific swell sweeps up the harbour but never quite reaches the land because of the braking effect of the shelving beach.

Descending spurs radiate from the eastern rim of the Akaroa crater in a regular pattern, but on the rocky, eroded northern flank spurs and ridges, knobs and gullies dovetail into one another along a long valley. This opens into Pigeon Bay, a 7 km long fiord, 1.5 km wide at its broadest point. Its flanking hills are lofty, with well-marked walking tracks along their crests, and a rough vehicle track, down to Mackintosh and Decanter Bays, small, wide-open indentations.

The landscape, inclined to bareness, is rounded crests and blunt-edged ridges, patched here and there with small stands of bush and dotted with waterholes where the rains have collected in small, rock basins.

▲Gaunt headlands slope down to the ocean all around Banks Peninsula, enclosing quiet bays

The western bastion of Pigeon Bay is a 580 m ridge, which splits at its seaward end into finger-like spurs forming headlands. The westernmost is the rocky, eastern head of Port Levy, another long fiord almost identical to Pigeon Bay. It is walled off from Lyttelton Harbour by the eastern rim of the Lyttelton crater, which rises up from Adderly Head, where the sea is rimmed with the white of waves breaking on the narrow reefs protecting the coast, to Mount Evans at 703 m. Then the crater rim slopes down to the saddle where the Port Levy road climbs up from Purau Bay on Lyttelton Harbour's eastern coast, and lifts up again to Mt Herbert, crown of the rumpled, mountainous landscape of Banks Peninsula.

◄Hall's totara trees, remnants of the forest that once clothed Banks Peninsula, grow on some of the peaks. The prevailing wind has shaped the crowns of these specimens

▼The hills of Banks Peninsula are seldom truly green, and summer bleaches them to yellow ochre

'High above all, towering into the sky'

▲*From the rushing Hooker River, in a view that has become almost the official one, Mt Cook appears as a perfect triangular peak*

Since humans first set eyes on Mt Cook they have tried to capture its essence in words, but no words quite prepare one for the exhilaration of seeing New Zealand's highest mountain rear into view above the broad, brown tussock flats of the alpine basin.

As much as anyone, it was the geologist Julius von Haast who opened the eyes of the country to the extraordinary beauty of the isolated Mt Cook region. Haast, who was later knighted by both Queen Victoria and the Emperor Franz Josef of Austria, first led an expedition to the region in 1862 and returned time and time again, exploring the Hooker, Mueller and Tasman Glaciers and writing the first scientific reports on the area. Of Mt Cook, he wrote that it 'stood high above all, towering into the sky. As far as the eye could reach everywhere snow and ice and rock appeared around us, and in such gigantic proportions that I sometimes thought I was dreaming, and instead of being in New Zealand, I found myself in the Arctic or Antarctic mountain regions.'

Samuel Butler, high-country sheepfarmer and author of *Erewhon*, was one of the first Europeans to venture among the foothills, ranges and beyond into the distant highlands where Mt Cook stands. 'I was struck almost breathless by the wonderful mountain that burst upon my sight', he wrote.

The mountain is an enormous mass of rock with three peaks, its broad, steep faces mantled with snow, iridescent against the infinitely clear, blue sky. It stands alone, 3764 m high, overshadowing even its lofty neighbour Mt Tasman, whose crest lies only

▲*The bulk of Mt Cook is so enormous that the mountain seems to tower straight out of the still waters of Lake Pukaki, even though it is 20 km away*

▶*Even from far away in the Mackenzie Country, Mt Cook appears dominant on the hazy horizon*

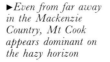

264 m below. Its base is immense, its summit ridge more than 1.6 km long, and it lies in a national park which is entirely alpine and covers an area of 69 923 hectares.

The Maoris have their own name for this great mountain—*Aorangi*, 'cloud in the sky'. Legend says that Rangi, the sky father, and Papa, the earth mother, joined together to procreate the children of the sky. Four of their sons came to live on earth, led by Aorangi, the eldest. They travelled by *Te Waka-a-Aorangi*, the canoe of Aorangi, and when they arrived the canoe turned to stone, becoming the South Island of New Zealand. The children became mountains. Aorangi is Mt Cook, and his brothers Rangiroa, Rangirua, and Rarangi-roa are Mt Dampier, Teichelmann and Silberhorn respectively. Around their feet live the people of earth and around their heads the dwellers of clouds.

There are other legends too—of Aorangi, a survivor of the wrecked sea canoe *Arai-te-uru*, who went looking for food at night and was petrified by the first rays of dawn. And of a party who, making their way north, spied the mountain and named it for a boy who, being carried on the shoulders of his grandfather, was also higher than those around him.

Mt Cook is never more imposing or more beautiful than when seen soaring, like an unreal backdrop, beyond the vivid turquoise waters of lakes Tekapo and Pukaki. The water of these lakes is cloudy, the result of tiny particles of rock flour, ground from the mountainsides by the force of glaciers and washed down by the rivers.

Ironically, Captain Cook probably never saw the mountain that was to be his finest memorial, since his log reports that the weather was bad and the cloud heavy. It was first spied by the explorer Thomas Brunner who, with his companion Charles Heaphy, made an epic trek down the West Coast in 1846-48. Two years later it was named in Cook's honour by John Lort Stokes, captain of HMS *Acheron*, during a detailed survey of the coast.

▲*Late afternoon light catches the three peaks of Mt Cook. One is separated from the others by a summit ridge which stretches for more than 1.6 km. Beside it is Mt Tasman, the second highest mountain in New Zealand*

▼*Mt Cook stands apart from the Main Divide of the Southern Alps in its own range. Its summit rises about 3000 m above the floors of the Tasman and Hooker valleys, to the east and west of the range respectively*

Climbing Mt Cook by ridges and faces

▲*Mt Cook from the Haast ridge. Beneath the peak the Hochstetter Icefall begins its descent to the Tasman Glacier*

▼*The eastern face of Mt Cook rises above the Grand Plateau. The summit was not reached by this face until 1961*

William Spotswood Green, an Irish clergyman and member of the London Alpine Club, saw photographs taken 'by a gentleman lately returned from New Zealand. They showed me enough to convince me that Mount Cook was a splendid peak, and his conquest well worth the trouble of a long travel'.

But Green had also read Julius von Haast on the geology of Canterbury and Westland, and he realised that success would depend on expert help 'such as could not be found in the colony'. He therefore engaged two experienced Swiss alpinists

Green's party made three attempts to reach the summit. The last, on 2 March 1882, was nearly successful, but a rising storm and the approach of night forced them to descend to a ledge where the three men perched up-

right until morning. Green wrote that ' . . . sometimes a blast would come upon us with such force as to compel us to crouch low and drive in our axes firmly, to guard against our being blown off into space . . . From the moment we had gained the arête, anxiety about beginning the descent had filled our minds—as should darkness overtake us on the summit . . . our chances of ever returning to the haunts of men would be but slight.'

By the time they reached their base camp they had been on the mountain for 62 hours. It was a great disappointment; but in the following years numerous other attempts were made by enthusiastic local climbers. George Mannering, armed with Green's chart, made five attempts between 1886 and 1891. The last took Mannering within 15 m of the top,

▶ *The southern face of Mt Cook. Ascent from the south is popular with climbers because it allows them to reach all three peaks on the summit ridge*

but capricious weather defeated him too.

In 1894 impetus was given to the assault on Mt Cook when news arrived that an English climber, Edward Fitzgerald, and a renowned Italian guide, Mattias Zurbriggen, were coming. That summer 24-year old Tom Fyfe, already the conqueror of Mts Malte Brun, de la Beche, Darwin and the Footstool, turned to the untried Hooker side of Mt Cook. At 1.30 pm on Christmas Day, 1894, he and his companions, George Graham and Jack Clarke, 'exultantly stepped onto the highest pinnacle of the monarch of the Southern Alps'. Their brilliant climb, up the Hooker Glacier and the north ridge, was not emulated for 61 years—on the 100th ascent.

Fitzgerald was piqued and decided against Mt Cook but Zurbriggen made the first solo ascent up an eastern ridge that now bears his name and is probably the fastest of the more than 20 ways so far found to the summit. The most popular route, however, is Green's path up the Linda Glacier though it was not tackled with success until February 1912.

Since 1882 there have been many notable first climbs. In 1913, seven hours of constant step-cutting took Freda du Faur, an Australian, and her guides, Peter Graham and Darby Thomson across the icy, notched 1.6 km long summit ridge. The traverse along the toughest ridge, to the middle peak, was achieved in 1938. In 1948 a party including Edmund Hillary, the conqueror of Mt Everest, overcame the daunting, sunless south ridge. But climbing up the faces instead of the ridges began in earnest in 1956. The 2100 m Caroline face was the last to be vanquished. In 1970, two separate parties reached the top within three days of each other. They were surpassed soon afterwards by a daring solo ascent.

▼ *Mt Cook seen from the north, with Mt Tasman, to its left. It was from the north that the first successful ascent of Mt Cook was made in 1894, by three New Zealand climbers, Jack Clarke, George Graham and Tom Fyfe*

Views from the summit of Mt Cook

◄*The summit of Mt Tasman seen from the summit of Mt Cook, 267 m above it*

▼*This view of the mighty Tasman Glacier flowing down from its parent* snowfield rewards the efforts of climbers who reach the summit of Mt Cook

'One would indeed need to be phlegmatic not to get a little excited on such an occasion', observed Tom Fyfe, the first man to stand on the summit of Mt Cook, 3764 m above sea level. Fyfe and his two companions looked 'into the very heart of the Southern Alps . . . range after range, peak after peak in wild confusion, which impressed one with an almost overpowering sense of desolation and solitude'.

The mountains are static, but their appearance can change, hour by hour, even minute by minute, as shadows move across their snow-bound summits and down their sombre rock faces. Clouds roll in, thick and dark sometimes from the west, or cluster like dervishes around the peaks. At other times streamers of cloud or mist lie deep in the valleys, dispersed on bright days by winds and the heat of the sun.

At dawn the mountains are first to catch the light and they stand out above the shadowy land below. At sunset they undergo a transformation, their jagged outcrops and embrasures of stone softened by pastel and orange lights. The departing sun is reflected from millions of pure white crystals and below, the deep ice of the glacier turns a spectral blue.

To those who reach the summit in clear weather, the western coast and the Tasman Sea are visible. Perhaps even the Pacific Ocean, 130 km to the east, will come into focus, a band of light beyond the distant hills and plains of Canterbury. At other times patches of cloud, heat haze or mist give the land below an ethereal quality, with a landscape now visible, now hidden from sight.

To the southwest, aloof from all around it, is the distinctive arrowhead of 3036 m high Mt Aspiring, the highest mountain outside the Mount Cook National Park and centre of its own national park. More than 140 km separates the two giants.

Closer at hand, the summit ridge, 800 m long, sweeps down to the middle peak, and beyond it to the low peak where the Tasman Glacier lies to the east. With walls of sheer ice, the ridge is serrated and precarious, and below it heavy folds of snow lie fluted by the wind and broken by harsh outcrops of rock. To the north rises the pyramid of Mt Tas-

man, and through the wide triangle between the high and middle peaks Lake Pukaki appears thousands of metres below, sprawling across an ancient glacial basin.

But some climbers do not reach the summit in clear weather and are battered by the elements. When Mattias Zurbriggen became the first to reach the summit alone a gale was blowing, 'and one could distinguish little by reason of the drifting mists and powdery snow, which was being raised in great clouds by the gusty winds'. After taking three or four photographs—the first taken from the summit—he retreated thankfully to the shelter of the rocks below.

And the Reverend W. S. Green found the same threat on his unsuccessful attempt with his two companions. 'The weather was settling in for a thoroughly bad night', he wrote. 'The storm at present blowing was sufficiently unpleasant; if it came to blow any harder we would not be able to hold our grip. There was no chance of a view. We were hundreds of feet above any rocks, so that we could build no cairn, or leave any record of our ascent. We were all agreed that we were fairly on the summit of the peak and that we ought to commence the descent . . .'.

Mrs Doreen Urquhart, in the first successful women's party was luckier. 'How good it was to sit on the summit in the still of that perfect day. From ocean to bush valleys to mountains of rock and ice our eyes wandered. We sucked coffee-soaked snow and seldom spoke . . .'.

▼To the south there is a view along the summit ridge of Mt Cook and beyond it the Tasman Valley, between the Burnett and Ben Ohau Ranges, and Lake Pukaki

On the longest glacier in New Zealand

Slicing south through the Mount Cook National Park, between the white wall of the Main Divide and the red rock faces of the Malte Brun Range, is one of the largest glaciers in the world outside the polar zones. It is the Tasman Glacier, a mammoth ribbon of ice, 29 km long and up to 3 km wide in some places. Once the ice stretched another 50 km to the end of present Lake Pukaki. The moraine ridges enclosing the southern end of the lake were built prior to about 13 000 years ago. At that time the extended Tasman Glacier still joined with others in neighbouring valleys to form a giant glacier system occupying much of the Mackenzie Basin. All the glaciers have shrunk drastically since their last major advance, which probably occurred not long before they were first seen by exploring Europeans.

Except for occasional advances, the Tasman Glacier has been slowly, imperceptibly melting away ever since. In 1882 a party had to climb about 10 m up a moraine wall to reach the surface of the ice. Today the ice lies almost 100 m below the same spot.

The effects of glacial action on the sides of the mountains display the power of this tight-packed river of ice. Piles of black ice at its foot are the last stage of melting. As the water slips away into the Tasman River, the mountain sediment and debris remain, forming beds up to 40 m deep on the valley floor.

In 1891, a hut was built above the Ball Glacier and seven years later plans went ahead for a second hut farther up the Tasman Glacier. The site chosen was a high grassy terrace hard at the foot of Mt Malte Brun, about 150 m above the glacier. With its superb views, from the Hochstetter Dome at the head of the valley to Mt Cook in the southwest, the two-room hut was soon a favourite and a growing number of visitors trudged up the glacier to enjoy it, not all without misadventure.

Protection against avalanches was provided by a stone parapet erected on the side of a huge rock. This worked for 40 years until the hut was finally shattered in 1930, and had to be rebuilt with more modern techniques.

More recently, the hut has suffered a catastrophe of another kind. As the glacier receded, the moraine walls, no longer supported by the pressing ice, began to weaken and collapse. The hut, like that above the Ball

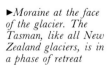
▲*A crevasse on the Tasman Glacier*

▶*Moraine at the face of the glacier. The Tasman, like all New Zealand glaciers, is in a phase of retreat*

▲*Tourists, at bottom right, appear as mere specks below the contorted formations at the foot of the Hochstetter Icefall, a tributary of the huge Tasman Glacier*

Glacier farther down the valley, was removed in 1979. Present plans are to build a replacement in the nearby Beetham Valley.

From the Mount Cook village, an interesting road leads up a trough in the old glacial moraine to the tiny Blue Lakes and from there it is a short walk to the grey, debris-torn terminal of the glacier.

Ten kilometres farther on at the site of Ball Hut, there is the sudden spectacle of ice merging into moraine. Above, two tributary glaciers, the Ball and the Hochstetter, feed snow from the eastern faces of Mt Cook and Mt Tasman onto the gigantic blue-tinged river of ice. As snow piles on snow, the bottom layers are gradually compressed. Seismic surveys have shown the ice opposite the Ball Hut site to be more than 600 m thick.

The Hochstetter is so steep and so violent in form that it is called an icefall. From its source in the Grand Plateau on the flanks of Mt Cook, it plunges down for almost 1000 m, a tortured mass of huge ice blocks and pinnacles. Its north side is contained by the Haast Ridge, a favourite route of ascent onto Mt Cook, and site of a hut which is also used by adventurous climbers tackling the Silberhorn and Mts Tasman and Haidinger.

It is a region which attracts skiers too, and the smooth ice of the Tasman Glacier provides one of the most exciting and unusual ski runs in the world. Until 1955 skiers faced the problem of how to get to the top.

Ski planes were in wide use by then but an enterprising aviator named Harry Wigley invented the retractable ski. It enabled aircraft to take off and land either on snow or on a regular airstrip.

Wigley's ski-plane has revolutionised the national park, not only for skiers and mountaineers but also for sightseers. Every season the planes of Wigley's company ferry thousands of visitors onto the Tasman Glacier and up, over the snow-crested Main Divide to the famous companion glaciers of Westland, the Fox and the Franz Josef. It is a dizzying and unforgettable experience, enhanced by the realisation that superb views of mountains and glaciers can be captured without apparent effort.

◄*The Hochstetter Icefall begins its steep 1000 m descent and the ice fractures into a chaotic mass. The icefall was named by Sir Julius von Haast after a fellow Austrian geologist and explorer, Ferdinand von Hochstetter*

▼*The Tasman Glacier begins its 28 km long journey on the flank of the Hochstetter Dome. The peak's name, inappropriate to it, results from years of misunderstanding of the name originally given it by a German biologist and climber — Hochstetter Dom. The German word* dom *means 'cathedral' not 'dome'*

The steep and challenging slopes of Mt Tasman

'Of all the mountains I have ever seen, in reality or even in dreams, Tasman is the most faultlessly beautiful . . .', wrote an English climber, H.E.L. Porter, of New Zealand's second highest mountain.

Mt Tasman holds some of the steepest, most challenging ice climbs in the world within its 3498 m. Edward Fitzgerald, the English mountaineer who had travelled to New Zealand for the sole purpose of conquering Mt Cook, found himself beaten at the eleventh hour and turned to Mt Tasman as an alternative. In early 1895 he set out with

▼*Mt Tasman rises to 3498 m above sea level. Mt Cook, at 3764 m, is the only higher mountain in New Zealand*

his Italian guide, Mattias Zurbriggen, and 18-year-old Jack Clarke, to make the maiden ascent of the peak. He had already asserted that 'he looked upon Sefton, Haidinger and the Tasman as much more difficult than Mt Cook as their slopes are steeper'.

After climbing the neighbouring Silberhorn ridge, they made their way to the summit of Mt Tasman. Their route has attracted climbers ever since, not least for the splendid, uninterrupted views to the east and west. Below the summit, the icy fingers of the great western glaciers, the Fox and the Franz Josef, stretch towards dense rainforest.

And the agile chamois is also seen in this region, often at considerable heights, cling-

ing to the most precipitous rocks with great aplomb. The animals were introduced in 1907, a gift to the New Zealand Government from Emperor Franz Josef of Austria. The chamois is prized by hunters and it was to enhance shooting as a sport that the Emperor had responded to the request of one of his naval officers who had been hospitably received in New Zealand. Two male and six female chamois were released near Mt Cook and so multiplied that a herd of at least 70 was counted in 1919.

Now dispersed widely both north and south of the site of their original release, chamois have been observed hundreds of kilometres away. The mountainous areas of

▲The peak here dominated by Mt Tasman is Silberhorn, another of the great mountains of the Southern Alps. It is 3322 m high, and in Maori mythology it is Rarangi-roa, one of the younger brothers of Aorangi, or Mt Cook. It shares its German name with a mountain in the Swiss Alps

the South Island offer a perfect environment and the New Zealand herds are the only ones in a natural state outside their central European habitat. But in Europe they are now protected from the hunter; in New Zealand they are a target for anyone with a permit, as culling of the herds is an urgent necessity.

The chamois is distinctive in appearance, in spite of some similarity to the goat. Long legged, graceful in movement, its pointed ears and slightly curved, vertical horns mark it out from the goat and the thar. The thar was introduced from the Himalayas and also enjoys high altitudes but has spread less rapidly than the chamois.

But the greatest heights of the Mt Cook region belong to the intrepid climbers. Freda du Faur, an Australian, joined this select company, and was also the first woman to achieve the summit of Mt Cook, on 3 December 1910, with Alex and Peter Graham. But it was two years later that she fulfilled another ambition and scaled the icy ridges of Mt Tasman with these two famous guides in gale-force winds. 'We were appalled at its steepness', she wrote later, but she exulted in the experience nonetheless.

Twenty years later, another route, equally steep and equally perilous, was forged across the Syme Ridge to the North Shoulder. The bottom of this testing ice climb passes through an area so prone to sudden, devastating avalanches that it has earned the cautionary nickname, 'the mad mile'.

Climbers who set out to ascend Tasman by either ridge from the hut on the Grand Plateau which lies below Mt Cook, must first overcome the ice and snow that clings to the mountain's east face. No part of this face was climbed until as late as 1960.

Heights of the central Southern Alps

►*Mt Malte Brun, 3155 m high, was first climbed by a solo climber who managed to beat an avalanche on the way down*

More than 150 mountains in the Mount Cook National Park are more than 2000 m high. Their names—though not all are named—have many associations. Some recall early climbers, explorers and other pioneers. For example, Mt Chudleigh, in the Malte Brun Range, was named after a farmer in the nearby Rangitata district by the explorer Arthur Harper. Co-founder of the New Zealand Alpine Club in 1891, Harper helped to chart nearly every glacier in the central southern Alps. The mountain he named Chudleigh is 2952 m high, just overtopped by the flattened cone of Mt Malte Brun, which is 203 m higher.

Another mountain named after a farmer is Mt Johnson, looming 2683 m above the Dorothy Glacier in the Malte Brun Range.

P. H. Johnson, a former army major who ran the Mt Torlesse sheep station in mid-Canterbury, was one of a small band of New Zealanders who tried to reach the summit of Mt Cook in the 1880s. Overseas mountaineers like Dr von Lendenfeld had set examples of great endurance in climbing and Johnson, with his companions, Mannering and Dixon, made a courageous attempt on Mt Cook in 1889, but without success. But the Malte Brun Range—named by Julius von Haast after an eminent French geographer—offered plenty of other challenges. Its magnificent red rock faces, etched with cracks, clefts and overhangs, always attract rock climbers.

The first ascent of Mt Malte Brun, in 1893, was spectacular. Tom Fyfe, a 24-year-old

plumber from Timaru and a brilliant rock climber who took part in the first ascent of Mt Cook in the following season, scaled the 3155 m mountain alone. Fyfe's descent from Malte Brun has become an enduring legend. Detecting an avalanche of rocks starting above him, he used his ice axe as a third support for his body, bent forward a little, and glissaded at breakneck speed down the long snow gully of Mt Malte Brun and beat the rocks to the bottom.

No second attempt was made until 13 years later when a Dutch alpinist, Henrik Sillem, and the guide Peter Graham pioneered a traverse from Beatham Glacier in the south to Bonney Glacier in the north.

Graham, chief guide at the Hermitage from 1906-28, also broke new ground on the

◄*The Sealy Range rises to the west of Mount Cook village. The Mueller Glacier flows along its western side and loops round its northern end into the Hooker Valley*

steep-angled buttress of another peak in the Malte Brun Range, the Aiguilles Rouge. In March 1909, Graham and L. M. Earle, a visitor from the London Alpine Club, set out up the slopes behind the Malte Brun hut, crossed the Beatham Glacier and climbed the north ridge up to its 2967 m high summit. Delighted with their victory, Earle exercised his right as first climber to give the mountain its name, and he called it Aiguilles Rouge—'red needles' in French.

But it was not Earle's only distinction in these mountains. Two weeks before he had been a member of the four-man team which conquered Mt Cook from the less popular western side, working its way up a prominent rib now known as Earle's Ridge.

Another mountain which presents a distinctive shape in the Southern Alps is Mt Haidinger. Its south peak is 3066 m high, its north just 8 m lower, and it has a truncated appearance with a wide, flat top. It was conquered by Fitzgerald and Zurbriggen in 1895. The whole of this mountain's eastern face is smothered in a fantastic confusion of ice, twisted into deep splits and chasms so daunting that it was not until 1960, with advanced techniques and equipment, that anyone succeeded in climbing it to the top.

The more felicitous approach is from the west, a route that offers a sound rock climb— a rarity for rock climbers, who consider these to be notoriously brittle mountains.

▲*Many fine peaks lie between the Mount Cook and Arthur's Pass National Parks, including these on the Arrowsmith Range*

▼*The Minarets cluster on the Main Divide between the Tasman and Franz Josef Glaciers. The highest of the peaks is 3048 m*

The summits of the Southern Alps are easier to negotiate when the snow is firm, and climbers often set off in the early hours of the morning to avoid the risk of the sun softening the snow and starting avalanches. If any reminder of the danger is needed, the Albert Glacier, below Mt Haidinger's western buttress, displays huge deposits of debris, and the first fatalities in these mountains occurred in an avalanche on the Linda Glacier in February 1914.

Freda du Faur, the Australian climber, was no stranger to the dangers of mountaineering and once described how she felt on being left alone while her companions went ahead to plug steps for the next climb. She wrote that 'the hours passed quickly enough in observing a phenomonon I have met before in the great silent places. Every now and then a voice seemed to rise from nowhere in a faint cry. Again and again I have started up, sure that someone was calling me, to confront only the silent snow-clad mountains. Some stone falling from the heights, the gurgle of an underground stream, or the wind sweeping into a hidden cave and raising an echo from the distant ridges—clear and distinct it comes, this call of the mountains, sometimes friendly and of good cheer; but often eerie, wild, and full of melancholy warning as if the spirit of the mountains bade you beware how you tread her virgin heights, except in a spirit of reverence and love.'

Westwards across the Copland Pass

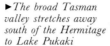
▶ *The broad Tasman valley stretches away south of the Hermitage to Lake Pukaki*

The Southern Alps form a natural boundary between two totally different worlds, as can be seen from the summit of the 2133 m high Copland Pass. To the west, encouraged by the moist north-westerly winds from the Tasman Sea, dense, lush rainforest spreads over the land. The Copland Valley is a maze of stately podocarps and graceful tree ferns, its understorey a tangled web of shrubs, vines and moss. The east, in sharp contrast, is quite barren—the bleak lower reaches of the Hooker Glacier, the bare shale faces of Mt Wakefield and the seemingly endless brown tussock of the Mackenzie Country.

For over a century, this windswept pass has provided the fastest and most accessible passage by foot over the Main Divide. Climbers and trampers still use the pass, mostly from the east, knowing that there is relief from tramping in the hot springs near Welcome Flat on the western side. The trip takes three or four days, with overnight stops at three huts along the way. Though much of it is not difficult, the possibility of icy conditions and abrupt changes in weather makes it inadvisable for people without alpine experience to attempt it.

From Mount Cook village, the route starts along the Kea Point track before branching off after a short distance into the Hooker Valley track. Across the Hooker Flats are the remains of the original Hermitage, an old cob

and iron building erected in 1884, alongside the moraine rampart of the Mueller Glacier. In the summer of 1913, torrential rain added to the normal flow of Mueller meltwater, which flooded over the moraine wall. Boulders, trees and ice rampaged onto the valley floor, demolishing part of the hotel and spreading thick silt through the battered main building.

The 11 km track, a pleasant three-hour walk, continues over two swing bridges above the Hooker River to the Sefton Stream, close to the terminal face of the Hooker Glacier. Built in 1901 so that pack-horses could carry

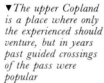
▶ *Unicorn (left) and Dilemma are high peaks on the Banks Range, to the north of the Copland Pass*

▼ *The upper Copland is a place where only the experienced should venture, but in years past guided crossings of the pass were popular*

in the materials for a hut at the foot of the pass, the track is decked in summer with the white blooms of mountain daisies.

Beyond Hooker Hut, the real climbing begins. After winding through a gully, the track heads up a steep, dangerous ridge plagued with loose rock and almost wholly exposed to the elements. About 100 m from the top of the pass stands the Copland Shelter. Beyond is perpetual snow and ice, negotiable only with crampons, ice axe and rope. The weather in this region can change daily. The best months for crossing the Copland are February and March.

◄Everlasting daisies
are among the
pleasures of the upper
Copland in summer.
The moister western
side of the pass has
more plant life than
in the east

▲Mt Cook, seen from
the Copland Shelter.
The shelter, just below
the top of the pass,
provides protection
from the wind for
those who overestimate
their prowess or are
caught by a sudden
change in the weather

▼The Mueller Glacier,
which flows between
the Main Divide and
the Sealy Range, is
passed near the start of
the track up the
Hooker Valley towards
the Copland Pass

Austere beauty of the Mackenzie Country

►*The bare hills of the Mackenzie Pass and, at right, the lower slopes of the Ben Ohau Range*

From the eastern boundary of the Mount Cook National Park, three major lakes reach southward to the edge of a vast and treeless basin of austere beauty. It is a bare, brown, tussocky place called the Mackenzie Country. It can be entered by road from Central Otago or North Otago, but its individuality perhaps impresses itself most sharply upon the eye and mind of the traveller who arrives from the gentler scenery of South Canterbury.

Twenty-two kilometres west of the leafy South Canterbury town of Fairlie, Highway 8 runs into the Mackenzie Country at Burkes Pass. The pass, 670 m high, lies between the Two Thumb Range in the north and the Dalgety Range in the south. It is named after Michael John Burke, an Irish pioneer who is credited with its discovery in 1855, although the Maoris had long known of it.

Those with a sense of history may prefer to make a different entry into the Mackenzie Country. A road leads off Highway 8 at the settlement of Burke Pass and runs southward, then westward to cross the Dalgety Range at the Mackenzie Pass. This is where, according to legend, a Scottish drover named James McKenzie discovered the highland plains of the country that now bears a version of his name.

Many romantic tales are told about McKenzie, and recent research suggests that most of them are untrue. But it is certain that one evening in March 1855 he was caught near the Mackenzie Pass in possession of a mob of 1000 sheep which did not belong to him. McKenzie thought they belonged to the Otago farmer who had hired him to drive the mob to Otago by a back-country route. But they had in fact been stolen from the Levels Station, near Timaru.

McKenzie escaped from his captors, but he was later caught by the police at Lyttelton, where he was trying to find a ship to take him away from Canterbury. He was tried,

◄*Erosion has created these spires and ravines near Omarama, at the southern end of the Mackenzie basin*

◄*The head of Lake Ohau. The lakeside country is a popular recreation area in both summer and winter*

▲*The Mackenzie Country is virtually treeless and it can seem bleak in its austerity, but it is not easily forgotten*

found guilty of sheep-stealing and sentenced to five years' imprisonment. He was also held to be 'mute of malice' for remaining silent throughout his trial, even though the proceedings were conducted in English, a language of which the Gaelic-speaking McKenzie had scant knowledge.

McKenzie escaped from the Lyttelton prison three times, and was recaptured each time, but he had served only nine months of his sentence when he was pardoned by the Governor of New Zealand. He left for Australia and is said to have spent the rest of his life there, farming in Queensland.

McKenzie's exploits not only prompted a flood of legend about him but also focussed attention on the country where he was captured. In 1856 the first sheep run in the Mackenzie Country was set up on the Mary Range, and other settlers soon followed. There were no permanent inhabitants in the Mackenzie Country in those days, but the coastal Maoris had long made seasonal visits to harvest the rich bird life of the plains. These visits continued for little more than 30 years after European settlers began to drain the swamps and set fire to the vegetation—to make the tussocks more agreeable to their grazing sheep. Destruction of habitats soon depleted the bird life.

The rivers of the Mackenzie country flow into the great Waitaki River, which forms the boundary between Canterbury and Otago. Lakes Tekapo, Pukaki and Ohau were originally drained by correspondingly named rivers, but the lake waters have been diverted for the purposes of hydro-electric power generation. The water is conveyed, through several power stations, by canals to the huge, man-made Lake Benmore, where it is stored before it passes through more power stations. The Ahuriri River, which rises high up in the Southern Alps and enters the Mackenzie Country in the west, also contributes to Lake Benmore.

►*Lake Ohau is the most westerly of the three great natural lakes of the Mackenzie Country. In the south it curls round the southern end of the Ben Ohau Range. The name of the range combines Scots Gaelic and Maori words. Such combinations are not uncommon in the southern half of the South Island, where many of the early settlers were Scots*

Glacier-fed lakes

▶Lake Tekapo in winter. The weather is highly changeable in the Mt Cook region

▲Chamois, introduced from Europe, were first liberated in New Zealand in the Mt Cook region, in 1907. They spread widely and are now regarded as a nuisance, whereas they are protected in their original European homelands

▼The simple Church of the Good Shepherd stands picturesquely near the outlet of Lake Tekapo. It was built, in local stone, as a memorial to pioneer runholders of the Mackenzie Country

The big natural lakes of the Mackenzie Country, like other lakes in the South Island, are said in Maori myth to have been scooped out by a great *ko*, or digging stick, wielded by the giant Rakaihautu. The geologist's explanation of the origins of Lakes Tekapo, Pukaki and Ohau is that they fill glaciated valleys which were dammed by moraine about 17 000 years ago.

The easternmost lake, Tekapo, lies along the western side of the Two Thumb Range at an altitude of 707 m. Fed by the Godley River and its tributary the Macauley, it covers 83 km² and stretches about 25 km southwards. An unsealed road runs along the eastern side to the Macauley River. On the western side another unsealed road runs as far as the Cass River, which enters the lake about midway along the shore.

In the southwestern corner, a beautiful small lake named Alexandrina drains into Lake Tekapo by way of the even smaller Lake McGregor. Lake Alexandrina was named after the Danish princess who married Edward, Prince of Wales, and later became Queen Alexandra.

These small lakes are much darker in colour than the big lakes, which have waters of

◄*Across the water from the tiny settlement at Lake Tekapo lies a small island which is called Motuariki. In contrast to the surrounding hills, it carries forest*

an extraordinary pale turquoise. This is because the small lakes are fed from rainwater, whereas the big lakes are fed from glaciers. The glacier meltwater carries 'rock flour', ground off the mountains by the moving ice. The rock flour is held in suspension by the lake waters, giving them opacity as well as their pale colour.

The water of Lake Tekapo is taken through a 1500 m long tunnel to a power station, which was built in the 1950s. A control dam was built at the outlet of the lake to permit the great volume of water released by the spring and summer thaw in the mountains to be retained for use in the system in winter.

Not far from Lake Alexandrina is Mt St John, where the University of Pennsylvania has established an international observatory to take advantage of the exceptionally clear night skies of the Mackenzie Country. The United States Government has a satellite tracking station nearby.

The central lake, Pukaki, is fed by the Tasman River, which drains a huge catchment, including the Tasman, Hooker and Murchison Glaciers. Highway 80 runs along its western shore, at the foot of the Ben Ohau Range, to the village below Mt Cook.

The smallest of the three big lakes, Lake Ohau covers about 60 km². It lies 519 m above sea level and is fed by the Dobson River and its tributary the Hopkins. The Dobson River rises on the main divide of the Southern Alps and flows between the Ben Ohau and Neumann Ranges. Seen from above, the lake is shaped rather like a hockey stick, curving round the 1244 m high Ben Ohau peak at its southern end.

It is said that the name should properly be spelt *Ohou*, which means 'the place of Hou' and refers to a companion of the mythical superman who formed the lake.

►*The interplay of sunlight, clouds, water and landforms in the Mt Cook region produces spectacular effects of light and colour. This dazzling display occurred at Lake Tekapo*

Lakes enlarged to provide hydro-electricity

▲*In fine weather Mt Cook provides Lake Pukaki with a backdrop of matchless grandeur. Clouds often obscure the peak*

▼*Lake Pukaki reaches towards the Mackenzie country and the ranges that separate Central Otago from South Canterbury*

The Waitaki River falls some 700 m on its way to the sea and this potential for power generation was recognised early. Development was proposed in reports to the New Zealand Government in 1904, but it was not until 1928 that work began on the first dam. This was the concrete dam, 354 m long and 37 m high, which holds the 6 km long Lake Waitaki. The power station has a generating capacity of 105 000 kilowatts.

In the 1950s a power station generating 25 000 kW was built at Lake Tekapo. In 1956 the 540 000 kW Benmore station came into operation and in 1968 the 220 000 kW Aviemore station. Lake Benmore, the biggest man-made lake in New Zealand, covers 80 km^2 and has a shoreline of 116 km. The water is retained by a huge earth dam which extends 823 m between rock abutments on either side of the Waitaki Valley.

The Aviemore dam, 18 km downstream from Benmore, is partly concrete and partly earth. The concrete section, on the Canter-

▶ *The Burnett Mountains run along the eastern edge of the Tasman valley, and extend beyond the head of Lake Pukaki*

bury side, is 335 km long and built on solid rock. The earth section, 457 m long, is built over a geological fault. The lake covers 2.85 km² and has 40 km of shore.

Further development of the Upper Waitaki for hydro-electricity was completed in December 1978. The scheme raised the level of Lake Pukaki by 37 m, making five canals to combine the outflows of Lakes Tekapo, Pukaki and Ohau at a higher altitude than before, and the building of four new power stations. The Fork Stream, which used to flow into the Tekapo River, was diverted into Lake Tekapo, making its water available for

generation of power. A canal carried the outflow from Lake Tekapo 27 km across country to the new Tekapo B power station on the shore of Lake Pukaki.

The storage capacity of Lake Pukaki was trebled by building a 60 m high dam about 500 m downstream from the existing control dam and the lake now holds 35 per cent of New Zealand's total storage capacity. Another canal carries the outflow of the lake 13 km across to the Ohau A power station on the north bank of the Ohau River. Raising the maximum depth of Lake Pukaki from 70 to 107 m increased the length of the lake from

22 km to 32 km. And a new road was built to Mt Cook because the old one was covered by the rising waters.

Lake Ohau has not been raised in level, though a control dam has been built at the outlet. The outflow is carried along a 10 km long canal to the Ohau A power station, where it is joined by the 13 km long canal from Lake Pukaki. A 42 m high dam below the Ohau A powerhouse forms a small lake which feeds the Ohau-Benmore canal. The Ohau B power station is built on the 10 km long canal, and the Ohau C power station is on the shore of Lake Benmore.

▶ *The valley of the Tasman River runs from the Tasman Glacier to Lake Pukaki. Along the western edge of the valley and the lake runs the highway to Mt Cook village*

Wildflowers of the mountain slopes

▶New Zealand edelweiss is not found in other lands, but is so similar to Swiss edelweiss that it was given the same name as the Swiss one

▲Numerous species of buttercups, members of the genus Ranunculus, grow in the mountains. Some display flowers of buttercup yellow, such as Ranunculus seriophyllus, which grows in crevices between rocks. Others, including the so-called Mt Cook lily, have white flowers

▶The Mt Cook lily, or giant mountain buttercup, in bud and (below) in full bloom

In the wild and apparently barren highlands of the Mount Cook region, buffeted by every extreme the elements can muster, strange and beautiful communities of alpine plants not only survive but seem to flourish.

Almost half of New Zealand's native plants grow exclusively among high mountains and do not appear at all on the lowlands.

In the Mount Cook National Park alone there are more than 400 species of ferns, mosses, trees, shrubs, herbs and grasses. Those in the true alpine zones cling doggedly to the bare rocks among the perpetual ice and snow. Other plants in the lower, subalpine belt are often covered with snow during the winter months. They emerge in spring and summer to flower amidst the soft green and brown tussock, or on the grey and bare moraine left behind by the glaciers, or even cover whole slopes with their blossoms.

But almost all alpine flowers are white, harmonising with the snow and ice that dominate their environment. And none is more exquisite than the famous Mt Cook lily, the largest ranunculus in the world. All through spring and early summer, the shiny, saucer-shaped leaves of this giant buttercup—for it is falsely called a lily—are topped with masses of pure white flowers.

In December the mountain daisies come into their own, the largest displaying long stems of round, yellow-centred flowers from clumps of thick silver leaves. There are 58 endemic species of mountain daisy, *Celmisia* being the third largest plant genus in New

◄The snowberry grows in lowland montane shrubland. Berry-like fruit appear in profusion, transforming this small shrub, a species of the genus Gaultheria, *into a plant of great beauty*

◄Distinctive wild-flowers can also be found in the alpine grasslands. This is a gentian from the Mackenzie Country

▼Mountain daisies grow in alpine scrub and grasslands. This, the large mountain

daisy Celmisia coriacea, *is one of 58 species. It flowers in the month of December*

Zealand. These plants have adapted to many environments. They bloom brightly among tussock, scrub, grass or rock, and they range from the robust *Celmisia coriacea* to the mat-forming *Celmisia sessiliflora*.

Alpine plants extend from the tree line at about 1200 m to the permanent snowline around 2000 m. As the mountains are young in geological time, the plant communities on them have had to contend with extensive fluctuations of heat and cold. Alpine plants have shown many adaptations, the most extreme being to the unstable shingle slips. The plants there have had to contend with shifting stones, lack of water, burning hot days and freezing nights. These plants usually have long roots, with leathery or succulent leaves of pale grey to reflect the light more easily. They appear as tight rosettes or cushions and have woolly surfaces.

Another unusual growth form is the 'vegetable sheep', inhabiting rocky subalpine and alpine areas. Densely crowded short branches spread from a central woody root which acts as an anchor. At their tips the branchlets are covered with small, whitish woolly leaves, forming a dense, hard convex mass, filled with water-storing peat formed from the plants' own leaves.

In the subalpine and alpine zones there are many shrubs of the genus *Hebe*, the largest plant genus in New Zealand, with more than 100 members, most of them endemic. Adaptation to fluctuating geological conditions and climate in the subalpine and alpine zones has led to the evolution of many species of *Hebe*. Their leaf forms are extensively varied. The most unusual is whipcord hebe, which appears to mimic a cypress.

Westland National Park

Shining glaciers amid high mountains, primaeval rainforest, silent lakes and rushing rivers all make South Westland a region of sublime beauty

West of the Southern Alps, a narrow coastal strip lies between Greymouth and the Haast River. Just over 238 km long, it is bounded by the Tasman Sea and by a long, incredibly straight wall of mountains which rise to an altitude of 3450 m in less than 32 km. Coastal flatlands vary in width from 20 km to a metre or two of cliff-bound beach where the spurs of the high ranges come right down to the sea. Of this strip, a 160 km length is covered by Westland National Park of 117 547 hectares, with additional associated areas, all of superlative and unspoiled beauty.

The region is entered from the north by Highway 6, which winds through kahikatea and rimu forest starred with tree-ferns. Lake Ianthe is the first along the highway of a string of lovely lakes, each seemingly more enchanting, more primaeval in the quality of its surroundings than the last.

The 12 sizeable rivers and innumerable tiny streams along this coast are swift and brawling, rushing down from the terminal faces of glaciers or from watersheds high in the adjacent mountains. Where the land is flat, the river meadows are grazed by some sheep, many cattle and sometimes deer. Rivers dawdle through vast swamplands and into and out of lakes of mirror-like stillness that reflect the highest alpine peaks and their eternal snows with photographic perfection.

There are glaciers along the way, descending from the lofty *névés* in the ever-freezing heights, sliding down between walls of wet and glistening rock, to terminate near vegetation of sub-tropical luxuriance.

In some places, the Southern Alps seem almost to lean over the dwindling coastal shelf. In others they stand back far enough to be a backdrop for another landscape.

The forests on the heights are often largely rata and beech, but along the coastal areas and lower slopes the variety of ferns and trees and shrubs is phenomenal. The dark greens of the forest are flecked with the lighter green of ferns, starred with hohere and climbing clematis blossom and, in season, splashed with scarlet rata flowers.

The bird life is rich. In the forest, ruru, the morepork owl, New Zealand falcon, native pigeon, South Island kaka, parakeet, tui, bellbird, brown creeper, silvereye, grey warbler, fantail, rifleman, yellow-breasted tit, robin, shining cuckoo and long-tailed cuckoo are all commonly seen. In some areas the great spotted kiwi and the more widely distributed South Island brown kiwi are plentiful but, being nocturnal, are seldom seen.

The weather in this spectacular land can be wet, particularly when the north-west wind, laden with moisture from the Tasman Sea, strikes the mountains. But it is seldom forbiddingly cold at coastal altitudes, for a warm current sweeps close inshore, and there are beaches edged with broad-leaved growth and nikau palms.

▶ *Westland National Park is but part of the natural splendour of South Westland. There are also many forests and scenic reserves*

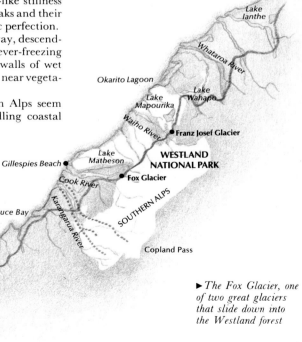

▶ *The Fox Glacier, one of two great glaciers that slide down into the Westland forest*

204

Forest-fringed lakes and lowland swamps

▼*Kahikatea forest inhabits shallow swamps and very wet ground. Much has been drained and cleared*

►*Lake Mapourika. It was named not by the Maoris but by gold miners—after a ship which ran between Australia and the West Coast*

Lake Ianthe was named by a surveyor and explorer who was fond of Byron's poetry. *Childe Harold's Pilgrimage* was dedicated by Byron to a child named Ianthe, and the explorer felt Ianthe would be a pretty name for a pretty lake. Its waters, some 900 hectares in area and 18.3 m deep, are fed by bush streamlets and girdled by kahikatea and matai forest. This includes a gigantic matai, estimated to be more than 1000 years old, with a bole 5.2 m in diameter.

About 50 km south of Lake Ianthe by good road, both the Whataroa and Waitangitaona Rivers wend deceptively easygoing ways out to sea. The Whataroa is a tangle of gravel-bedded waterways which flow out from the Whymper Glacier, high in a hanging valley between the 3109 m high Mt Elie de Beaumont and a chain of peaks on the Main Divide. The Waitangitaona is a much swifter stream which spreads across the flats from the crumbling flanks of the Price Range. It brings down such enormous quantities of gravel during winter floods that it inundates good pasture with stones and is choking a large area of kahikatea forest. On the southern edge of the Whataroa flat, within a fringe of forest, is Lake Wahapo, slightly smaller than Lake Ianthe, but equally well stocked with brown and rainbow trout.

The district was a scene of feverish gold-seeking between 1868 and 1907. At the Okarito Lagoon, a township grew up with pubs, dance halls, casinos, banks and stores, and about 5000 miners panned, cradled and sluiced. But today silence has returned to the forest, and fern and kahikatea have hidden the untidy tailings of river gravels, Okarito Lagoon is now a sanctuary and nesting place for the white heron, or *kotuku.*

Lake Mapourika, 5 km south of Lake Wahapo, is the largest South Westland lake. It covers 1813 hectares and is 37 m deep, filling the hole left by the melting of a huge block of 'dead' ice deposited by an ancient

◄The crested grebe, a shy and graceful bird which is found on many of the lakes of South Westland

▼White herons breed in New Zealand in the swamp forest at Okarito. The white heron is an immigrant from Australia. Since the 1940s it has been joined by another big, graceful, white bird from Australia, the royal spoonbill. Both species disperse throughout New Zealand after the breeding season

glacier. From the road near the head of the lake, the snow-covered peaks of the Fritz Range, southern wall of the great Franz Josef Glacier, rear back above forested heights in a gap between two eminences on the lake's eastern shore. Mapourika is a safe, calm lake, abounding in trout. It has a well-kept jetty and a small curve of good bathing beach situated quite near the road.

▼Lake Mapourika fills a hole left by the melting of a huge block of glacial ice

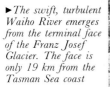

▲*The Geikie snowfield, high in the Southern Alps, feeds the Franz Josef Glacier, a great river of ice which descends to merely 300 m above sea level*

▶*The swift, turbulent Waiho River emerges from the terminal face of the Franz Josef Glacier. The face is only 19 km from the Tasman Sea coast*

The Franz Josef Glacier can no longer be seen from the road or the village, but on a dull day there is no mistaking where it lies, for a pale light seems to shine from its deep valley. To see the 11 km long glacier in all its shining beauty, the visitor must drive into the valley. The glacier comes into view with dramatic suddenness, a white and turquoise stretch of gleaming ice flowing down from its névé, or snowfield, high in the mountains between the Baird and Fritz Ranges.

The present Franz Josef Glacier is less than 7000 years old. More than 14 000 years ago it had an ancestor with huge lateral moraines—debris shed by the glacier—right down to the coast. A classic, 30 m high, crescent-shaped ridge known as the Waiho Loop and rising abruptly above the river flats is a terminal moraine formed about 11 800 years ago, when the glacier advanced again after a spell when it had been in retreat.

About 3 km from the present face are heaps of terminal moraine left by the glacier during halts about 1600, 1750 and 1825. Since 1893 the glacier has edged forward several times, but since 1950 it has receded, apart from a 400 m advance in 1965-67. These fluctuations are governed by snowfall, the glacier advancing when the snow accumulates faster than it melts, and retreating when melting prevails. Because the melt rate is high at the lower altitudes and the valleys are steep, the Franz Josef Glacier and its neighbour, the Fox Glacier, are highly sensitive to climatic change.

The glacier feeds the swift and turbulent Waiho River—the name means 'smoking water', and refers to the vapour constantly

Franz Josef Glacier

◄*The sharp contrast between lush temperate rainforest and jagged snowy peaks is highly characteristic of the scenery of Westland National Park*

▼*Peter's Pool, a calm, sheltered kettlehole formed about the year 1800, reflects the peaks at the head of the glacier*

rising from its ice-cold surface. It carries great chunks of ice which continually break away from even greater chunks too big to float in the shallow water. The valley is magnificent, with steep rock walls and slopes along which can be seen the 'trim-line' where successive build-ups of ice have shorn ancient forest and new growth has sprung up.

A five-minute walk along a track off the approach road leads to Peter's Pool, a kettle-hole. These are formed when a glacier has retreated, leaving behind it a new valley floor, covered with outwash gravels deposited by its melt-water. Small, separate masses of 'dead' ice are left behind, and eventually melt. The gravel deposits subside, the hollow fills with water and a clear, cold tarn is formed. Peter's Pool was formed in this way around the year 1800.

There are other walks. Sentinel Rock, largest of a string of *roches moutonnés* (sheep-like ice rounded rocks), is reached by a well-cut track leading past displays of gorgeous mosses, and through tall forest to a grandstand view of the glacier. Roberts Point Track requires fitness for a spectacular scramble up to a vantage point high on the glacier wall, where a manmade gallery hangs out high above the ice. The 1909 advance piled ice up to this point, and smashed the first gallery.

It is an hour's ramble to Lake Wombat, another kettlehole, on a terrace above the approach road. This walk leads through groves of tree-ferns on which may be seen little hanging straps with tiny needles angled downwards, and a small green or brown capsule near the tip on the inner surface. This plant is *Tmesipteris tannensis*, and its ancestors were common before flowering plants, ferns or conifers appeared, 160 million years before the first dinosaurs.

A full day's walk, past Lake Wombat and up to Christmas Lookout, 274 m high, leads to an area of mountain meadow, with snow-grasses and a veritable garden of alpine flowers, including the beautiful mountain buttercup *Ranunculus lyallii*. All the longer walks call for fitness and stout footwear.

The mirror of the mountains

►*Lake Matheson, perhaps the most photographed water in New Zealand. Here the celebrated reflection of the great peaks of the Southern Alps is slightly ruffled by a gentle breeze*

◄*Most of Lake Matheson is edged by rich forest, through some of which a boardwalk runs*

From Fox Glacier Village a road runs eastward across a scrub-patched flat where cattle graze, towards a tangle of forested spurs of ancient moraine. About 3 km from the village, the Clearwater Stream chatters around the foot of a loop of moraine, abandoned long ago by an ancester of the Fox Glacier. Forest covers the moraine and through it runs a boardwalk which skirts the charming little Lake Matheson.

The walk is easy, through rimu, kahikatea, koromiko and lancewood. Bellbirds' chiming accentuates the stillness, and fantails flutter and flicker within arm's reach. A proliferation of ferns, from the miniscule umbrella fern to the *wheki*, slimmest and most palmlike of the tree-ferns, fills the hollows and clothes the humps of the moss-carpeted table of morainic rocks. Flying-buttress roots of kamahi form many fairy-like caverns in which tiny wedgewood-blue fungi stud the dark greens and doubtful browns of decaying leaf mould.

The lake appears suddenly, like a mirror glimpsed through a leafy filigree. There are steps down to a moored raft, from which the lake spreads out placidly. The boardwalk goes on to the head of the lake. Lake Matheson is often catspawed by errant puffs of breeze, but on a reasonably calm day photographs of the reflections of the great alpine peaks can be so perfect that one is uncertain which is the right way up.

There is another branching track from the Lake Matheson track, an hour and a quarter's walk to Lake Gault, deeper in the complex of spurs. Lake Matheson is the fairer, but Lake Gault is the richer in bird life. The rare great crested grebe, a shag-like bird with two quills protruding from its head, is seen there. The kaka is often seen near the highest point of the walk, and the tiny, green rifleman, commonest of the three surviving native wrens, flashes its white breast among the foliage. The yellow-breasted tit and the bellbird and the native pigeon are plentiful.

The view of the mountains from Lake Gault is even finer than that from Lake Matheson. It ranges over a wide panorama from the Fritz Range on the left, past Silberhorn and Teichelmann, to Mount Cook.

The higher spurs west of the lakes are covered with fine stands of rimu. The narrow road which winds over these ranges commands splendid vistas of valleys filled with forest, splashed with scarlet rata in summer, and fringed with golden-flowered kowhai. The road runs out onto Gillespies Beach, 24 km from Fox Glacier township. It is the site of a vanished gold-rush township which had enough people to support several pubs. Gold was found in the beach sands in the 1860s and fortunes were made before the easier lodes petered out in the 1890s.

The beach curves around between Otorokua Point, along low, forested headland, and Gillespies Point. It is a wild, driftwood-strewn beach with broad bands of gravel, sprinkled with gleaming schist flakes and white quartz pebbles and black-streaked golden sand. It is separated from the morainic spurs by the gorse-grown tailings and reedy trenches left by the dredges, and by a swampy wilderness of flax and manuka.

A 40-minute walk from the carpark runs out to the lagoon on Gillespies Point. From there, a track around the lagoon's pebbly inland bank runs into regenerating bush, where kahikatea and silver pine struggle for dominance over the manuka scrub. An old miners' road, silent and grass-grown, is cut into the hillside and hidden by forest from the sea. There is also a tunnel which begins in a place of green, cool shade and opens out into the full glare of the restless, pounding Tasman Sea. A narrow path descends to the beach, and to a seal colony.

The Fox Glacier

◄*Perfect calm on the water of a lake near the Fox Glacier*

The 13 km long Fox Glacier is, perhaps, a grander spectacle than the Franz Josef. The approach road runs between stands of matai and kamahi for some 5 km, over and around ancient moraines and across gravel outwashes founded on 'dead' ice. It crosses flattened piles of debris fallen from crumbling mountainsides no longer supported by glacial ice. After advances around 1600 and 1750 AD, the glacier has receded between projecting spurs. Minor waterfalls trail narrow veils down wet and vertiginous rock faces, and little streams riffle over shingle fans, down to the Fox River.

The face of the glacier is partly buried in terminal moraine, but there is still a stupendous tumble of broken ice, arching out over a cave from which the Fox River issues, white with powdery 'rock flour'. Here and there it is checked by the mighty rubble from steep, crumbling mountain walls. The whole valley is founded on ice of unknown depth. It has been sounded to more than 300 m without positively reaching rock bottom.

The glacier ice is pristine white on its surface, except where it has been soiled by rubble, but its hollows and fissures are turquoise. Glacier ice is not a smooth and glassy sheet. Its centre travels faster than its sides, which are slowed by their grinding friction against the rock walls, and this causes a crisscross pattern of diagonal fractures within the ice, with crevasses and ridges at the surface.

As at the Franz Josef Glacier, walking tracks explore the surroundings. There is a steep climb, strictly for the physically fit but needing no more special equipment than strong footwear, to the 1337 m top of Mt Fox. It rises through heavy forest of sub-tropical luxuriance, past the timber-line to steep mountain slopes. This area, through the summer months, is daubed liberally with alpine flowers. From the summit there are fine panoramic views; though magnificent views of the glacier itself are obtainable from vantage points much more easily reached.

Phenomenal growth of the glacier in the 14th and 18th centuries caused it to spill over into the saddle where the Chalet Lookout is now situated. Two spillovers began to encircle an eminence known as Cone Rock; but the advance was then halted by a period of warmer winters, and the glacier receded.

The glacier thereafter receded sporadically, leaving lateral mounds of moraine across the mountain's face. The High Valley Walk crosses seven of them, piled like great terraces across the general slope.

Nature is repairing glacial damage. Small plants find footing in the gaps and silt-filled pockets between the stones on the gravelly ground, rotting down to provide humus in which wind-blown and bird-carried seeds of shrubs like tutu, broadleaf and wineberry can grow. These provide shelter for the seedlings of large trees such as totara, rata, kamahi and miro.

There are short walks adjacent to the village, such as the Minnehaha Track, a 20-minute ramble, close to the main road, through kamahi forest. The kamahi begins life as a parasite, growing in the trunk of a tree fern. But it sends down roots into the soil, which gradually encircle and choke the tree fern. The fern dies, leaving a kamahi tree standing on flying-buttress roots which form caverns filled with ferns and fungi.

The little Minnehaha Stream chatters softly over small rapids, or slips silently through a succession of pools. In its shallows, under stones, are the larvae of lacewing, mayfly and caddis fly. Above, fantails perform their aerial dances, catching the adult insects in full flight. The long-tailed cuckoo summers here, heard more often than seen, and at night *ruru*, the morepork, exchanges cries with his kind amongst the trees.

◄*The Fox Glacier stretches for 14 km and descends steeply from 2750 m above sea level to 245 m*

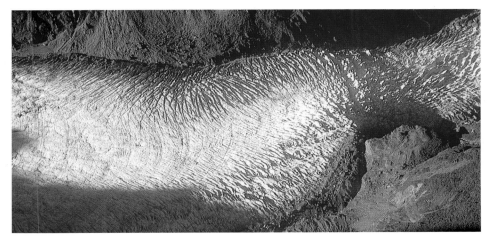

◄An aerial view of the Fox Glacier shows the pattern of internal fractures. These are caused by friction at the sides impeding the flow of the ice

▼Humps and pinnacles on the glacier are created by pressures within the ice, arising from movement over ridges of hard rock

Crossing the Copland Pass

►River boulders of schist at Welcome Flat, end of the first stage of the popular Copland Track

◄Boiling pool at Welcome Flat, where cooler hot springs also await weary trampers

The western side of the Copland track begins with a quiet four-hour stroll through the forest, and may be undertaken with neither special equipment nor a guide. The track enters the forest through a gap between thickly wooded gully-riven hills. There are brief glimpses of the jagged, snow-crowned tops of the Hooker Range, and dark, precipitous mountainsides, torn with scree slides, the tops lost in tatters of cloud. The way crosses the well-named Rough Creek and plunges into the bush, which closes overhead and leaves the tramper with the companionship of the Karangarua River and, presently, its tributary the Copland, up the long, climbing valley between the Copland, Navigator and Karangarua Ranges.

The forest through which this first stage passes is largely ancient rata and kamahi. The immense ratas have a huge spread of branches, laden with orchids and other perching plants whose weight frequently causes branches to collapse. The giants are interspersed with groves and clumps of tree ferns and some tall shrubs.

The Karangarua River, swift and often deep, is fed by the Douglas River, the Copland River, Regina Creek—all fierce, glacier-fed streams—and many small forest streams. The forest floor is littered with rotting logs, dressed in a brilliant green livery of lichens, mosses and filmy ferns.

The track meets the Copland River at its confluence with the Karangarua, following it closely for a winding 3 km, crossing McPhee Creek and the brawling Architect Creek, from where it begins a diagonal haul up the

flank of the westward-trending spur of the Navigator Range. It crosses the sometimes torrential Palaver and Open Creeks, and Shiels Creek before sidling down to the Welcome Flat Hut. This is as far as most inexperienced trampers wish to go. The remaining two days of the track can be a testing experience for the practised mountaineer.

Welcome Flat itself is about 1500 m upstream from the 16-bunk hut. The river has to be forded to reach it. It lies along a stretch of river opposite the confluence of the Ruera River, a short and turbulent torrent whose mouth is screened from view by a bush-crowned islet and a wide and gravelly delta. The eastern extremity of Welcome Flat is bounded by Scott Creek, rushing down, over and between ice-scratched morainic rocks from the Scott Glacier on the looming Sierra Range. All these swift mountain streams must be treated with respect. They can flood with frightening rapidity.

The track follows the south bank of the Copland River for about 9 km, over the points of spurs which descend from the Sierra Range, across Bluewater Creek and around the unstable lower end of a titanic slip which has gashed the foot of the range beneath Scott Peak. High above the track, on the right, may be glimpsed the Takano Glacier, beneath Welcome Pass, a notch in the top of the mountain wall .

The second day's walk ends at the Douglas Rock Hut, almost opposite the confluence of the Strauchon and Copland Rivers, in a deep valley between the Sierra and Banks Ranges. There the Strauchon Glacier once pressed down from the Baker Saddle to butt its head against the 2400 m Sierra Range, but receded at last, leaving great boulders.

On the third day the track begins to reach up into mountaineers' country. It crosses streams more often and finds itself in thinning woods. It leaves the forest at the crossing of a rumbustious creek which boils down from the side of the Footstool, one of the major peaks of the Southern Alps at 2765 m. Ahead, it zigzags up precipitous slopes beneath a towering bluff. An impressive array of peaks stands like mighty crenellations in the 2000 m saddle that is crossed by the 1830 m Copland Pass between La Pérouse, rising to 3079 m, and the Footstool.

There is a shelter in the Copland Pass, a

barrel-shaped emergency refuge built to withstand avalanches, a reminder that this is no place to linger. If the weather is clear, though, a little time may be well spent looking back to the Tasman Sea, stained by the outflow of the Karangarua River, about 50 km distant. Ahead to the east looms the Mt Cook Range, rising up to the awesome Mt Cook itself, 3764 m high. Below is the Hooker Glacier, a shining ice-mass dribbling off into a long valley.

From there, the climb leads down over a steep way, a 2 km path over wet rock and scree to the Hooker Hut, for rest before tackling the last 9 km walk down the lateral moraine to Mount Cook village.

◄*Immense rata trees splash scarlet over the mountainsides in Westland National Park in late summer*

▲*The second day's walk ends near Strauchon Junction, where the Strauchon and Copland Rivers flow together*

▼*The Copland Valley from the Copland Pass. Only experienced mountaineers can reach this point*

Lakes and coast southwest of the park

◄*Luxuriant tree ferns grow at the edges of the forest, some species as tall as palms*

For some 37 km south of the Karangarua River, the Highway 6 route is supremely spectacular, swinging towards the coast, where long spurs terminate in lofty bluffs above the sea. There are lonely, driftwood-littered, pebbly beaches where the wind off the sea sighs through the trees that screen the shore from the road. There are sandy-banked lagoons where the sea is said to be driving back the land, and placid little bays sheltered by rugged headlands, where seals or penguins bask in the sun. And always there is the forest, where the paler green of tree-ferns waves over bracken-covered verges, and tall trunks are tufted with flax-like kiekie.

There are frontier farms, hacked out of the bush and kept clear of fern by prodigious labour, where Hereford cattle are bred and raised. This is truly pioneer farming, except that axe and firestick have been replaced by bulldozer and chain saw. The farmhouses are the simple cottages that pioneers of last century knew, though here and there more substantial dwellings have been built in recent times. Today a good road serves the area and cattle are trucked to market, but not so long ago they were driven down the Windbag Valley, named for the whirlwinds which rush down from time to time.

The Windbag Creek emerges from the valley to feed Lake Paringa, which curls about the trout-like snout of Fish Hill, and teems with rainbow trout, brown trout and landlocked quinnat salmon.

Paringa can be rendered as 'flowing tide'. The lake is curved and narrow, and at flood times it visibly flows, surging out to sea by a creek which flows into the Paringa River. Kahikatea forest rises behind the flax-fringed lake like a backdrop curtain. There are deer in the forest, and the lakeside rings with the song of tui and bellbird, and the kingfisher flashes jewel-like from the high branches.

Ten kilometres south of Lake Paringa is the Moeraki (or Blue) River, which has become choked with old glacial deposits and dune sands to form Lake Moeraki. This lake, larger than Lake Paringa, is sheltered by the tall trees of forests in which wild pigs and deer are hunted.

Moeraki is the name of a kind of sweet potato brought to New Zealand by Maoris during their migrations from their South Pacific homelands. It is difficult to understand how such a calm, beautiful water acquired such a prosaic name. The lake proper spreads over 6475 hectares, and averages a mere 4 m in depth. It is one of the haunts of the graceful white heron.

The road climbs around Knights Point, a rugged and bush-crowned headland with a skirting of secluded, golden-sand beach where granite pinnacles and rocky islets fringed with surf offer a sanctuary and a fishing ground for seals. The point was named after a surveyor's black Labrador dog, whose head it was said to resemble.

The road from Knights Point dips down and almost immediately climbs again to the grimly named Epitaph Cutting, 183 m above the sea, and then undulates with steepening climbs and descents, down to Breccia Creek, up to Seal Point at 153 m, down again to Grant Creek, over Bullock Creek and up to Sardine Terrace, 61 m above the rocky

◄*The mountains are close to the coast in South Westland, and high peaks seem to thrust almost directly out of the lowlands*

◄Windbag Creek ripples into Lake Paringa, which teems with fish—brown trout, rainbow trout and landlocked quinnat salmon

coast—a roller-coaster scramble over the toes of the Alps. At last the road descends and swings out towards the sea at Taiperikaka River, known also as Ship Creek because the remains of a ship lie buried in the sand about 100 m downstream from the bridge, near a prominent sandstone outcrop.

The road south from there runs across forest-covered sand dunes and a number of swamps, and the trees crowd up to the roadside almost to the end of the Callender-Hamilton Bridge, the longest of its kind in New Zealand, which spans the Haast River. The wide, swift river rushes and swirls through rock-strewn deeps to the coast and out to the Tasman Sea.

▲Pioneer Hut perches 2600 m above sea level at the head of the Fox névé. Behind it is Douglas Peak

►One of the many state forests in South Westland covers the coastal hills between Tititira Head and Heretaniwha Point, south of Bruce Bay

Mount Aspiring National Park

A majestic and shapely mountain, sometimes called 'the Matterhorn of New Zealand', stands at the centre of this rugged region, through which run some of the country's finest walking tracks

Mount Aspiring National Park stands astride the Main Divide of the Southern Alps. Its focal point is the magnificent Mt Aspiring, 3027 m high, the highest New Zealand mountain outside Mount Cook National Park. It is a majestic peak, with four main ridges rising to the summit.

The park was established in 1964 and now extends over 289 657 hectares, stretching from the Haast River in the north to the Humboldt Mountains in the south. It is a rugged, mountainous region, supporting more than 100 glaciers of varying sizes, though most of them are in steady retreat.

The advances of glaciers about 15 000 years ago shaped the landscape of the region. At that time the surface of the ice stood at 1500 m or more across the Main Divide, covering many of the lesser peaks. In the vicinity of Mt Aspiring the ice reached up to more than 2100 m. Today there is permanent snow and ice above about 2000 m. Lake basins, moraines, hanging valleys, cirques and deep glacial valleys are numerous.

A wide range of vegetation types, from lowland to high alpine, is found within the park and there is one of the greatest ranges of alpine vegetation in the world in the 1000 m between the treeline and the snowline. About 93 per cent of the species of alpine plants are found only in New Zealand. Silver beech grows throughout the park but red beech and mountain beech are erratically distributed

and are restricted to the southern half of the park. The wetter western regions support a much denser forest than those in the east. Mixed beech-podocarp-hardwood forest is found west of the divide, and ferns, mosses, liverworts and lichens are abundant there.

Introduced animals, such as deer, chamois, goats and hares, have drastically modified the vegetation and scrub in many areas, especially west of the divide. Red deer have caused the greatest damage but where their numbers have been severely reduced, recovery is evident. Possums do not seem to have done great harm to the forests, but cattle and sheep have noticeably damaged the forest understorey in several valleys.

Stoats, weasels and feral cats threaten the bird population but do not appear to have made heavy inroads. Birds are very plentiful, though more needs to be known on their habits and distribution. In spring and summer birds are active in forest and scrub; migratory and shore birds dot the river-beds and the kea surveys them all from above.

Lakes Wanaka and Hawea, and the coastal strip south of the Haast River are not within the park, but they lie along the main approaches to the region, and in many ways they come under its influence.

▶ *The Routeburn, Rees and Dart Valleys give access to the southern section of the park. The Matukituki River valleys provide entry to the east and centre, and the north is entered from the Haast highway. Access to the west is over high passes from the east or by a long walk up difficult valleys*

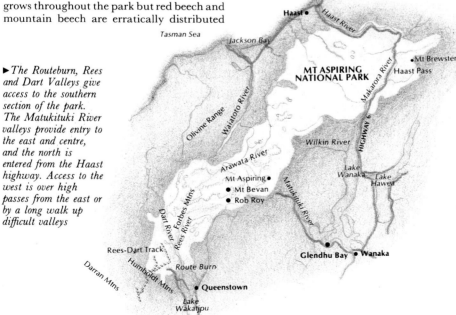

▼Bad weather in the
Dart Valley. Cattle
feed on the river flat

Over the Haast Pass by long-awaited road

▼*Enormous boulders of schist jam the gorge of the Haast River between Thunder Creek and the Wills River. The gorge is crossed by the Gates of Haast bridge*

▶*Rich forest in the lower Haast Valley is a mixture of podocarps, beech and hardwoods*

The Haast Pass, at 562 m the lowest pass on the Main Divide, was long a Maori greenstone trail, but it was not until January 1863 that Charles Cameron, a Scottish gold miner and explorer became the European discoverer of the route. Later the same month the geologist Julius von Haast and four companions battled through to the coast and back in continuous rain.

From late last century packhorses and cattle were driven across a formed track but the building of a road across the Haast Pass did not begin until 1929. It was another 31 years before Wanaka and Haast townships were linked by road, and only in 1965 was the road pushed through to Paringa, completing Highway 6. Much of the road is still not sealed, but it is not so difficult except when there have been washouts or slips, and it is seldom blocked by snow.

From Haast Junction to Wanaka is only 146 km. There is so much to see and experience that the journey should not be rushed. The contrast between the magnificent Westland rainforest and the lakes and open spaces lying east of the Main Divide is something to savour and remember.

On the western side of the pass the Haast River flows to the sea, and on the eastern side the Makarora River flows down a widening forested valley to the head of Lake Wanaka. The Makarora rises under the south face of Mt Brewster (2423 m) and flows through a deep gorge before emerging into the main valley just north of Davis Flat, about 2 km south of the Haast Pass.

Before the Europeans came, the lower Makarora River flats were thickly covered by a mixture of cabbage trees, flax, shrubs and fern. Timber mills started up in the valley in 1861 and kahikatea, matai, and silver beech were pitsawn, lashed together and rafted down the rivers and lakes to the goldmining towns of Clyde and Cromwell. Flaxmilling was practised for 30 years from 1890.

On the east side of the valley, 9 km from the head of Lake Wanaka, part of the Mount Aspiring National Park runs north

▲ *Tree trunks tossed onto huge boulders at the Gates of Haast show the river's power*

from White Creek to Brady Creek. There are remnants of the original forest—kahikatea, rimu, matai and miro—near the Makarora Ranger Station.

The valley between Makarora and the Haast Pass, about 18 km long, provides a deeply satisfying variety of scenery—with rollicking rivers and skittery streams; subtle variations of forest green; high meadows and alluvial fans. Tracks lead off to the east into the headwaters of Camerons Creek and the Makarora River, and from Davis Flat it is a short walk through mature silver beech forest to the Stewarts Creek Falls.

On both sides of the valley above the Haast Pass, subalpine scrub occupies most of the first 100 m above the treeline. Above this narrow band, tall snow-grass tussocks and herbs are dominant. Herbaceous plants, such as the great mountain buttercup, spear-grasses and mountain flax, flourish in the shelter of snow totara, celery pine, small-leaved coprosmas and daisy shrubs.

Rainfall is heavy, especially near and west of the pass. The wettest spot is at the Roaring Billy, on the Haast River, about 22 km from the coast, where the mean annual rainfall is 5840 mm and rain falls on 182 days a year. Makarora, protected by the Main Divide, records 2440 mm from 125 rain days.

Ten kilometres from the pass the Haast River plunges into a gorge crammed with colossal schist boulders, and 2 km farther on are Thunder Creek Falls. A walk of about 100 m through silver beech forest, and the 30 m falls are seen pouring from a notch in rock that was once the floor of a glacier flowing into the Haast Valley. In 1863 Haast found the forest, in which matai, miro, rimu and kamahi grow, 'alive with woodhen and many kakapos'. It is no longer so.

The road skirts Pleasant Flat and reaches Clarke Bluff, where the mighty Landsborough River joins the Haast River. Southern rata flowers in late summer, splashing scarlet along the beech forest and olive-green rimu. From there to the sea the river runs wide and deep, swinging from side to side across a valley up to 1 km wide.

Deep lakes that feed the mighty Clutha

Lake Wanaka is one of the most benign of the southern lakes, and only Wakatipu and Te Anau are larger. Covering 181 km², it is 45 km long and 4.8 km at its widest. Its surface is 274 m above sea level, and its deepest point is 311 m. The Makarora River feeds the lake from the north and the Matukituki from the west, and the lake itself is the source of the mighty Clutha.

Lake Wanaka and nearby Lake Hawea, fill glaciated valleys. It is everywhere obvious how the glaciers of the ice ages smoothed and rounded the landscape below the sharp peaks. Massive rivers of ice thrust as far south as the junction of the Clutha and Lindis Rivers. Moraines built up and as ice thawed the lakes filled.

Wanaka is a corruption of *Oanaka*, from the name of a Maori chief said to have once visited the area to fish. Before Europeans came Maoris roamed the area, hunting moas, fishing and sometimes journeying west to trade in greenstone. According to Maori mythology, the chief Te Rakaihautu dug out the beds of Lakes Hawea and Wanaka with a huge *ko* (digging stick) and he piled high the spoil, forming ranges of mountains.

European land-seekers were intensely active in the Wanaka area from the early 1850s. In 1853 Nathaniel Chalmers, a young Southland settler, persuaded an old Maori chief, Reko, to take him into the interior. By the time they reached the junction of the Clutha and Hawea Rivers, Chalmers' enthusiasm had waned as dysentry had waxed.

▼*Stream-riven faces of the Four Peaks loom above the northern shore of Lake Hawea.*   *Nearby is the Neck, a narrow isthmus which separates Lake Hawea from Lake Wanaka*

▲*The Clutha River winds out of the southern end of Lake Wanaka to meet the Hawea River at lower right. At the centre of the horizon, Mt Aspiring soars high*

▼*Terracing of the shore of Lake Hawea has resulted from control of the height of the waters by gates built across the exit in 1958*

Reko constructed a raft from the dry stems of flax flowers, lashed together with flax and they set off down river. After four fearful days in the gorges they arrived at Balclutha. By 1863 sheepmen and surveyor-explorers were familiar with the region surrounding the two lakes and miners were busy in the valleys.

In winter the lake shores can look bleak and desolate, with skeletal trees standing by cold blue waters, but with the coming of spring the land takes heart and in summer the drive from Wanaka to Glendhu Bay, 13 km to the west, is enchanting. Limes, willows, poplars, rowans, maples and the golden flowers of kowhais enrich the scene. Ten kilometres from Wanaka, the snow-covered spire of Mt Aspiring is seen soaring above the intervening ranges.

On flats near the mouth of the Matukituki River, black-fronted terns flit over the fields and finches are numerous. Pied oystercatchers, white-faced herons, Canada geese and black swans are seen near the lake edges.

Lake Hawea, 345 m above sea level, is starker than Lake Wanaka. It measures 31 km long, 8 km wide at one point and 119 km^2 in area. Its maximum depth was increased by the installation of control gates in 1958 from 392 m to 410 m. The waters are well stocked with brown and rainbow trout and there are some land-locked salmon.

About 20 km north of Hawea township, the road swings north-west to The Neck, a narrow rocky saddle cut by ice. It once interconnected the glaciers which filled the valleys of Lakes Wanaka and Hawea. This brackencovered saddle was the site of a Maori village which was abandoned about 1836.

In the shadows of Castor, Pollux and Alba

◄*In the upper Wilkin, where grassy flats offer fine views of the mountain peaks*

►*The Makarora River flows down a broad valley from Haast Pass. Shortly before it runs into Lake Wanaka it is joined from the west by the Wilkin River*

The Wilkin Valley is one of the most beautiful in Mount Aspiring National Park but, except when the Makarora and Wilkin rivers are low, access is difficult. Quicksands are a danger and the rivers flow with deceptive power. Boats are frequently used to cross the Makarora and a jet boat service up the Wilkin is popular with fishermen, trampers and climbers who wish to be dropped off just below Kerin Forks at the confluence of the Siberia Stream. It is a swift and exhilarating way to cover the 20 km from Makarora.

The Wilkin River, named after an early runholder, and its tributaries drain a wild 32 km length of the Southern Alps. Cattle and sheep feed on the broad grassy terraces of the lower Wilkin, and paradise shelducks are numerous along the surging blue-green river. Big brown and rainbow trout lie in the pools above and below Kerin Forks. Fine silver beech forest grows down to the valley floor.

Near the head of the Siberia Valley, to the north, a small stand of coniferous-broad-leaved forest, unusual in an area dominated by silver beech, grows at an altitude of 650–900 m under Mt Dreadful (2027 m). There is a similar stand in the north branch of the Wilkin River. The Siberia Valley is a gorge lower down but opens onto pleasant flats ringed by high-walled peaks. Mt Alba (2355 m), is the most impressive.

An abundance of birds is one of the special joys of the Wilkin. Tomtits, yellow-heads, riflemen, brown creepers, kakas, parakeets, and fantails live in the forest and scrub. And hikers who climb well above the valley floors are likely to see New Zealand falcons, keas and rock wrens.

About an hour's walk upstream from Kerin Forks, the Newland Stream joins the Wilkin from the northwest. Like all the side valleys, it is a gorge in its lower reaches but soon there are grassy flats, the floor of a wide hanging valley with splendid views of Mts Alba and Achilles (1875 m).

The track from the Newland Stream to the Wonderland Stream never strays far from the river as it slavers and thunders from one cataract to the next. Along the western margins of the Wonderland Stream is a chain of 2000 m high peaks with the evocative classical names of Vesta, Iphigenia and Juno.

Half an hour's walk through the bush and the wide Jumboland Flats are reached. In summer, grazing cattle intrude and cut up the ground, along which yellow ragwort grows in riotous profusion. At the junction of the south and north branches of the Wilkin River the scowling, riven bluffs of Mt Ragan (2259 m) tower 1500 m above the valley floor. The south branch, in which the subalpine scrub is dense and varied, leads to a difficult crossing into the East Matukituki valley.

The north branch provides the wildest and most spectacular mountain scenery in the Wilkin. Rocks rattle and clatter down the bluffs of an uncompromising mountain landscape. Ice breaks from the large hanging glaciers on Mt Castor (2516 m) and Mt Pollux (2542 m), the most formidable and majestic peaks in the valley. The explorer Charles Douglas named Castor and Pollux after two peaks in the Swiss Alps which took their names from the twin Roman divinities. They have high *névés* whose meltwaters feed Lake Castalia and a smaller lake at the foot of Pollux's swarthy bluffs across the flat from tarn-like Lake Diana.

Substantial moraines have to be negotiated on the way to Lake Castalia, named after a nymph who drowned herself in a spring while trying to escape from the god Apollo. The head of this valley is a place of supreme isolation and beauty.

'A glorious pyramid of ice and snow'

The mountains of the Mount Aspiring National Park offer limitless variety and scope to all who yearn to explore the majestic world of high and silent places above the bushline. And while other peaks have their own special appeal, it is to the peak of Mt Aspiring itself that many are drawn.

It is 3027 m high, an aloof imperious mountain, standing alone west of the Main Divide, in the path of severe northwest storms. Blizzards also strike from the southwest and evil weather may hit suddenly at any time of the year. The mountain is so well protected it scorns the bumbler and receives only the fit and determined. There are four ridges, rising from the contortions of the Bonar, Therma and Volta Glaciers. The northwest ridge is the least difficult and is usually attempted from the Colin Todd Memorial Hut, built at 2100 m on the Shipowner Ridge. Perhaps the purest and most beautiful route is the snow-and-ice-covered southwest ridge, rising from the Bonar and steepening to about 60° near the summit. The impressive castellations of the east arête ridge—known as Coxcomb—provide exposed and difficult mixed climbing. An approach via the Therma Icefield leads to the steep rock arête of the northeast ridge, which joins the Coxcomb ridge ice shoulder east and slightly below the summit of Mt Aspiring. North of Mt Aspiring, the Volta and Therma Glaciers form a bow about 30 km long, the whole ice-shelf draining into the Waiatoto River. The Bonar Glacier grinds for about 8 km along the southern flanks of the mountain before spilling into the Waipara River.

The Maoris called Mt Aspiring *Tititea*, the 'upright glistening one'. It was given its

▼*Mt Aspiring, 'the Matterhorn of New Zealand', seen at sunrise from Glendhu, on Lake Wanaka*

English name by the first European to see it, J. T. Thomson, chief surveyor for the Otago Provincial Government. On 18 December 1857, he stood on the summit of Grandview Mountain (1387 m), above Hawea Flat and saw in the northwest, beyond brown and green hills and the shining waters of Lakes Hawea and Wanaka, 'a glorious pyramid of ice and snow'.

The first climbers to attempt an ascent of Mt Aspiring tried from the west in 1908, but they were defeated by the Waiatoto River and the glaciers at its head. On 23 November 1909, Major Bernard Head and the guides Jack Clarke and Alex Graham made the first ascent, by the southwest face. They had approached by the West Matukituki River.

Whatever the weather, whatever the conditions, whatever the time of the year, there is no easy way to approach Mt Aspiring. It has claimed many lives in testimony to this fact.

South of Mt Aspiring across the Bonar Glacier are the splendid viewpoints of Mts French (2341 m), Joffre (2082 m) and Bevan (2030 m). To the southwest are Mt Barff (2243 m) and Governors Ridge, separating the West Matukituki from the head of the Dart Valley and Dart Glacier. Major Head

▲*Glaciers fill enormous cirques between the arrêtes of the peak*

▼*Mt Aspiring towers above the west Matukituki valley*

named Mt Liverpool (2446 m), the glacier-overridden Islington Dome (2402 m) and Plunket Dome (2158 m) after three Governors of New Zealand.

Northeastwards along the Main Divide are the Aeroplane, Moncrieff and Fastness Peaks, the dark concave wall of the last rearing above Ruth Flat. Fastness Peak (2377 m) is perhaps the finest position from which to view the peaks of the Haast Range which jut between the Bonar and Therma icefields.

Although none of the mountains in the north are as commanding as Mt Aspiring, many have distinct characters of their own. Mts Pickelhaube (2262 m), Pollux (2542 m), Castor (2523 m) and Alba (2355 m) are but a few of the outstanding peaks on the divide between Aspiring and Mt Brewster (2423 m), which stands above the Haast Pass on the extreme northeast boundary of the Park.

Southwest of Governor's Ridge above the West Matukituki is the Dart-Barrier Range, the glaciers of which have been shrinking fast in recent years. The Humboldt Mountains straddle the southern boundary of the Park and include several striking peaks up to about 2300 m in height, including Chaos, Poseidon, Tantalus, Somnus and Erebus.

▲*Highly specialised plants grow in almost no soil on the scree slopes of the mountains*

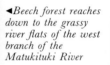

◀*Beech forest reaches down to the grassy river flats of the west branch of the Matukituki River*

▶*Mountain foxglove, or ourisia, is a plant of the alpine zone*

medal from the Royal Geographical Society for his explorations in North America, crossed from the West Matukituki over a high saddle to the Waipara and Arawata rivers. He returned the same way, over what is now known as Hector Col.

About 7 km from Cameron Flat the road skirts the base of Niger Peak (2012 m) and swings northwest. The view is stunning. Straight ahead the curving icefields and jagged east ridge of Mt Avalanche (2438 m) stand behind Homestead Peak (1999 m), above the junction of the east and west branches of the Matukituki River. Mount Aspiring Station homestead is seen on the left soon after fording the Niger Stream. Both the Niger and the next stream, Glenfinnan, can be impassable in wet weather. And it rains hard and often. Mount Aspiring Station records annual averages of 138 rain days and 2770 mm of rain.

From Cameron Flat it is a drive of about 8 km up the west branch over an often washed-out road to Raspberry Creek, 54 km from Wanaka. On the north bank opposite Cameron Flat is Hell's Gate—high, slimy, evil-looking bluffs guarding the entrance to the west branch of the Matukituki.

On the south side of the valley above Raspberry Creek is the fang of Sharks Tooth (2094 m). Beyond the creek the track wanders over a hummocky moraine, with a view of flat parklands and the scintillating river, to the New Zealand Alpine Club's Aspiring Hut. Above are the glistening bluffs and shining snowfields of glacier-worn Plunket Dome (2158 m). It is worth allowing five or

The Matukituki River flows to Lake Wanaka from the west and gives the easiest and most convenient access to the eastern boundary of the Mount Aspiring National Park. In Maori legend the river was called 'the white destroyer', though the literal translation of its name is 'dashing stream'.

The road from Wanaka is sealed only for 11 km to Glendhu. From there it is unsealed and in parts corrugated and rutted. After passing the 60 m high cataracts of Twin Falls at about 21 km, and the start of the access road to the Treble Cone Skifield, the road approaches the Cattle Flat homestead and

outbuildings, sheltered by tall trees. Cattle Flat Station and Glenfinnan, farther up the valley, began as sheep runs in 1876. In the terrible winter of 1878, snow lay more than a metre deep for four months and Glenfinnan lost 8000 of its 9000 sheep.

The first European to visit the valley was most likely the Government surveyor James McKerrow, searching for the elusive pass to the West Coast in March 1862. He discovered no pass but he did express 'awe and veneration at the stupendous forces of nature'. The next summer, James Hector, 28 years old but already the holder of a gold

six hours for the walk to the hut and back.

A variety of forests grow in both branches of the Matukituki. Subalpine silver beech is found in the upper west branch, and also in the east branch from Junction Flat to Ruth Flat. Mountain beech grows on the east bank in the lower east branch and mountain and red beech can also be found in some parts of the west branch. Leatherwood subalpine scrub makes its unique appearance below Liverpool Bivouac in the upper west branch. The slopes opposite Homestead Peak are dominated by bracken where fire has destroyed beech forest.

Near the head of the east branch, above Ruth Flat, is the most extensive stand of coniferous-broadleaved forest in the whole national park. The east branch is not so accessible as the west branch because the west branch has first to be crossed from the road head at Cameron Flat.

The walk across the flower-strewn flats to Glacier Burn (known locally as Snowy Creek) and up a track to its source below Avalanche Glacier is delightful. There and back takes three and a half hours. A good track follows the west bank all the way to where, in the words of the writer and mountaineer Paul Powell, 'a venerable silver beech stands on Junction Flat where the East Matukituki River leaves the Bledisloe Gorge and meets the Kitchener Stream. The flat is covered with browntop and native grass, violets and thin-stemmed slender daisies'. There is a fine view of the peaks above the Kitchener Cirque, with the soaring spire of Mt Aspiring beyond.

▲*In winter a thick mantle of snow softens some of the harsh contours of mountains but emphasises others. This is Rob Roy (2606 m). It carries a glacier from which the Rob Roy stream flows into the west Matukituki*

◄*Mt Bevan (2030 m) stands above the Hector Col, the saddle between the West Matukituki and Waipara Rivers. It was discovered in 1863 by James Hector, who later became director of the Geological Survey*

Along the valleys of the Rees and the Dart

▲*Mt Earnslaw is the highest point of the Forbes Mountains, the massif that lies between the Rees and Dart valleys*

▼*The Rees Valley climbs gradually up to the Rees Saddle, where the track crosses the Forbes Mountains at an altitude of 1506 m*

Maoris knew of the lower reaches of the Dart and Rees valleys at the head of Lake Wakatipu, but until Europeans came in search of gold no one had found a way into the headwaters. The surveyor James McKerrow pushed up the Rees as far as Hunter Stream, east of Mt Earnslaw, in February 1863. The next year Patrick Caples crossed the Rees Saddle in an unsuccessful search for gold.

After that miners concentrated their efforts on the lower Rees, with good results. A quartz battery began operating on Invincible Creek, east of the Rees River, in 1882 and continued until about 1900. Relics of the operation are still visible.

Mountaineering in the region also began in 1882, with an unsuccessful attempt on Mt Earnslaw. The party was led by the Rev. W. S. Green, an Irishman who despised 'gold-grubbing' and wished for the settlement of 'industrious Swiss settlers in beech chalets'. A notable tourist industry quickly sprang up, based on scenic excursions and guided climbing. The chief guide, Harry Birley, made the first ascent of the 2819 m East Peak of Mt Earnslaw in 1890, climbing alone. The more difficult West Peak (2816 m) remained unclimbed until 1914.

Surveyors and geologists were slow to explore the upper Dart after Caples in 1864. No one seems to have gone there until 1897, when William O'Leary, the legendary and secretive Arawata Bill, became the first to cross the Barrier Range to the Joe River. Finally, between 1911 and 1914 Major Bernard Head and his companions surveyed the Dart Glacier and climbed several peaks in the upper valley. Prospectors and runholders

◄The Rees Valley, in which most trampers begin their walk along the Rees-Dart track

►Small leaves enable Hebe subalpina to resist being dried out by cold winds in its subalpine habitat

▼Approaching the Rees Saddle, the Rees-Dart track climbs into this subalpine country near the source of the Rees

cut the first tracks in the district. Men on relief work during the Depression and, later, contract workers cut a track through virgin bush from Cattle Flat to the Dart Hut, built in 1937 for the New Zealand Alpine Club. The job was completed in 1939 and after World War II the Rees-Dart round trip became popular. It is usually done in four or five days in favourable weather.

The Rees-Dart Track is well-marked, easily accessible and within the scope of the average tramper. It provides the finest alpine scenery. Cars can go as far as the carpark at Muddy Creek in the Rees Valley. Most trampers start in the Rees Valley for two reasons—the open nature of the lower valley and the gradual climb to the Rees Saddle, the highest point of the trip.

The walk up the Rees is fulfilling. Streams gurgle down from the Richardson Mountains in the east, friendly grey robins inhabit the bush, grasses flourish on the flats and the river bounds along.

Near 25-Mile Creek the summit of Mt Earnslaw comes into view and across the river the spectacular Lennox Falls pour from Kea Basin. Oystercatchers, paradise shelducks and spur-winged plovers patrol the flats and hares lope among the tussocks.

The subalpine ground approaching Rees Saddle is a delight. Shrubs, bushes and flowers stand out in early summer, especially the golden-headed spaniards. From the saddle the descent down to the Snowy Creek and the Dart Hut is steep and a little awkward, with speargrass to jab the flesh.

From the Dart Hut begins the long slog down the valley to Paradise—through bush, up and down bluffs, across clearings and flats. Across the Dart River are views first of the Barrier Range, then the Cosmos Peaks and finally, the falls from the hanging valley of Lake Unknown, a tarn, with the Humboldt Mountains beyond.

In the upper Dart more than 70 per cent of the forest is silver beech, and the remainder mountain beech. But lower down the Dart Valley has one of the last great stands of red beech forest in New Zealand. Some of the largest trees are 1300–1500 mm in diameter and 30 m tall. Mountain beech grows in association with red beech, which has an upper limit of 650–850 m, depending on the warmth of the location.

Up and down
the Routeburn Track

◀The Routeburn
Falls, where the Route
Burn tumbles down
from Lake Harris

The increasingly popular Routeburn Track can be walked with equal ease from either end, starting in the west from The Divide, between the Eglinton and Hollyford Rivers in Fiordland National Park, or in the east from the Route Burn in Mount Aspiring National Park. Before Europeans came the Route Burn was of considerable importance to the Maoris, who established villages near the mouth of the river, searched for precious greenstone and went to and fro, trading with settlements in South Westland.

In the early 1860s the province of Otago was alive with rumours, not only of gold, but of convenient easy routes to the West Coast, the idea being to open ports for fast trade with Australian cities. Prospectors explored the valley in 1862 and 1863 and reached but did not cross North Col at the head of the north branch of the Route Burn. It was left to Patrick Caples to discover the Harris Saddle (1277 m) and to go on to make a solo journey down the Hollyford Valley in 1863.

News of Caples' exploit did not reach the provincial government's chief geologist, who was keen to find a route for a road from Lake Wakatipu to remote Martins Bay and linked the Greenstone and Hollyford valleys in 1863. But not until 1870 did the authorities look closely at the possibility of cutting a trail up the Route Burn and over the Harris Saddle. James McKerrow said a bridle track could be cut for £400. He was wrong, and

four years later the work was abandoned in the lower Routeburn. But a good packhorse track was cut and used to carry mail to a settlement at Martins Bay.

Harry Bryant and Harry Birley took tourists from Kinloch and Glenorchy to the Harris Saddle and places farther west in the 1880s and 1890s. Then in 1912, a livewire Minister of Tourism, Sir Thomas Mackenzie, suggested extending the track from Harris Saddle to Lake Howden. Birley looked, and discovered Lake Mackenzie, and the work began in 1913. By the time war erupted the section was complete except for the zigzag above the lake.

Until the early 1930s, when the Milford road was advanced to The Divide, the walk involved a return trip by way of the Greenstone valley. Later, the withdrawal of the Lake Wakatipu steamer *Earnslaw* and the opening of the Dart road bridge in 1974 took some of the magic out of reaching and walking the track.

There are huts at modest intervals along the track. Routeburn Flat and Routeburn Falls each have 20 bunks, the Harris Saddle shelter is for emergency use only, Lake Mackenzie hut has 40 and Lake Howden hut has 20. First come, first served is the general rule. Trampers virtually must stay at

▶The tussocky upper
Routeburn basin may
seem bleak but in
summer the walker
will find many
wildflowers

◀Flowers of Anistome
haastii, a native
member of the carrot
family

◄Red beech forest reaches down to the river flats in the Routeburn Gorge, seen here from the brink of the Routeburn Falls

these huts as camping is not permitted within 500 m of the track.

Camping is not permitted within 500 m of the track between Routeburn Flat and the Milford Road, nor are firearms permitted without a permit either from the national park authorities or the New Zealand Forest Service in Queenstown.

Waterfalls, bluffs and red beech down to the river—this is the scene at the start of the track at the Route Burn end. Mist often swirls in the gorge. The sense of confinement is not shed until, about two hours after leaving the road, the din of the gorge is left behind and the track crosses the tussocky Routeburn Flats. At the western end the Routeburn Falls dive down the bluffs.

The track soon enters the forest again and gradually climbs the southern slopes of the valley to emerge by the hut at the top of the falls. From Routeburn Falls Hut to the Harris Saddle is a world of tussock basins, boulders, broken ridges and, especially in early summer, pockets of subalpine flowers in sheltered or damp places—daisies, gentians, ourisia, coprosma and the voluptuous giant mountain buttercup.

Lake Harris appears below and to the right of the hewn track, and then suddenly the view from the Harris Saddle bursts upon the walker, compelling a stop. From this windy perch the bush-filled Hollyford Valley is spread out below and across the valley are the vertical faces, waterfalls and hanging valleys of the Darran Mountains. The coarse-grained, hard diorite of the Darrans is some of the oldest rock in New Zealand.

From the saddle to Lake Mackenzie the track insinuates itself above the bushline and is exposed to harsh weather from both north-

west and south. No one should linger on this section for lives have been lost there in storms. Lake Mackenzie is an angelic spot, with reflected and real views of Emily Peak (1820 m). Podocarps are numerous in the mixed forest and in summer rata blossom flares. Apart from the climb up to Earland Falls, the track is mostly downhill to Lake Howden and on to the Milford road.

Lake Howden is on the Greenstone River, down which the Hollyford Glacier diverged

and flowed about 20 000 years ago. It is worth climbing the 120 m to Key Summit above the track from Lake Howden to The Divide. Key Summit merges into bog and swamp with a considerable range of alpine bog plants, stunted beech trees, bladderworts, orchids, and other species. Three major drainage systems radiate from Key Summit—the Hollyford, Eglinton and Greenstone Rivers. There is also a fine view northwest into the deep Marian Basin.

►Lake Harris lies near the highest point on the Routeburn Track. This popular track links the Dart valley in Mount Aspiring National Park with the Hollyford valley in Fiordland National Park

Remote wilderness of the Arawata and Waiatoto

The country north of the Barrier Range is a crazy jumble of sharp ridges, deep gorges, broken glaciers and inhospitable mountains. A prospector, Alphonse Barrington and two companions were the first to explore the Olivine region, in 1864. They spent several gruelling months in the area, suffering appalling privation and several times nearly starved to death. With winter beginning to maul them, in desperation they decided to attempt to force a direct route back to lake Wakatipu. One day they climbed what Barrington called 'a mile of pure ice, as pure as crystal', and discovered the peak-bound Olivine Ice Plateau. At the southwestern end of the Olivine Range, this vast silent *névé* is about 13 km long by 3 km wide.

Eventually Barrington, his companions and their dog, slid down frozen snow into the Route Burn, where they shot seven kakas. They devoured these instead of the dog and, like 'living skeletons', staggered to Lake Wakatipu and hospital. Observers said 'their

cheek bones and noses, besides their elbows, hips and other parts . . . were protruding through the skin in places'. It was perhaps the most heroic journey in the history of New Zealand exploration.

Other brave, explorers have been drawn to the region. William 'Arawata Bill' O'Leary (1865?–1947), immortalised in the poetry of Denis Glover, spent a lifetime exploring and prospecting in the area. Another to feel the call was the legendary Charles 'Mr Explorer' Douglas, who went up the Okuru River, south of Haast, in 1885, finding four passes into Otago that were 'utterly useless for road or railway', fit for none but 'an Alpine Explorer or other Lunatic'.

In the 1930s the adventurous J. T. Holloway and various companions, over four summers visited and mapped the southern Olivines. Holloway gave many of the peaks suitably dramatic names, among them Blockade (2173 m), Climax (2423 m), Darkness (2073 m), Typhoon and Tempest.

▲*The Arawata River, 68 km long, flows through remote and inaccessible country*

The Olivine Range runs along the western boundary of the Mount Aspiring National Park and beyond, its highest peaks and the Olivine Ice Plateau forming the southern section of the park's glacial wilderness. Westerly weather predominates and the mean annual rainfall in the middle-to-upper Arawata and Waiatoto valleys is 5000 mm or more. In some tributaries it is a good deal wetter and travel in these gorged, heavily-bushed valleys is always slow and difficult.

The whole area from the Olivine River to the Te Naihi River, about 68 km to the north, has been zoned a 'wilderness area', meaning that it will be preserved in its natural state for as long as possible. The region of the Arawata and Waiatoto rivers and their tributaries is among the most remote, inaccessible and uncompromising in New Zealand.

The Arawata River, 68 km long, rises on

▶*Jackson Bay, where the Arawata River meets the Tasman Sea. The west coast road reaches its southern extremity here*

the western slopes of the Dart Range and flows west until met by the Joe River at Williamson Flat, one of the largest enclosed amphitheatres of flat land in the whole Southern Alps. The Arawata enters the sea to the northeast of Jackson Bay, a small settlement whose origins go back to 1875. A few fishing boats unload at the wharf or jog at their moorings in the bay while the grey Tasman Sea rummages among the rocks of the shore.

The Waiatoto River rises beneath the glaciers of Mount Aspiring and the peaks at the southern end of the Haast Range. As with the Arawata, Joe and Waipara rivers, its headwater tributaries are usually hanging valleys. The Waiatoto flows northeast through gorges and across flats before swinging northwest to the Tasman Sea about 8 km north of the mouth of the Arawata. To the west is the Haast Range, to the east the Main Divide, then progressively down-valley the Commissioner, Drake and Selbourne Ranges. Extensive glacial moraines fill the

head of the valley, where there is a large lake below a massive fall of glacial melt-water.

The knowledge of this region has been hard-won, yet, 'the impulse which impells us to search the wild places of the Earth is good'. Those words are from the diary of Charles Douglas who, in 1891, alone but for his dog Betsy Jane, explored the Waiatoto, its gorges and glaciers, its passes and mountains.

▼*The upper Waiatoto Valley, seen from Bonar Flat, is a 'wilderness area'. Mt Aspiring (3027m) stands at the head*

Central Otago

One of the most visited regions of the South Island, Central Otago is at the same time one of the least known. Tourists travel through it on the way to alpine resorts on its fringes, but few of them know the rock-studded ranges and the bare, lonely plains at the heart of the plateau

Central Otago is a great fragmented schist plateau. It rises 600 m and more above the coastal strip and holds several broad basins which run generally in a northeast to southwest direction, and lie between wide, gently-graded ranges of hills and mountains. The landscape alone, with its rock-studded brown hills, exerts a magnetism that draws people back. There are signs of past human activity everywhere and nowhere else in New Zealand is the past so pervasive.

The precise geographical boundaries of the region are hard to define, but it is generally accepted that the Dunstan Mountains and St Bathans and Hawkdun Ranges form a boundary in the north, along with the Kakanui Mountains farther east, and that it extends as far south as the Garvie and Umbrella Mountains. The region includes the Upper Clutha basin to the shores of the Lakes Wanaka and Hawea, and reaches west to Queenstown, the Remarkables and the Hector Mountains overlooking Lake Wakatipu. The Barewood Plateau, between the

Strath Taieri plain and Dunedin, marks the southeastern limit of the region.

One of Central Otago's greatest attractions is its continental climate—dry all year and frosty in winter. Compared with other areas of New Zealand it is a region of climatic extremes, with some of the lowest winter and highest summer temperatures in the country.

Many parts of Central Otago are arid and barren but they were not always so. About 1500 years ago, for example, the land was swathed in thick tussock and scrub, and there were still signs of a dying forest, mostly matai and totara. From the 10th century to at least the middle of the 14th century the moa hunters came, relentlessly pursuing the giant flightless birds. They set fire to the forest cover to drive the birds out. So began man-made erosion and it has continued into the 20th century. Burning, sheep-grazing and an ever-growing population of rabbits nearly denuded the landscape of vegetation.

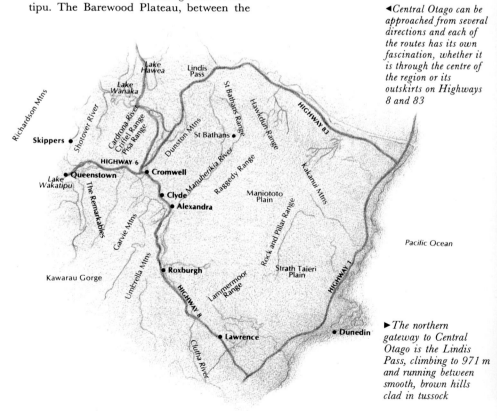

◄Central Otago can be approached from several directions and each of the routes has its own fascination, whether it is through the centre of the region or its outskirts on Highways 8 and 83

►The northern gateway to Central Otago is the Lindis Pass, climbing to 971 m and running between smooth, brown hills clad in tussock

236

Ranges and valleys of the east and interior

▶ *The Kakanui Mountains form the eastern boundary of Central Otago. They are crossed by only one road, which goes through Danseys Pass at 935 m*

Everywhere in Central Otago there is remoteness and there is desolation. The rock-freckled brown hills roll into the far distance; there are solitude and space and the broad sweep of blue skies.

Across the Manuherikia and Clutha Rivers east of Alexandra is the Knobby Range, a craggy inhospitable area of shallow valleys and low ridges, studded with rocks of the most bizarre shapes. Here and there deep valleys, such as the Manorburn, carry substantial streams draining the higher country, and creating a 'fretted landscape'. This kind of landscape occurs again farther north along the western slopes of the Raggedy Range and Rough Ridge. Hot northwesterlies, common in summer, have helped to denude the western slopes of these ranges of nearly all but a blue-grey scabweed.

Farther east, at the southern end of the Ida Valley, the Maniototo Plain and the Strath Taieri, is a landscape over which are scattered tors, or pillars of rock, 6–9 m high. They are weathered and indented and sit on a thin surface of soil covering bedrock.

In a basin south of the Knobby Range and to the north of the Lammerlaw and Lammer-moor Ranges lies Lake Onslow, made by the damming of the Teviot River, which joins the Clutha opposite Roxburgh. Remote and windswept, it is 37 km from Roxburgh and 23 km from Millers Flat over a dry-weather road. On dull days this bleak spot can be uninviting and featureless, but all that changes in clear weather, when dragonflies patrol the lake and the water erupts if one crosses the path of a cruising trout.

In the 1860s prospectors battled their way up the east bank of the Clutha, many of them after leaving Gabriel's Gully, 5 km northeast of Lawrence. There on 20 May 1861, Gabriel Read, an Australian, had discovered gold 'shining like the stars in Orion on a dark frosty night'. Within weeks the tents of thousands of miners crammed the gully and by the end of July more than 11 000 people beavered in the Tuapeka goldfields. Charged with hope and anxiety, miners spread throughout Central Otago, northwards through the Paerau and Serpentine areas of the upper Taieri River to the diggings at Kyeburn and Naseby.

In April 1862, about 3000 rushed to Waipori, farther south, but only a switch to quartz mining enabled the settlement to survive. Soon after World War I, however, a 12 m dam—later raised to 38 m—was built at Waipori Falls to supply power to Dunedin and this committed the former township to the depths of Lake Mahinerangi.

In the 1860s the shortest and most used route from Dunedin to Alexandra and Clyde was over the old Dunstan road. From Outram the trail wound over broken country, crossing Lee Stream and Deep Stream before rising to more than 1000 m over the desolate Lammermoor Range. This cruel stretch was impassable in winter and was never to be taken lightly. After crossing the Taieri River at Styx, now called Paerau, the road traversed Rough Ridge and the Raggedy Range before reaching 'the Dunstan'. Wagon trains went that way and travellers used 'buffalo chips' (dried dung), 'yellow pine' (straw), and 'kaladdies' (the stem of the flax flower) for fuel.

The fertile Strath Taieri plain—its name a mixture of Gaelic and Maori—lies east of the Rock and Pillar Range. Thunderstorms are common there, and huge cloud formations, called 'the Taieri Pet' by locals, often tower above the range. By driving north, over the lower slopes of the Rock and Pillars, one reaches the exposed inland plain known as the Maniototo—'the plain of blood'.

Raw winds whistle across the Maniototo and in winter ice-skating and curling are practised on ponds and dams, especially at Naseby and Oturehua. Naseby was one of the first gold-mining settlements in the region, a strike being reported in 1863. Ranfurly stands on Hog Burn, a river given one of many unimaginative names suggested for

◀*Interplay of light and shadow on the Ida Range dramatises the rounded hill forms that* *characterise much of Central Otago. The Ida Range is north of the Maniototo Plain*

tributaries of the Taieri River by Otago's chief surveyor, John Turnbull Thomson, in irritation after his first choices had been rejected. To his surprise, his more prosaic suggestions, which also included Sow Burn, Ewe Burn and Wether Burn, were accepted.

Although the Maniototo is desolate in winter, birds are numerous in summer. Harrier hawks seen in the area are said to be redder in plumage than usual. According to Maori legend, Mapuika, the goddess of fire, was angry with Maui for playing a trick on her and set the land ablaze. He escaped by changing into a harrier but his feathers were scorched.

Between Rough Ridge and the Raggedy Range lies the Ida Valley, the second largest irrigated area in Central Otago. In the Maniototo, dams are being built in the Paerau Gorge and the Great Moss Swamp, near the head of the Taieri River. Waterfowl frequent the unique system of ox-bow lakes in the swamp, which is one of the most vital wetland areas in Otago. The dam projects have attempted to take account of this and, if anything, they will enhance the area's suitability for waterfowl and fisheries.

Slowly agricultural development has been transforming the eastern ranges, basins and valleys of Central Otago but while patches of green seep across the dun-coloured plateaux, there is a limit to how far the landscape and the climate will allow them to go.

▶ *The Raggedy Range was so named by explorers because of its rocky outcrops and irregular skylines. In the distance are the Dunstan Mountains, rising to 1600 m*

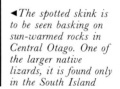

▲*Strange rocky tors stud the ground in the Lammermoor Range and many other parts of Central Otago near the Strath Taieri*

◀*The spotted skink is to be seen basking on sun-warmed rocks in Central Otago. One of the larger native lizards, it is found only in the South Island*

The turbulent and rocky course of New Zealand's biggest river

Travellers on Highway 8 to Roxburgh get their first view of the Clutha River at Beaumont, a farming and fruit-growing area 53 km from Milton. The river swings from the gorge and flows powerfully over ribbed rocks and under the main road bridge.

In the 1860s, at the height of the gold rushes, thousands of miners combed the riverbanks. Drownings were common, and in 1863 a very heavy flood swept the bodies of miners and animals out to sea. Perhaps the greatest flood of all occurred in 1878, during a winter regarded as one of the worst Otago has known. The effects in the lower Clutha were calamitous. Balclutha was inundated and the river carved a new outlet to the sea, closing Port Molyneux to shipping.

The Clutha is fed by three major lakes— Wakatipu, Wanaka and Hawea. They contribute to the Clutha's average discharge into the Pacific Ocean of 650 cubic metres of water per second, more than any other river in the country.

The Clutha begins its journey to the sea when it slips away from the outlet of Lake Wanaka. This is a favourite spot for trout fishermen and both brown and rainbow trout are found between the outlet and Albert Town. In 1862 a whaleboat was used to cross the river to Albert Town, and ferries and punts operated there until the present bridge was opened in 1930. Above and below the bridge the water is blue and green like

▲The Clutha River rushes to meet the Kawarau below the township of Cromwell

▼The wild Cromwell Gorge was doomed when it was inundated by an artificial lake.

jade. Mature poplars, weeping willows, gorse, broom and matagouri line the banks.

The Hawea River joins the Clutha a few metres below the bridge and then flows in wide bends until just south of Luggate, where the basin narrows before opening out again beyond Queensberry. A spectacular sequence of river terraces near Luggate shows

how deeply the river has cut into the gravels. Three main levels are obvious, but six in all can be distinguished along the Clutha, Hawea and Kawarau rivers.

From Queensberry to Lowburn the river flows through perhaps the driest region in the Clutha basin; the farmland is poor, and scabweed, sorrel and harestail clover are common. The river broadens and the gravels have been extensively worked for gold. Parallel lines of tailings are visible near Lowburn and the most recent workings are white, with little or no vegetation. Dense willows inhabit the gravel flats where the river is braided.

Below Lowburn the older tailings are home to Californian poppy and sweet briar but these soon run out where the river rushes wildly into a narrow gorge a kilometre north of Cromwell. This little town has a most dramatic setting on a promontory at the confluence of the Clutha and Kawarau Rivers. To its north the blue and white-flecked buffer of the Pisa Range forms a backdrop and rises to 1961 m.

Much of the most interesting part of Cromwell has unfortunately disappeared beneath waters impounded by a high dam at Clyde. There has been considerable opposition to the scheme, although the campaign has not gained as much support as did the campaign to save Lake Manapouri. It has, however, highlighted the differences in outlook between those who value the Clutha for its

recreational and scenic attractions, and those who regard it primarily as a resource.

Until the waters rise, the 21 km down to Clyde is the wild and rocky Cromwell Gorge. The river accelerates, swirls and boils down the narrow defile, and is often coloured by sediment brought down by the Kawarau.

The road through the gorge is narrow, with a low stone wall on the river side. The bare Cairnmuir Mountains in the west and the Dunstan Mountains in the east rise to heights of about 1070 m and provide excellent shelter for the orchards along the east bank. A few hundred metres upstream from Clyde is the site of the dam. Scarred hillsides, dust and the roar of heavy earth-moving machinery defeat the voice of the river.

Clyde, originally known as The Dunstan, boomed after Horatio Hartley and Christopher Reilly struck gold south of Cromwell in 1862. By the end of that year 1984 kg (70 000 ounces) had been deposited in the Treasury at Dunedin. In the 1880s gold dredges began appearing and between 1890 and 1900, 30 were operating on the 10 km stretch of river from Clyde to Alexandra. By 1900, 187 dredges were working in Otago. Only a few remained after the 1930s; the last finished work on the Earnscleugh Flat in 1963.

Alexandra is situated on the north bank of the Clutha at its confluence with the Manuherikia River. The hydro-electricity storage lake formed by the 365 m-long, 76 m-high Roxburgh dam extends as far as Alexandra, 32 km upstream.

A smaller number of quinnat salmon continue to run up the Clutha from January to March each year and are sometimes caught where they congregate below the dam. From there on the river is broad, flowing with immense strength between banks thickly lined with willows.

Between Roxburgh and Dumbarton the river flows through a short shallow gorge before swinging across wide flats past Ettrick, where the remains of hundreds of moas were found, and on to Horseshoe Bend, 13 km below Millers Flat.

From Horsehoe Bend it is no more than 10 km down another gorge to Beaumont. Beyond Beaumont the Clutha leaves Central Otago behind. It flows on past stands of larches, glorious in autumn, and on through South Otago to the sea.

◄*The Cromwell Gorge, bleak and forbidding in winter, when the willows can no longer soften and colour the landscape with their foliage*

▼*The Clutha beyond Lake Wanaka, where it begins. It is a big river from the outset*

Ranges west and north of the dry core

Northwest of Alexandra, the Dunstan Mountains form a broad barrier between the basins of the Manukerikia River in the east and the upper Clutha in the West. The mountains provide good grazing for sheep during summer but for the rest of the year they are usually unstocked. Even in summer, snow can linger in shady hollows on the east face. Tors spot the crests and rolling tops, where peat bogs and swamps occur and subalpine plants grow. The mountains rise to over 1500 m, with Mt Makariri, towards the southwest end, reaching 1615 m.

To the south and west of Alexandra the Old Man Range stands guard against the worst of the foul weather from those quarters. In the stifling heat of summer its rippled slopes below 1500 m look inoffensive, but

▼*Snow can settle on the mountains of Central Otago at any time of the year. It was in February that this photograph of the Hawkdun Range was taken*

◄*Beneath the snow are the prickly dried-out flower heads of a wild plant called the teazle*

severe snowstorms can come at any time of the year. In 1863, such a storm resulted in an appalling loss of life, when 30 of a party of about 200 goldminers perished while retreating from the summit of the range.

From a distance the range looks barren but there is evidence that native forest once grew on the slopes. The whole range can be divided into four altitudinal zones—montane, from 150 m to 750 m, subalpine (750–1000 m), low alpine (1000–1450 m) and high alpine (1450–1695 m)—in which eight major vegetation types are recognisable.

All over the summits are tors, isolated rock

pinnacles standing up to 16 km above the bare crests. The range itself is named after Old Man Rock, a large tor standing 26.8 m above a base tapering to 8.5 m. According to Maori legend, the rock is *Kopuwai*, a giant able to step from one mountaintop to another, but in petrified form. Ten two-headed dogs lived with him. In retribution for his having captured a young girl whom he kept in his lair, a party set out and clubbed both Kopuwai and his freakish beasts to death.

The region around Alexandra is often described as the 'dry core' of Central Otago. Looking at uncultivated parts of the land-

scape today, one finds it hard to believe the reports of the earliest runholders, who wrote of luxuriant tussock and pockets of matagouri and manuka.

The rabbit can be blamed for the barren nature of much of the land. Once the hillsides were alive with them. Some landowners in desperation gave up traditional farming and farmed rabbits instead. Rabbits were released in Otago between 1864 and 1867.

They proved uncontrollable even by ferrets. Trapping became popular, and provided a lively export trade in skins but this declined after pest-destruction boards were established in the 1950s.

Sheep farming and arable cropping are vital to the area and patches of vivid green contrast with brown hills wherever water is diverted onto pastures. Fruit-growing is of primary importance around Alexandra, and

▲*The highlights on the Dunstan Mountains are heightened by winter snow. These ranges* *return to life after the thaw, when the snowbank-community plants bear flowers*

Clyde too has its orchards. One of the first commercial growers in the area was a Frenchman, Jean Désiré Feraud, who planted trees and grape vines in 1864 and irrigated his orchard with water from a miner's race. To the general surprise, he produced a passable wine.

Evidence of the frenzied search for gold is visible everywhere. Bare cliffs of yellow and white quartz gravel stand among sweet briar and wild thyme in Conroys Gully, southwest of Alexandra. Up the Manuherikia Valley, 61 km northeast of Alexandra, is the captivating tree-lined village of St Bathans, set close to the lip of Blue Lake, a crater 800 m long and over 50 m deep, gouged out by resolute sluicing for gold last century.

The western slopes of the Dunstan Mountains, about 26 km northeast of Cromwell, bear the remains of long-abandoned goldmining centres—Bendigo, Logantown and Welshtown. As the alluvial mining ran out, some of the richest gold-bearing quartz reefs in the country were discovered there. When quartz mining declined in the 1870s, so did the towns and they were virtually dead by the end of the century.

Twisting gorge of a violent, turbid river

►*This spectacular and spiky flower belongs to a plant with lance-like leaves which is to be encountered in tussock grassland. A member of the carrot family, it is called a spaniard*

The Kawarau is a brawling, tempestuous river which flows through one of the most uncompromising gorges in Central Otago. Its name—literally meaning 'many rapids' —is mispronounced 'K'worra' by many people in the district, but not out of disrespect, for it is a river that commands awe. It contributes about 35 per cent of the total flow of the Clutha River, as recorded at Cromwell, where the two great rivers merge. At the entrance to the Cromwell Gorge, the muddy green waters of the Kawarau join the clear Clutha. The sinister colour of the Kawarau is due to sediment from the Arrow and Shotover Rivers, upstream near Queenstown.

Nearly half the 63 km journey from Cromwell to Queenstown is through the twisting, narrow and sometimes frosty Kawarau Gorge. Before the gorge begins at Ripponvale, a road on the outskirts of Cromwell turns left and crosses the Kawarau to Bannockburn. Today Bannockburn consists of a stone church and a few houses, but in the late 1860s up to 2000 people lived there, most of them involved in sluicing for gold on the flats near the town. When the gold was exhausted these miners moved onto the barren slopes of the Carrick Range, no more than 7 km away, to work the quartz reefs. It is a steady 4 km climb, needing reasonable fitness, up to the site of their Carricktown, where mullock heaps mark the positions of mine holes, the remains of stamper batteries lie scattered like rusty fossils and the ruins of stone cottages squat among rocky outcrops.

The men who searched for gold in Central Otago left behind them many stony wastes. Some of these have been colonised by introduced plants hardy enough to cope with the rigours of a climate in which bitterly cold winters alternate with hot dry summers. Garden thyme, wonderfully fragrant when trodden, occupies many hectares in places. Sweet briar, now that there are few rabbits to crop its young shoots, has become a troublesome weed, and foxgloves abound.

Sweet briar, poplars and matagouri grow together near an automatic power house

◄*The Roaring Meg, said to have been named after a loud-voiced redhead who tended a bar on the* *goldfields, rampages towards the Kawarau Gorge. It passes through a power station before it joins the Kawarau*

where the Roaring Meg bursts out of the southern end of the Pisa Range, about 10 km up the gorge. When Meg is in full spate water jets from the power house as if from a huge fire hose. In frosty weather the roadway for several kilometres on either side of the Roaring Meg ices up and demands extreme care.

Not far upstream from the Roaring Meg is a jumble of rocks where the river is pinched into its narrowest point. They mark the remains of a 'natural bridge' first used by Maoris. Twenty-three year old Nathaniel Chalmers used the bridge in 1853 on the way to becoming the first white man to see Lakes Wanaka and Hawea and in the 1860s miners crossed it. It later collapsed.

The road today travels much the same route as that followed by drays and pack-horses, and then coaches in the 1860s. It was a hazardous trip. The route followed the north bank to the Nevis punt; the south bank to another punt-crossing near Gibbston, and on as far as a punt over the Lower Shotover. Bridging came later; the Shotover was spanned near Arthur's Point in 1875, the Kawarau at Nevis Ferry—Victoria Bridge today—in 1878, and at Gibbston in 1880.

About a kilometre downstream from the Victoria Bridge, the Nevis River flows in from the south through a narrow gorge. The Nevis runs northeast from its sources in the Hector and Garvie Mountains down a valley bounded by the Remarkables on the west and the Garvie and Carrick Ranges on the east, before joining the Kawarau River. The Nevis Valley must be approached with the utmost care, for the road is poor and the silences of this empty region are barely endurable to some.

After the road passes under the massive blastings of the Nevis Bluff it crosses the river on a bridge built above an old suspension bridge. The old bridge, built in 1880, is preserved as a historic landmark. The Kawarau Gorge now opens out onto the tree-studded pastoral flats at Gibbston. The Arrow basin is a little beyond, and it is a relief to leave the gorge and the malevolent river behind.

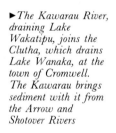

►The Kawarau River, draining Lake Wakatipu, joins the Clutha, which drains Lake Wanaka, at the town of Cromwell. The Kawarau brings sediment with it from the Arrow and Shotover Rivers

Lake with a beating heart

►*The heights of the Richardson Mountains loom over Queenstown, which lies beyond the little peninsula*

The name Wakatipu means 'space where the demon lies' and a Maori myth attempts to explain the making of the lake. A demon captured the lovely daughter of a Maori chief and took her to his mountain home. Exhausted by struggling against a wild nor'wester, he lay down to sleep with his head at Glenorchy, his knees at Queenstown and his feet at Kingston. The girl's lover stole up and set fire to the demon, whose flaming fat burnt deep into the earth. All that remained was his odious heart, beating in a trench which, as rain fell and snows melted, filled with water in the shape of the evil giant, and began to oscillate and pulsate.

The lake still pulsates, but the more prosaic European has determined that these natural oscillations of the water, called 'seiches', are caused by wind or variations in atmospheric pressure. At Bob's Cove, some 15 km west of Queenstown, a transverse seiche creates a maximum variation in the level every 4.5 minutes; over the whole length of the lake it takes about 51 minutes.

The Z-shaped lake is 77.2 km long and covers an area of 293 km². Only Lake Te Anau in the South Island and Lake Taupo in the north are larger in New Zealand. It is 4.8 km across at its widest point and plunges to a depth of 378 m—which is 68 m below sea level. The depth is surprisingly constant, except for the expected shelving at the head of the lake. Lake Wakatipu lies in the valley of an ancient glacier which built up a terminal moraine at Kingston, blocking the outlet down the Mataura River valley. All round the lake sharp broken summits reach above glacier-rounded hills.

The town of Queenstown rests in the shelter of Queenstown Bay at the junction of the south and central arms of Lake Wakatipu. Queenstown Hill, 900 m high, provides a view of the lake. The Remarkables rise up beyond the Frankton arm, and swinging west towards the Eyre Mountains, the Cecil and

▲*The Frankton arm of Lake Wakatipu. The Kawarau River flows out of the lake at the head of this arm*

►*The Rees (right) and Dart Rivers (left) flow into the head of Lake Wakatipu, separated by Mt Alfred and, beyond the* *Mt Earnslaw massif. Between Alfred and Earnslaw is the resort of Paradise, on the shore of the beautiful Diamond Lake*

Walter Peaks stand out. Ben Lomond rises to 1732 m, cloaked in tussock and other native grasses, herbs and small shrubs. It is possible to leave Queenstown around midnight in summer and scramble to the summit of Ben Lomond to watch the suffusion of colour as the sun rises over The Remarkables and lights up the glaciers and spire of Mt Aspiring in the north.

The drive to Glenorchy, 50 km away at the head of the lake, is rewarding. Unsealed for most of the way, the road skirts the lake or climbs high above it, negotiating rock bluffs covered with native bush and scrub.

After 7 km a narrow, steep, unsealed road—dangerous in wet weather—leads off to the right over a low saddle for another 7 km until it reaches the small Lake Kilpatrick and its larger neighbour Moke Lake. Patches of beech forest grow in side valleys and in summer buttercups and daisies appear.

Eventually the Glenorchy road swings north and 25 km on there is a magnificent view of the mountains, bush and valleys at the head of the lake. From the shoulder nearby the Pig and Pigeon Islands can be seen and Mt Bonpland and the Humboldt Mountains to the northwest. Straight ahead the icy towers of Mt Earnslaw rise—the East Peak to 2819 m and the West to 2793 m.

A land of golden autumns and white winters

The Remarkables are a sierra-like range rising steeply above the eastern side of the south arm of Lake Wakatipu. The highest point of the serrate skyline is the 2343 m peak of Double Cone. The shattered crumbling rock of the westward-facing ridges and gullies was shaped by the glacier which gouged out the trench now filled by Lake Wakatipu.

Northeast and out of sight behind the peaks of Double Cone is the small, icy and remote Lake Alta, which nestles in a cirque at a height of about 1830 m. Lake Alta can be

▲*The Remarkables, whether bare in summer or snow-covered in winter are among the most celebrated sights of Central Otago*

▶*Introduced trees are virtually the only trees in Central Otago and in autumn the deciduous species provide spectacular displays of colour*

reached by fit, experienced climbers by way of the moderate northern slopes of The Remarkables and the Rastus Burn. The view from Double Cone is extraordinary—mountains and valleys on every side. Mts Earnslaw and Aspiring to the northwest, the blue waters of the lake below, and far away to the north, Mt Cook.

There are few more photogenic lakes in the region than Lake Hayes, fringed by exotic trees and set in the shallow trough about 15 km east of Queenstown. The Maori called the lake *Wai-whakaata*—'water that reflects objects'. Its European name is derived not from the Australian stockman Donald Hay, who is thought to have discovered it in 1859, but from the legendary blackbirder and pirate 'Bully' Hayes (1832-77), who was on the Arrow goldfields in 1863.

Lake Hayes is a wildlife refuge noted for its breeding of Australian coots, sooty-black and dark-grey birds about 380 mm long. Scaup, pukekos and the secretive marsh crake also live around the lake fringes, and brown trout and perch lurk in its waters.

Arrowtown, 21 km northeast of Queenstown on the west bank of the Arrow River, dates back to the ecstatic days of 1862, when William Fox discovered gold. An undulating old road leads up the Arrow Gorge to Macetown. It is 10 km long and has numerous river-crossings; the best part of a fine day is needed to walk in and out. A few stone walls, fruit trees, rose bushes, and other exotics remain among the lush grasses as relics of the period when 3000 hopeful souls endured winters there in the 1860s before the gold gave out and they steadily moved away.

The climate in the Arrow basin is a little moister than in the basins further east because of the proximity to Lake Wakatipu, The Remarkables and other high ranges a little farther north and west. The landscape is more varied and the soils less arid than in many eastern areas; in addition, pockets of beech forest can be seen in a few of the side valleys, and these things enhance the character and appeal of the area around Lake Hayes.

▶*First snow of winter on the Remarkables. In summer this region is warm and sunny, but in winter the weather is often bitterly cold*

Lonely mountains where gold-seekers once toiled

◄*The Shotover River was named not with any allusion to its wild nature, but after a property in gentle Oxfordshire, England*

There are times when it is uncannily still in the country to the north and west of the Pisa Range, a burly chain of block mountains extending northeast between the Cardrona and Upper Clutha valleys. To the east of the central ridge, Mt Pisa rises 1961 m as the highest point and snow lies high in cirques on the east face for most of the year. Tors up to 16 m in height crown its tops.

There is a 70 km scenic route from Wanaka to Queenstown via the Cardrona Valley and the Crown Range, most of it over an unsealed and unsettling road which is closed in winter. The Cardrona Valley is terraced and open in its lower reaches, where 5.5 km west of Wanaka there is a memorable view of Mt Aspiring soaring to 3027 m in the north. The road winds on through the valley to reach Cardrona, 26 km from Wanaka.

Gold was discovered there in 1862 and mining went on until the early 1900s. On the nearby Criffel Range are the remains of one of the highest significant goldfields in New Zealand. It was mined in the early 1880s. Water was scarce and conditions were bitter at 1220 m, yet those who toiled there obtained good returns.

A few kilometres past Cardrona the valley narrows. Steep tussock-covered slopes rise on either side and the river, now a stream, chatters close by. After a stiff climb, the narrow road reaches the pass over the Crown Range, 40 km from Wanaka and at 1121 m the highest main road in New Zealand. Crown Peak at 1729 m is the highest point on the range trending north from the pass. The view from the pass is startling—the Kawarau River green and slithering far below—but it is not until the road winds steeply down to Crown Terrace, above the Arrow Basin, that the magnificent panorama of lake, mountain, river and sky can be fully absorbed.

An even more nerve-wracking road runs from Queenstown to Skippers in the Shotover River valley—29 km of narrow and unsealed road with few passing places and many precipitous drops—but it is now closed to private cars. After crossing a saddle, the road winds down Long Gully, past the striking sentinel Lighthouse Rock towards the ribbed and quilted Richardson Mountains, until it swings north on a terrace overlooking the gorge of the Shotover River.

Mica schist flashes like semaphore from

◄ *The Criffel Range, on the western side of the Cardrona Valley, was the site of gold mining in the 1880s. The range reaches an altitude of 1339 m*

the scarred hills and the river is a vindictive force in the gorge below. Some people have to steel themselves to cross the Skippers suspension bridge, which hangs 100 m above the river. In the 1860s as many as 700 people lived and worked there but the miners gave little thought to the wild beauty of the place; they endured it for the sake of the gold.

Deer and goats infested the Harris Mountains, east of Skippers, and the Richardson Mountains until the 1970s, when they were drastically culled. They had added seriously to the erosion in the Shotover catchment. A phenomenal amount of sediment is carried down by both the Shotover and Arrow rivers and this contributes to the silting-up of the Roxburgh dam on the Clutha. From Arthur's Point it is possible to travel up and down Shotover Gorge by various sorts of tourist craft, but it is not a river to take lightly.

► *No road enters the Pisa Range, which runs northward from the Kawarau Gorge. It was named because a rocky outcrop was thought to resemble the leaning tower of Pisa*

▼ *The notorious Skippers road terrified many motorists until it was closed to private traffic. There is still the Crown Range road for those who enjoy narrow roads winding above precipices*

Bare, tussocky hills of the Lindis Pass

◀Erosion-scarred
mountains and tussocky
valleys are the essence
of the Lindis Pass

The Maoris were familiar with the Lindis
Pass, which links the Waitaki basin and
Mackenzie Country with Central Otago,
long before the Europeans discovered it.
Hunters and those on their way inland in
search of greenstone used the pass.

The Otago surveyor John Turnbull
Thomson was the first European to discover
the Lindis route. He went that way on 17
December 1857 and named the pass after the
island of Lindisfarne, off the coast of North-
umberland in England.

To the south of the pass Old Man Peak
rises to 1827 m, the highest point in the Dunstan Mountains, while in the north, Longslip
Mountain rises with pleasing symmetry to
1247 m. Omarama is 32 km to the northeast
and Tarras 40 km southwest.

From Tarras the road passes over open
downs and level, dry country, thence through
the picturesque Lindis Gorge to the famous
Morven Hills Station, and then up the steady
climb for about 15 km to the pass itself.

The view from·the pass is remarkable—
tussock-clothed mountains rising to tops
scarred and eroded by snow, wind and rain.
Longslip Creek wriggles off to join the
Ahuriri River in the north.

According to a Professor Morris who went
through the Lindis Pass by coach in the early
1890s, it was 'a tolerably continuous climb'
during which the scenery changed 'from the
pretty to the grand' but the whole ascent was
'far too treeless for perfect beauty'. Mata-

▲The harrier, or
hawk, preys on other
birds and rabbits in
the Lindis Pass region
and its grasslands

▼Spectacular clouds
often float above the
Lindis Pass ranges
and cast dramatic
shadows on them

▲The Lindis Pass, the
northern gateway to
Central Otago, is bare,
lonely country, far from
settlements. Snow is
likely to dust the
mountaintops at any
time of the year.

gouri and sweet briar grow in the Lindis Valley and willows gird the stream but otherwise there is little substantial vegetation.

There are few birds to be seen but visitors who move off the road and remain inconspicuous may be lucky enough to see a chukor or a New Zealand falcon. The fiercely territorial falcon in this terrain derives most of its food by preying on the pipit. A piercing whistle or shrill scream means a falcon is on the wing.

Prospectors looked for gold in the Lindis area and in 1861 Samuel McIntyre and 40 others claimed a reward from the Government for discovering a payable field in the Lindis Valley at Goodger Flat. It was a complete failure and McIntyre's claim was shelved. But if the pickings were thin for the miners, prospects looked good for run-holders. John McLean was farming on the Canterbury plains when a passing Maori told him of vast uninhabited tracts of open country in the interior farther south. McLean set off to see for himself in the autumn of 1858 and upon meeting the chief Te Huruhura got him to guide him to the pass. McLean was mightily pleased by what he saw—unending tussock country offering limitless scope for the sheep man.

After a struggle with the authorities, who were reluctant to lease a vast area of land to a single applicant, John McLean and his brother Allan were given approval to manage and develop four runs amounting to 161 844 hectares. The huge run was called the Morven Hills Station, after the hills facing the Isle of Man. In 1874, when the McLeans sold out, the sheep numbered 135 154, an impressive count anywhere.

Undoubtedly the most impressive of the rambling station buildings is a massive stone woolshed from the early 1870s. Social distinctions were rigidly observed and two doors stood side by side, one for the boss, the other for the men.

Morven Hills is about 15 km on the southern side of the pass over which, last century, teams of 14 bullocks hauled wagons loaded with up to 30 bales of wool. The teams usually travelled three at a time for mutual support while crossing streams and bogs.

Near the summit a monument commemorates the centenary of the liberation of red deer in Otago. The seven deer freed in the vicinity were shipped from Scotland by the Earl of Dalhousie. They quickly spread north, south, east and west with devastating effect.

Fiordland National Park

The wildest, wettest and most isolated part of New Zealand is Fiordland, in the extreme southwest of the South Island. There mountain and water join in forming a dramatic landscape

In the west, fingers of the Tasman Sea probe a precipitous coast. In the east a string of lakes with lyrical Maori names partly separates the region from the drier expanse of Southland. Three rivers, the Hollyford, Eglinton and Waiau complete this boundary.

The broad southern coast faces the western entrance to Foveaux Strait, the 'famous and dreaded Solander whaling ground' of the last century, where the gales and seas of the Roaring Forties beat up on the shore. It is a run of some 200 km from there to Martins Bay, a sandy beach, after which the seaward precipices fade into a blander landscape.

The western heights are greatly affected by the winds of the Roaring Forties and rain falls in almost unbelievable amounts—

7274 mm a year on average at Milford Sound, for example. Fiordland is one of the wettest places on earth. This rainfall nourishes the rich Fiordland forest—largely of small-leaved, evergreen native beech—which throws a rather sombre cloak over the land up to the tree-line about 1000 m.

Within the forest, the damp air and soil sustain a rich, shaded undergrowth of ferns and mosses, lianas, creepers, shrubs and lesser trees. Higher, nearer the tree-line, stunted beech, leatherwood, and mountain fuchsia survive, their branches draped with a straggly lichen called old man's beard. It gives the forest an air of incredible antiquity.

The land rises steadily from south to north, reaching its most spectacular form in the precipices, icefalls and summits of the Darran Mountains. During an ice age which ended 15 000 years ago, glaciers ground out perpendicular-walled troughs. On the west coast these became fiords as the sea rose with the melting of the ice. In the east the glaciers deepened the basins of the larger lakes.

But if this last spectacular shaping was in recent geological times, the rock beneath is much, much older. Most of it was laid down under the sea as sediment about 400 million years ago. It was later hardened by pressure and heat deep in the Earth's crust to produce the metamorphic rocks that form much of Fiordland today—crystalline granites, banded gneisses, serpentine, quartzite and marble—and then folded and uplifted. Injections of molten rock from below form the rock of Darran Mountains, and the peaks west of Lakes Te Anau and Manapouri.

Then all this land was submerged again for some 40 million years—until it was sharply uplifted about 2 million years ago—during which more sediments were deposited, among them the limestone now visible along the shores of the eastern lakes. But most of these sedimentary rocks have been worn away, exposing older schists and gneisses, themselves now greatly eroded.

▼*It is northern and central Fiordland that tourists and trampers see. The wilderness farther south is rarely visited by anyone*

Martins Bay
Lake McKerrow
Darran Mtns
Hollyford Valley
Mt Tutoko
Mitre Peak ● ●Milford
Tasman Sea
Sutherland Falls
Sutherland Sound
Bligh Sound
Lake Ada
Milford Track
Mackinnon Pass ●Mt Balloon
George Sound
Caswell Sound
Charles Sound
Nancy Sound
Thompson Sound
Murchison Mtns
Lake Te Anau
HIGHWAY 94
Doubtful Sound
Kepler Mtns
●Te Anau
Dagg Sound
Lake Manapouri
Wilmot Pass
●Manapouri
Breaksea Sound
Hunter Mtns
Waiau River
Resolution Island
Dark Cloud Range
Lake Monowai
Dusky Sound
Cameron Mtns
Lake Hauroko
Chalky Inlet
Lake Poteriteri
Preservation Inlet

►*Fiordland valleys have broad, flat floors and nearly vertical walls—the classic U-shape that is the inevitable result of glacial scouring*

At the door of the wilderness, a lake with fiords

▶ *The flightless takahe, thought extinct for more than 50 years, was rediscovered in the Murchison Mountains, in 1948. Entry to the area is prohibited*

Lake Te Anau is the largest lake in the South Island. It is 340 km² in area and 66 km in length, and has an indented shoreline of about 500 km. Three large arms, the South, Middle and North Fiords, push west from the main body of the lake into the mountains. The Maori name for the lake is said to derive from the grand-daughter of one of the chiefs who discovered it, perhaps around the year 900. But a hint that the true name of the lake was Te Ana-au, 'rushing waters in a cave', led

▶ *Rich forest in the Lake Te Anau district extends as far as the eye can see*

to the discovery, in the 1940s, of the Te Ana-au glow worm caves.

The caves are a half-hour journey by launch from Te Anau township across the lake to the base of the Murchison Mountains, between South and Middle Fiords. The journey underground is made partly by track and partly by boats pulled along a wire. In the deepest part of the cave the blue lights of a myriad glow worms can be seen on the roof.

Higher up in the Murchison Mountains is

the last refuge of one of New Zealand's flightless birds, the takahe, which had been believed to be extinct until it was rediscovered in 1948. In the snow grass valleys, which are closed to the public, there are 100-200 takahe, but the number seems to be declining. Attempts to breed the takahe in captivity have been only moderately successful. It is a sombre experience to stand on the eastern lake shore in the evening, to look up at the high castellated silhouette of the Murchison peaks, and think of these few survivors of millions of years of evolution, scrabbling for food among the snow grass, nearing the end of the slow path to extinction.

During a scientific expedition to this region in the early 1950s, another interesting find was made. Under a rock shelter clearly used by prehistoric hunters was found the pelvic bone of a small moa. This bore evidence of cuts made by something sharp—a metal implement, according to one scientific opinion of the day, no longer accepted. If correct, it would have implied that some who had gone there were not prehistoric hunters but men who had encountered Europeans, and that at least one species of moa might have survived into historic times. Scientific advances in dating such material should eventually lead to an accurate dating of the bone, but the chances of any moas surviving now are nil. In spite of the terrain, every part of Fiordland has been crossed by man at some recent time.

Te Anau has the air of a frontier town. It could be nothing else, with the wilderness of Fiordland so near across the lake. Approaching from the east, the road slips between low, rolling hills and ahead the Fiordland peaks seem very close, without a hint of intervening water. Then abruptly the hills flatten, the road turns down a long slope, and lake and township suddenly lie ahead.

The town takes its prosperity largely from two disparate sources—tourism and deer. Late last century and early this century four kinds of deer—red deer, axis deer, wapiti and moose—were liberated in several parts of Fiordland. The axis deer may be extinct, the moose have not flourished, wapiti took a firm hold, but the red deer multiplied explosively. Many today can tell of the time when herds of deer grazed, like cattle on a ranch, in the high Fiordland valleys. In the 1920s, care-

fully protected red deer made havoc of the bush, accelerated erosion in a land of high rainfall and, through over-population, deteriorated physically. By the 1950s, when the animals must have numbered hundreds of thousands, they were declared vermin, and hunted for a bounty and their skins.

Then in the 1960s the European market for venison opened, and the demand was great. Prices were high and good livings were made by men working from isolated bush camps. The latest in the long line of exploiters and entrepreneurs of Fiordland, they followed sealers, whalers, and diggers for gold. But the 'meat-hunters' did more good for the region. For the first time in a generation the deer were reduced to reasonable numbers, and on slopes and in valleys the beleaguered vegetation started to thicken.

Now deer farming is a growing industry in New Zealand, and breeding stock has come from the wild animals of the hills. Riding helicopters, equipped with sophisticated nets and tranquilliser guns, the modern hunters ride the Fiordland ranges, plucking out the deer from thinner patches of bush, or wherever they are rash enough to venture in daylight. It is a hazardous occupation and helicopter crashes are almost commonplace. In 1989 the price for a deer was $400, but in the heady days of the deer 'cowboys', the prices soared as high as $1000. The war on the deer has been a good thing for the land.

▲ *The Dome Lakes and Dome Islands at the entrance to the South Fiord of Lake Te Anau. The distant ranges are the Livingstone Mountains*

▼ *Worsley Arm, one of the two extended arms at the head of Lake Te Anau. It is on the* eastern side of the *lake, at the mouth of the Clinton River, the Milford Track begins*

'Lake of a hundred islands' saved by popular protest

From 50 km to the east of Lake Te Anau, the peaks of Fiordland are discernible as a dark erratic frieze against the western sky. Distinctive amongst them is one that seems nearly perpendicular on its northern side. The first Europeans to see it, Charles Nairn and W. H. Stephen, sketched it in January 1852 as overhanging. 'Both Nairn and Stephen assure me that the overhanging peaks in the sketch are

▼*Hope Arm is one of four named arms of Lake Manapouri. The lake covers an area of 142 km² and reaches a depth of 433 m. The only deeper lake in New Zealand is Lake Hauroko, which lies farther south in Fiordland National Park*

literally true,' commented one authority after they returned from their journey. 'Unfortunately neither can inform me what rock it is which indulges in such absurd antics.' The peak was in fact Leaning Peak, which rises above the lake now called Manapouri. Lake Manapouri is well known to New Zealanders, even if most have never seen it. It is New Zealand's second-deepest lake, with soundings down to 433 m. It is often said to be New Zealand's most beautiful lake. If this is an unproveable claim in a land of beautiful lakes, there is no doubt that the summer traveller, arriving along the rather dry, dusty

eastern shore, looks suddenly out on an expanse of water of great beauty passing in the distance into the recesses of the hills of Fiordland. Even on the most brilliant summer days Lake Manapouri seems to emanate an atmosphere of brooding beauty, perhaps just drawn from the reflection of the dark bush around the waters.

The name is a corruption of *manawapora*, which means 'sorrowing heart', and there are Maori stories to suit. But that name belonged to another lake and was applied to Manapouri by a cartographer's error. The correct Maori name, as Nairn noted in his sketch, is

◄*Lake Manapouri's eastern shoreline is intricate. Forested islands dot the waters and give Manapouri a charm that is unique to it among the lakes of the South Island*

▼*Skeletons of drowned trees remain to tell of the destruction wrought in 1925, when the level of Lake Monowai was raised to permit the generation of hydro-electric power*

the equally appropriate *Moturau*, 'lake of a hundred islands'.

But to none of these things does Manapouri owe its particular place in the consciousness of New Zealanders. It might have continued to be known vaguely just as an attractive southern lake had not a proposal been put forward in the early 1960s to raise its level to generate hydro-electric power.

The map tells the story of Lake Manapouri's potential for generating hydro-electric power. In a straight line, the West Arm of Manapouri is separated from the easternmost extremity of Doubtful Sound by a mere 10 km, with an intervening ridge rising 670 m above sea level. The waters of the lake are 200 m above the level of the sea. No firm proposal to utilise this natural facility was made until 1959, when the establishment of an aluminium smelter in the South Island was projected, based on power from Manapouri. This entailed raising the level of the lake by damming its outlet.

Farther south on this fringe of Fiordland there was already a sad example of the consequences of such a project. A dam was built at the outlet of Lake Monowai in the 1920s, and the dead, grey trunks of the drowned bush still protrude like ugly accusing fingers from the lake's edge. The prospect of this being repeated at Manapouri proved unacceptable to New Zealanders in general.

The resulting debate provoked a great protest petition to Parliament and one of the significant protest movements of the 1960s in New Zealand. To some it marks the point at which New Zealanders, becoming aware of how little of the original landscape of the country was left, stood up and said: 'Stop here and consider.' To others it marks the start of a campaign for conservation that has hindered the country's necessary economic development. The debate is probably unending. But Manapouri, this sombre, beautiful lake far removed from the centres of population, was the first battleground.

Eventually the scheme went ahead, but without the raising of the lake. There is a dam on the Waiau River below the lake to control the natural outflow and, while some fluctuation in level does occur, Manapouri has largely preserved its form and shoreline.

The power project was eight years in construction, and formidable engineering problems were encountered. In places the conditions, and the technology required to deal with them, were unique, such as the plugging of water channels in the often unstable rock of the deep tunnels against the pressure of water coursing down through hundreds of metres of rock. Tunnelling proceeded from both east and west, and at Deep Cove, in Doubtful Sound, the workers were housed in the old trans-Tasman liner *Wanganella*.

From the intake at West Arm, seven penstocks take the water vertically down to turbines in a powerhouse 213 m below lake level, from where the water is discharged along a 10 km long tailrace tunnel, out to the sea at Deep Cove. The peak power output from this scheme is about 700 megawatts.

After all the controversy, the aesthetic and ecological results seem to be acceptable, and there are gains. The trip from Manapouri township across the lake to the power complex is well worth taking. At West Arm a coach takes the visitor down, down beside the unseen vertical penstocks with their plunge of water, to the powerhouse. The gradient of the tunnel is about one in ten, hewn through metamorphic gneisses initially laid down under the sea 400 million years ago. In the powerhouse, with its bare rock-hewn walls, are seven turbines, the heart of the whole scheme. The air is chill in this great cavern, and the traveller can feel that he has really glimpsed the bowels of the earth.

Then the bus grinds its way up again, out into the sunlight, climbing even higher to Wilmot Pass, 670 m above sea level. From the pass too there is a superb view of Doubtful Sound, winding between mountains towards the open sea. A steep descent, in only 7 km, leads to the valley of the Lyvia River and Deep Cove. There the waters of the tailrace tunnel churn out to sea. Across the head of the sound are the splendid Helena Falls. Man's little effort at construction seems puny in these surroundings.

Seldom-visited sounds of the southwest

▲*Walking in the Fiordland forest*

▼*A frozen lake high in the mountains near Doubtful Sound*

Doubtful Sound stretches to the west for 20 km between the mountains, to the Hare's Ears Rocks and the open sea. Few tourists see this part of Fiordland, a rock-bound coast, broken by a dozen fiords which become larger and more intricate farther south.

Captain Cook named 'Doubtful Harbour' in 1769, on his first voyage, because he was doubtful of the ability of the HMS *Endeavour* to enter and leave such a narrow entrance safely. Of the value of Dusky Sound, farther south, he was more certain: '. . . it is about 3 or 4 miles broad at the entrance and seems to be as full as deep. In it are several islands behind which there must be shelter from all winds, provided there is sufficient depth of water.' Of this he need not have worried. Most of the fiords reach depths over 200 m.

On the second voyage in 1772, Cook brought HMS *Resolution* into Dusky Sound, to refresh his men and repair the ship. Viewed from the sea, Dusky Sound remains as Cook saw it, except for a navigation beacon on the south headland. As always, Cook recorded meticulously the major features of landscape and wildlife, and he charted most of this extensive harbour.

The Polynesian forbears of the modern Maoris were already settled on the shores of the Foveaux Strait by 1200, and there is evidence that even the ferocious Fiordland coast did not intimidate them. They came in their canoes, exploring, camping at favourable sites and making one or two settlements.

But the Europeans who followed Cook were more exploiters than explorers. Sealing ships from New South Wales began landing gangs along the Fiordland coast in the 1790s. Their prize was the skin of the vulnerable southern fur seal.

The first known sealing gang to visit Dusky Sound was landed at Luncheon Cove in 1792 and isolated there for some ten months. In that time they collected only 4500 seal skins, which was regarded as poor work, but they were perhaps distracted by their construction of the first vessel of European type to be built in New Zealand. Subsequently named *Providence*, she was 16 m long. Three years later, with a motley crew of sailors, sealers, stowaways, and escaped convicts, she sailed to Norfolk Island and Sydney.

By the 1820s the sealers had nearly exterminated their prey from the Fiordland coast.

▶*Maori legend says a goddess created the biting sandfly (here greatly magnified) so that humans would not become too bold through enjoying the Fiordland landscape, which a god had made*

▲*Fiordland crested penguins breed only on the coast of Fiordland*

◄*Nearly vertical mountainsides plunge into the waters of Doubtful Sound. In this sound is a cataract called the Browne Falls, which drops 836 m*

▼*Several islands stud the entrance to Doubtful Sound. One of them, Secretary Island, separates Doubtful and Thompson Sounds*

Only now, a century and a half later, are large colonies of seals starting to flourish on some of the isolated low headlands. After the sealers came the whalers, seeking the southern right whale on its summer migration to Antarctica. The whalers used Preservation Inlet particularly. The southernmost fiord, it was closest to the great whaling grounds of Foveaux Strait. Then the whales went the way of the seals, and the camps were left to the encroaching bush.

Perhaps Fiordland would be spared further exploitation. The land was impossible. 'Not soil enough to nourish a potato,' noted Captain J. L. Stokes of HMS *Acheron*, on the hydrographic survey of the region in 1850. The steep highlands grow little timber suitable for milling. One visitor concluded that the region would remain 'a safe retreat for the distressed mariner, or where the man of science can retire for a while and examine

into the mysteries of nature and where the tourist can wander amongst scenes of beauty and grandeur which may be paralleled but hardly excelled'.

But at the end of the century the peace was broken by the discovery of gold in Preservation Inlet. Crushing batteries were set up, a town grew to a thousand people, with a store, a school and a pub. In 1898 the Gold Star Mine on the south shore of Preservation produced 58.3 kg of gold. Then the reefs ran out, the settlement faded, and ten years later the bush had returned.

Thereafter the Fiordland coast remained exceedingly isolated for nearly half a century, until after World War II. Then the crayfish of the coast began to be exploited and Fiordland has remained a major New Zealand crayfish fishery ever since. Catches have declined with the years, but rising prices have maintained profitability. Fortunately the

wild seas, dangerous coast and unpredictable weather of the region ensure that even if all sensible fishing regulations are ignored, this resource can never be worked out.

Other men, unusual men, have come to this coast for more altruistic reasons, out of an interest in some aspect of nature out there. Notable amongst these was Richard Henry, who between 1894 and 1900 transported many flightless birds, particularly kakapos and kiwis, to Resolution Island in Dusky Sound. He hoped they would flourish there, free from the stoats and other introduced vermin that were threatening to make them extinct on the mainland. He abandoned his task when he discovered that vermin could indeed swim and were establishing themselves on Resolution Island. 'I am very sorry to say I saw a weasel on Resolution', he wrote in his diary. And, months later: 'I feel I cannot stay here much longer.'

Over the Mackinnon Pass to Milford Sound

▼*Glacier action shaped the steep walls of the immense Clinton Canyon. The first stage of the Milford Track is along the canyon's floor*

It is not really clear who coined the epithet 'the finest walk in the world' for the Milford Track, but perhaps a telegram sent by Thomas Mackenzie, a Fiordland explorer and politician of unusual accomplishment, suggested it: 'The overland route to the Sutherland Falls and Milford Sound will be practicable in summer after cutting a track. The scenery is simply magnificent.'

Today the Milford Road approaches Te Anau township along the drier eastern shore of the lake. The Fiordland heights across the water gather most of the rain and the poor stony soil of the eastern side supports bracken, manuka scrub, and only the occasional patch of dry beech forest. After about 25 km the road turns down to the deep semi-circular boat harbour to Te Anau Downs, where launches leave during the summer months for the two-hour trip to Glade House, at the head of the lake.

For many years the 55 km Milford Track was open only to guided parties, who stayed overnight in Tourist Hotel Corporation huts, but now it is also available to un-guided 'freedom walkers', who carry all their own supplies and stay in Fiordland National Park huts. However well guided, no one should take the Milford Track lightly. It runs through a landscape as rugged as any in the world, and is renowned for fickle weather and torrential rain. Moderate fitness, stout footwear and a really good waterproof are basic requirements.

The Milford Track can be walked comfortably by trampers of average fitness in four days and three nights. From Glade House, the track crosses a new suspension bridge to the west bank of the Clinton River. From the bridge to the Clinton Forks, where the north branch of the river comes in, is an easy two-hour walk, passing through moss-festooned bush which is like something from a mediaeval fairy tale.

Above Clinton Forks the valley narrows, and at Hirere Falls there is a shelter, the THC lunch hut. The sheer walls of the glacial valley rise through bush to mossy rock and, high above, patches of snow. Then the track passes through bush again before opening into scrub at Hidden Lake. The Mackinnon Pass can now be seen at the head of the valley, with Mt Balloon towering to the east. The track climbs through rocky country

◄*The Milford Track winds across the top of the Mackinnon Pass, watched by Mt Hart in background and a kea in the foreground*

▲*Mt Balloon, 1829 m high, rises to the east of the Mackinnon Pass*

▼*An unnamed cirque lake typical of glaciated mountain country and common to Fiordland*

overgrown with bush to reach Pompolona Hut. This is the end of the first day for those walking in luxury, but the freedom walkers have another hour to the Lake Mintaro Hut.

Beyond Mintaro on the second day, valley and track swing westward, and the infant Clinton River is crossed. The track doubles back to the foot of the Mackinnon Pass and the climb now really begins, a long zigzag progress, up and up. Now there is only snow-grass, scattered with blue and red berries of gaultheria and coprosma, and white mountain buttercups. Wekas skulk in the snow-grass and keas turn and call harshly in the sky. It comes almost as a surprise when the track flattens out on the top of the pass, and northern Fiordland lies displayed.

Looking back, the immensity of the Clinton Canyon can be realised. Cut out by ice 15 000 or more years ago, it lay for millenia under the sun before it was ever seen by man. The route may have been unknown until 1888, when Quintin Mackinnon and Ernest Mitchell were contracted for £30 to blaze a track up the Clinton Valley from the head of Lake Te Anau. Three weeks of rain saturated their tent, their blankets became flyblown and they ran out of food. They returned down the lake for more food, then went back to the valley. Higher up they came to a lake which Mackinnon named Mintaro, Spanish for 'resting place'. But they did not rest. The pass to Milford, they were convinced, lay just above. They struggled over in wind and rain, and down the western side, into the Arthur Valley, where they then encountered Thomas Mackenzie and a companion, searching for a route to Te Anau. A few days later the four men returned over the pass.

Quintin Mackinnon became the first guide on the finished Milford Track in 1890, but in 1892 he was lost from his boat during a storm on Lake Te Anau. There is plenty of room to move about at the top of the pass he helped to pioneer. By walking a little to the east, the best view is gained of the Clinton, backed by its southern wall Pariroa, 'the long cliff'. Above this is the many-peaked Castle Mountain (2094 m), unclimbed until 1958, and directly east of the pass rises Mt Balloon, conquered in 1911. There are several tarns on the pass, from which to quench a thirst, or in which to cool hot face or feet. There is a shelter hut too. Mt Elliot and the icefalls of the Jervois Glacier to the north are reminders that this is alpine country.

From the north rim of the pass the night's resting place, the Quintin Huts, can be seen in the Arthur Valley, nearly 900 m below. It is a steep and jarring descent. Where the Roaring Burn is crossed, just above the bushline, is another shelter hut, Crow's Nest. The last kilometre through the bush to Quintin Huts seems to be the stoniest and steepest of all. The huts are about 100 m off the main track, on the same track that leads to the Sutherland Falls. Freedom walkers press on for another hour, to Dumpling Hut farther down the Arthur Valley.

Guided parties spend a night at Quintin Huts, and the main attraction is the Sutherland Falls, cascading in three giant leaps, 580 m to the valley floor. These are the fifth highest falls in the world, and are named

▲ *The Arthur valley from the summit of the Mackinnon Pass. The Arthur River flows into Milford Sound*

◄ *The cairn marking the pass was erected by the Government, the Gaelic Society and the Otago Rugby Football Union. The discoverer of the pass, Quintin Mackinnon, was a Scot and a fine footballer*

for Donald Sutherland, 'the hermit of Milford', who lived there from 1878 until his death in 1919. Sutherland's first estimate of the height of the falls was about 1000 m, which he later increased to 1500 m. Unromantic surveyors later reduced this, but the falls remain one of the most impressive sights of all Fiordland. A direct track from Quintin Huts leads to the foot of the falls, where the tramper can but gaze in awe at this magnificent sight.

The walker, seeing the falls, should think on Will Quill. This young surveyor who was working on the track, left Quintin Hut in March 1890 for the top of the falls. 'I began the climb about three or four chains to the east (true right) of the lower fall, reaching

the top without too much difficulty,' he wrote. 'But beyond this the face is smooth granite rock and one has to be careful. A steady hand and a strong nerve were all that kept me from slipping, where the least slip would send me down the perpendicular rock to be dashed to pieces hundreds of feet below.' Eventually he gained the top and described the scene: 'As I stood I turned toward the south and discovered a beautiful lake . . . the reservoir of the Sutherland Falls. The outlet is a deep chasm about a hundred yards in length. The water rushes through this chasm with great force and swiftness, making a terrible noise . . .'

Twice more that year the intrepid Quill climbed the falls. Then, in January 1891, he

◄*The Arthur River at Lake Ada. The track is flat from here to the end, where a launch takes walkers to shelter at Milford*

◄*In three leaps the Sutherland Falls drop 580 m. The falls were long believed to be the highest in the world*

►*The source of the Sutherland Falls is Lake Quill, named after the daring climber who discovered it. The lake is not visible from the valley floor but those who return from Milford to Te Anau by air catch sight of it*

fell to his death from the Gertrude Saddle, a few kilometres away, while attempting to find a route to Milford from the Hollyford Valley. In the mountains he so clearly loved, his name is commemorated in the glacial lake from which the falls take their waters.

The last day on the track is the longest—22 km from the Quintin Huts to Sandfly Point at Milford Sound. From Quintin the track turns round the western spurs of Mt Elliot as the Arthur Valley swings north and widens towards Dumpling Hill. The track passes through bush and fern, with glimpses of the precipitous Wick Mountains.

The Arthur River in its last rush to sea level is clearly heard, and at 10 km from Quintin, at Boatshed Shelter, the track crosses the river by suspension bridge. Here a short side track leads to the Mackay Falls and to Bell Rock, a sinkhole ground out by stones and river water and later overturned; several people may stand upright beneath it.

In denser bush now, the track crosses tributaries of the Arthur, and the mileposts are imaginative wooden signs carved with likenesses of native birds. The track skirts above Lake Ada, and then descends again to Giant Gate Falls, perhaps the most beautiful falls of the walk. Now comes the final wide, flat 6 km of track, first beside Lake Ada, and then the older, browner, more sullen Arthur River again to Sandfly Point. There is the tang of the sea, but the view of Milford Sound is limited. That must wait for the launch trip at the end of the track.

At Milford Sound

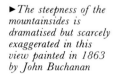

▶ The steepness of the mountainsides is dramatised but scarcely exaggerated in this view painted in 1863 by John Buchanan

The first Europeans to visit Milford Sound were sealers and it was one of them who, in 1822, gave it its European name. He was John Grono, a New South Welshman with memories of Milford Haven, in his native land old south Wales. Little is known of earlier visits to the area beyond that Maoris went sometimes to Anita Bay, at the entrance to the sound. They were seeking a kind of greenstone called *tangiwai*. This soft, semi-translucent gem stone sometimes flecked with black bears no close mineralogical relationship to the other variety of greenstone used by the Maoris, the tough, long-fibred *pounamu*, or nephrite. *Pounamu* was valued for

adzes and fighting weapons because it would take a sharp edge, while *tangiwai* ('waters of weeping') found its use in ornaments.

In 1851 Captain J. L. Stokes of HMS *Acheron* entered Milford, proceeding to the head to drop anchor in Freshwater Basin, where the launches and lobster boats are now moored. At that time the Cleddau River flowed into Freshwater Basin, but later during a flood it cut itself a new channel to the south, beyond the site of the airfield today. Now Freshwater Basin is quickly silting up, as the view at low tide clearly shows.

An unknown artist made the first painting of Milford Sound while HMS *Acheron* was at

anchor. The ship is shown in the extreme right of the picture, in Freshwater Basin, with all sail set, which must be taken as artistic licence. The features of the landscape are clearly shown—the Bowen Falls cascading from their high hanging valley; the snow-capped Mt Pembroke (2045 m) to the north; the Lion (1302 m), its walls plunging to the depths of the sound. Beyond the Lion are the Stirling Falls, and across the sound the sharp shape of Mitre Peak (1412 m), known from a thousand more recent pictures. It was named by Captain Stokes, who concluded: 'Milford is the most memorable Harbour yet visited by the *Acheron* in New Zealand.'

The Milford Hotel now stands on the flat land between Freshwater Basin to the north and the Cleddau outlet to the south. Across the last extremity of the sound are the outlet of the Arthur River and Sandfly Point, where the Milford Track ends.

To this place in 1878 came Donald Sutherland, determined to make his home there. He built a hut at Freshwater Basin. When two more huts were added he proclaimed the 'City of Milford'. He explored for gold in the surrounding valley, and forced a way up the Arthur River with a companion to discover and name the Sutherland Falls.

He named Mt Balloon, and must at least have looked keenly at the Mackinnon Pass. After Quintin Mackinnon had crossed it in 1888 Sutherland claimed that he had been on top of it years before, but had bothered no more with it because it did not lead in the direction of Queenstown.

In 1890 Sutherland married Mrs Eliza-

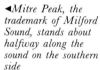

◀ Mitre Peak, the trademark of Milford Sound, stands about halfway along the sound on the southern side

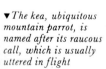

▼ The kea, ubiquitous mountain parrot, is named after its raucous call, which is usually uttered in flight

◄*A native buttercup, one of many species found in the mountains*

►*Mitre Peak from the top of the Bowen Falls. Sinbad Gully is to the left of the peak*

beth Samuel, a robust Victorian widowed three times. They built a 12-room accommodation house near the site of the modern hotel. For nearly 30 years, until Sutherland's death in 1919, this was the centre of human activity in Milford Sound, with a welcome for visitors from the track, fossickers and prospectors, sailors and early mountaineers. A visitors' book was kept, in which Sutherland sometimes added his own assessment after the visitor's departure. 'The two meanest scunkes that ever came into this sound', read one celebrated comment.

After Sutherland's death the Government purchased the accommodation house, gradually improving the facilities to those of the present-day hotel. During the summer months more spartan accommodation is available at Johnson's Hostel, 400 m back along the road from the hotel. For visitors to Milford there is the launch trip on the sound, fishing in the lower reaches of the Cleddau River, and the walk up Tutoko Valley, in the shadow of the Darran Mountains, to approach a little closer to the icefalls on the south face of Mt Tutoko. The monarch of Fiordland, it is 2756 m high.

Beyond the wharf at Freshwater Basin a narrow track passes hard against the bluffs and beside the crayfish boats at their moorings. Milford, with its road access, is one of their main Fiordland bases. Their colourful battered appearance makes these boats a favoured foreground for the view of Mitre Peak, and many of their crews have the blood of the Ngatimamoe in their veins.

Beyond the crayfish boats, the track soon reaches the foot of the Bowen Falls, named after an early Governor of New Zealand. These falls leap in two steps from a high glacial hanging valley and their energy is used to generate electric power for the hotel.

The launch trips leave from the basin, for an hour to Stirling Falls, which cascade directly into the sea beyond the Lion, or for two hours to Anita Bay. There the launch feels the long swell of the Tasman. The fossicker may find fragments of greenstone amongst the boulders of the beach. Seals bask on the rocks within the entrance to the sound, and if the visitor is lucky a school of dolphins may accompany the launch for some distance along the sound.

Mitre Peak forms the great south wall of the Sound. In 1883 Donald Sutherland attempted to climb it with a companion. They made their way up Sinbad Gully, the deep valley immediately to the south of the peak as seen from the hotel. The name Sinbad carries allusions of Oriental riches, but no gold was ever found in Sinbad Gully. However, it is now one of the last places where the kakapo, the flightless ground parrot of New Zealand, survives. For this reason Sinbad Gully is, together with the takahe reserve above Lake Te Anau, among the few parts of Fiordland to which general access is prohibited.

The decline of the kakapo has been sudden. In the 1860s explorers on the West Coast complained of being unable to sleep at night because of the din made by the curious booming call of the male birds. By the late 1880s introduced stoats and ship rats were spreading into Fiordland, and the ground-nesting kakapo seems to have been particularly vulnerable to them. A few birds still exist, on Stewart Island, in Tutoko Valley, and in Sinbad Gully. The extinction of the species may be inevitable. Perhaps up there behind Mitre Peak some day this century the last kakapo will die.

To Milford Sound by road

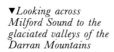
▲Sinbad Gully, a hanging valley which is a last haunt of the endangered kakapo

▼Looking across Milford Sound to the glaciated valleys of the Darran Mountains

►Water cascades down the rocky flanks of Sinbad Gully during a storm

If the Milford Track has claims to be the finest walk in the world, the road to Milford Sound must have equal claim to be the finest drive in the world.

From Te Anau, the road swings north up the Eglinton Valley. From a high curve there is a view of the Eglinton River, sweeping over stony shallows into deeper pools. Ahead the steep, bushed slopes of the Earl and Livingstone Mountains flank the valley. On the valley floor the road crosses wide tussock flats, natural parkland amid the beech forest. There are numerous camp sites with stone fireplaces. A track to Dore Pass, the overland route to Glade House and the Milford Track, is signposted, but it is not for novices.

Farther on are the small Mirror Lakes, and a view up Mistake Creek to the impressive spire of Ngatimamoe Peak (1849 m), named after the earliest major Maori tribe of the southern part of the South Island. Remnants of this tribe, not willing to be subjugated by the invading Ngai Tahu from the north, fled into the wilderness of Fiordland in the late 18th century, and fanciful stories of their survival there lingered well into this century.

The road passes Cascade Creek, site of a construction camp during the making of the Eglinton road in the 1920s and subsequently a tourist centre for accommodation, meals and petrol. A few years ago a fire destroyed the main building, but accommodation is now available at Lake Gun Motor Lodge.

Beyond Cascade Creek the road runs past Lake Gunn, a beautiful small lake set against the western mountains and completely surrounded by bush. Beyond it two smaller lakes lie on the other side of the road—Fergus and Lochie, both good Scots names reflecting the origins of early Europeans in this region. Then, still in bush, for this is the lowest pass on the Main Divide, the Eglinton Saddle is reached at 530 m.

The road now hugs the steep slopes on the west of the divide, a route blasted out of the rock in the 1930s. Stretching northward is the lower Hollyford Valley, one of the most beautiful bush valleys in all New Zealand. The road, unsealed and winding, descends very steeply to the west, and the precipices and peaks of the upper Hollyford Valley start to fill the view. Nearest are the awesome, sheer, moss-encrusted lower slopes of Mt Christina, 2502 m high.

At the bottom of the descent, a side road turns north into the lower Hollyford Valley. The road to Milford continues westward along the upper Hollyford, between the grey walls of the Darran Mountains and the Earl Mountains. There high snowfields and rocky summits slip into view. The road, though now climbing steeply, is deceptively flat in the immensity of the landscape.

The young Hollyford River roars over its bed, the bush becomes sporadic, and the valley floor is a wild scattering of old morainic boulders and more recent rockfalls, liberally coated with a fine red lichen. Snowgrass and mountain shrubs form most of the vegetation. The road winds steeply up the last slope to the portal of the Homer Tunnel at 900 m.

In 1889 a settler from Martins Bay, W. H. Homer, declared the Homer Saddle to be the route for a road to Milford Sound. Other visitors were more sceptical, though an official estimate of the cost of a tunnel through the saddle was only £2000 in 1890. Work eventually started in the early 1930s, but the tunnel was not completed until 1953.

Above the tunnel is a short signposted walk amongst the subalpine vegetation. A scramble over boulders and scree to the top of the Homer Saddle is also possible.

The road descends steeply in wet darkness through the tunnel, to emerge then into the Cleddau Valley, another steep-sided glacial valley, leading down to Milford. The road, well-surfaced now, turns down into bush again. A pause at the Chasm gives a view of the Cleddau River crashing through a deep channel. Down almost at sea level a superb view is obtained from the Tutoko River bridge of Mt Tutoko to the north. The road then passes alongside the now wider and gentler Cleddau River to reach Milford Sound.

◄Looking back up the Hollyford valley from Martins Bay. The first European to enter the valley, Patrick Caples, named it after his birthplace in Ireland

From the Milford road the Hollyford Valley runs northward for some 60 km to the coast. For the first few kilometres a rough unsealed road winds through luxuriant, fern-fringed bush. At 8 km is Gunn's Camp, a rude collection of huts, a small store and a museum on the banks of the Hollyford River. Eight kilometres beyond Gunn's Camp the road ends and the Hollyford Track begins.

The first European known to have travelled down the valley was Patrick Caples, a miner from Queenstown, in 1863, but it is likely that sealers had penetrated some distance inland 50 years earlier. The Maoris used the valley as a route to the West Coast and the names of some peaks in the Darran Mountains, to the west of the valley, honour great southern chiefs. Others immortalise erstwhile editors of the Melbourne *Age*.

From the roadhead the track hugs the eastern wall of the valley. In two hours it meets the river again, meandering down the valley. It is two and a half hours from the road to the Hidden Falls Hut and a further one hour's walk to Hidden Falls Creek. A bridge crosses the creek and a few minutes further is the Hidden Falls Hut. At Hidden Falls a walk on the flats between hut and river on a clear evening, in the shadow of the Darran Mountains, reveals Fiordland at its finest.

From Hidden Falls the track continues northward for approximately an hour on an upgraded surface which is in good condition. Then begins a steady half-hour climb, up to the Little Homer Saddle, almost entirely through the bush. At only one point does the bush open westward to give a fine view of the eastern bluffs of Mt Tutoko. The mountaineering history of the Darrans was enlivened by several attempts on Mt Tutoko in the 1920s by an eccentric English draper named Samuel Turner. Determined to be first to climb the mountain, he succeeded on his sixth attempt. His expeditions were run on the lines of a classical Himalayan trip. Turner was a man of firm ideas: 'When selecting men, either companions or porters, the question of good or bad temper is of

◄The Hollyford River runs turbulently after rain. All Fiordland rivers can rise with frightening speed

►Hidden Falls drop into the Hollyford River at the end of the first day's walk on the Hollyford Track

▲Mt Madeline, seen here from the Lower Pyke clearing, is the second highest peak in the Darran Mountains

▶Lake McKerrow viewed from Huroki Creek, where the Hollyford Track meets the lake shore

minor importance . . . it is of utmost importance to get non-snoring, early-rising, methodical men, non-clumsy and with a moderate appetite'.

From the Little Homer Saddle the track descends steeply to the valley floor, where the Bridal Veil Falls fill the air with fine spray. Then the track runs westward for half an hour, through thick bush, to meet the Pyke River. Guided trampers collected by jet boat nearby, are taken to a tourist company lodge, but others must walk on for 90 minutes or more to the national park hut on the shores of Lake Alabaster, in the Pyke Valley.

To gain the next stage of the Hollyford Track it is necessary to return towards the

Pyke clearing, where a suspension bridge crosses the deep green waters of the Pyke River below Lake Alabaster. From there a three-hour walk through thick bush ends on the shores of Lake McKerrow.

Thousands of years ago Lake McKerrow must have been the northernmost fiord. Now it is separated from the sea by a kilometre or more of low land. In part this may be due to silting of its entrance, but the land may have been raised too, for the Alpine Fault, running the length of the Southern Alps, crosses the seaward end of the lake. The lower reaches show a slight rise and fall with the tides.

The track leads down the eastern side of the lake, a switchback route long known as

the Demon Trail, and finally meets the lake shore at the northern end, near Hokuri Creek. From the Hokuri a two-hour walk passes along the thick shingle of the lake shore, then through bush and across open flats to reach the northernmost hut of the park and the final sweep of the Hollyford River as it enters the sea at Martins Bay. The view southwards of the surf beating on the sandspit and of the long valley of the Hollyford flanked by the Darran Mountains and the Skippers Range, is ample reward for those who have carried loads this far. The Hollyford cannot match the Milford Track in dramatic grandeur but it exceeds it in variety of beauty.

◀Mt Tutoko, the highest peak in Fiordland National Park, from the Little Homer Saddle, which lies to its east

▶Lake Alabaster, a long, narrow lake on the Pyke River, lies below the Skippers Range, a massif jutting between the Pyke and Hollyford river valleys

A miserable settlement reclaimed by the bush

The eastern shore of Lake McKerrow, where it forms the last part of the track to Martins Bay, is broken by a small indentation where the water is dark and deep and the kowhais fringing the shore are at their loveliest. There is nothing now to tell the uninformed traveller who passes, boots crunching the gravel of the lake shore, that a little more than a hundred years ago this small bay was much surveyed, or that for a brief period some half-dozen houses, a store and a pub existed on the site. This formed the scene of the abortive settlement of Jamestown.

In the 1860s the Otago Provincial Government was concerned about the Westland gold rush drawing trade and people from Otago. Martins Bay was examined as a possible western gateway to the province. Some early reports proved favourable. Fifteen hundred hectares of rich alluvial land were estimated to be available for cultivation. There were suggestions of gold and other mineral wealth.

A road inland, connecting with Queenstown, was deemed to present 'no difficulty' by the Provincial Geologist. The region lay on a favourable sailing route from Australia.

▲*Coastal forest at Martins Bay, where a settlement endured briefly in the 1870s*

▼*At Martins Bay the Hollyford River's entry to the sea is delayed by a long sandspit*

The river was, 'comparatively safe and easy for coastal steamers', declared one authority. There were dissenters too. One described the entrance to the river as very bad, and the surrounding country as unfit for settlement.

To settle the matter the ebullient James MacAndrew, Superintendent of the Province of Otago, visited the region himself in 1867. He travelled round the coast in the steamer *Geelong*, whose captain declined to enter the river. In a ship's boat, MacAndrew went up the Hollyford River and into Lake McKerrow. He and his party were impressed. They declared that the district could not contain less than 6000 or 8000 hectares of level timbered land which would be arable after clearing. MacAndrew guaranteed the road to Queenstown, the land was surveyed and settlement began. Its centre was to be Jamestown, named for MacAndrew himself.

In 1870 the first settlers came, and the houses, store and pub rose. Access proved difficult, and three of the first four ships to try to enter the river were either wrecked or ran aground. The difficulties of an inland route to Queenstown had been greatly underestimated. More than a century later there still is

◄*To the north of Martins Bay coastal lands become flatter and rivers can meander to the Tasman Sea*

▼*From Martins Bay to Milford Sound the Fiordland coast becomes increasingly higher and more rugged*

none, and the need has passed.

By 1873 a visitor could comment: 'Of all the miserable settlements I ever saw or read of, Martins Bay is the worst.' He had bitter comments on the land and on what the settlers had managed to achieve. But it was hardly the fault of the settlers, enticed and misled by miscalculations and promises.

In another couple of years most had left and Jamestown was virtually abandoned. A few settlers lingered, on larger holdings on the flat land nearer the sea. In 1880 James Park, professor of geology at the University of Otago, could write: 'We lodged with a settler named Webb whose wife regaled us sumptuously on fresh meat, homemade bread and succulent spinach.' Webb was growing tobacco, hops, wheat and oats, and ran cattle in the surrounding bush. Finally, only the Mackenzie family remained at the bay. They continued to run cattle through the region until the 1920s, when Davy Gunn took over their leases.

Davy Gunn guided tramping parties, using packhorses on the trails and a large sailing dinghy on Lake McKerrow. In 1936 he made a dramatic journey for help after a plane crash on the coast at Big Bay, covering the 90 km to the Milford road in 20 hours. He met his death by drowning in the Pyke River, in the midst of the land he knew so well, on Christmas Day 1955.

Jamestown Bay has reverted to its original appearance, described by one who accompanied MacAndrew as 'a sheltered nook in the bight of a lovely bay, quite sheltered from the wind'. Within the bush are three apple trees, still fruiting. Stone fireplaces are discernible in the undergrowth. A sycamore tree grows on the river bank, and an occasional rose bush. On the coast a cluster of Australian gums thrive, and open flats on the walk to the bay must also be reckoned as remnants of the era of settlement.

In rocks near the river entrance are rusted iron pegs, the remains of navigation marks for ships. Remarkably, a century after the abandonment of settlement and harbour, the *New Zealand Pilot*, a *vade mecum* for the mariner, still describes these entry beacons as if they were pristine and functioning. This must be the last official acknowledgement of the settlement's existence. The wilderness has come back almost completely.

The Catlins

In scale as well as area, the Catlins is smaller than most other great scenic regions in the South Island, but it offers perhaps the greatest variety of scenery—rivers, lakes, waterfalls, cliffs, caves, beaches and rainforest

One of New Zealand's least-known regions, the Catlins district is a wedge of rolling hill country whose sides run inland from the mouths of the Clutha and Mataura Rivers to meet at Gore. There is only one substantial settlement—Owaka, with some 400 people—even though the Catlins was settled early.

Sealers arrived in 1810, whalers followed in the 1830s, and settlers intent on farming arrived in 1840. In that same year, a Sydney whaling captain, Edward Cattlin, was sent to assess the navigability of the river that now bears his misspelt name. He found that it led to the most accessible forests in the South Island. For the equivalent of $184.50—$60 in cash and the balance in firearms and gunpowder—he bought from the Maoris a block stretching 32 km on each side of the Catlins River and 90 km inland. He claimed it when New Zealand became a British colony, but the authorities granted only a fraction of his claim—and that not until 1873, 17 years after his death. By then sawmillers were cutting the dense beech forests.

Ships loaded timber at Hinahina, on the shore of a broad stretch of the Catlins River called Catlins Lake. There was no busier timber port in the South Island in the early 1870s. Settlers moved into the cleared valleys. In 1879 a railway from Balclutha was started, but it did not reach Tahakopa, only 68 km away, until 1915.

By 1887 the easily-reached timber had been cut out and the port at Hinahina was defunct, but sawmilling continued. Even as late as the 1930s there were about 30 sawmills in the Catlins. Now the best stands of timber on the coast and in the valleys have been cut out and few sawmills are in operation.

People have left the Catlins. Small farms did not prosper and have been merged into large properties. Townships have disappeared or dwindled to a few dwellings. Abandoned houses, schools and churches are commonplace in the green valleys. The railway was closed in 1971. The Catlins district remains a frontier—perhaps the last in New Zealand—but, paradoxically, it is quieter than it was a century ago.

Most of the forests on the ranges and the surviving patches on the lowlands are protected in reserves and the scars left by the early timber trade are healing. Much of the forest is in the three great blocks of the Catlins State Forest Park. The land is not particularly rugged or high—the highest point, Mt Tautuku, is only 690 m—but the region is one of the least-known wildernesses in New Zealand. There are few tracks and the roads are nearly all unsealed.

▼*The Catlins coast is the most southerly part of the South Island. Much of it lies to the south of Bluff*

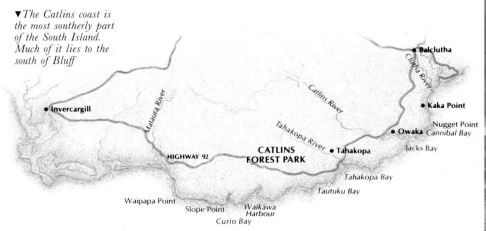

▶*Virgin rainforest covers the lowland and hills lying behind the sands of Tautuku Bay*

The Nuggets

▶*Nugget Point, its tip crowned by a lighthouse, is the end of the Razor Back ridge. One of the main landmarks of the southern Otago coast, the point is visible from as far north as the Dunedin hills*

Nugget Point is a fine place for the south-bound traveller to begin a visit to the Catlins. There are some who would not concede that the point is properly part of the Catlins district, but its wild coastal scenery is a fitting introduction to one of the most varied and wonderful stretches of coast in all New Zealand.

The long, narrow headland that terminates in Nugget Point is reached by turning off Highway 92 at Romahapa and travelling along the coast, past Kaka Point, an agreeable beach resort. Halfway along the rocky headland the road ends, and then a path leads along a sharp, narrow ridge called the Razor Back to a lighthouse, which stands on the last hump of the headland. Seventy-eight metres below are jagged islets where seals can be seen. These islets, called the Nuggets, are also a breeding ground for birds, including gannets, spotted shags, red-billed gulls and white-fronted terns.

At many places along the coast south of Nugget Point the yellow-eyed penguin, or *hoiho*, breeds in the bush. Its only other breeding grounds are on subantarctic islands. The species is protected and the birds and their nesting sites must not be disturbed.

The Catlins coast to the south of Nugget Point is an astonishingly beautiful sequence of coastal features—golden beaches fringing dense green forests; broad, calm estuaries; and towering cliffs, in places 200 m high.

◀*The handsome spotted shag is one of several species of seabirds that breed at Nugget Point. In the breeding season the male spotted shag develops a crest*

▲*Giant kelp fringes the rocks on the Otago coast, writhing to the motion of the water*

◄*A young fur seal, one of a colony flourishing at Nugget Point*

▼*From these jagged islets, which early whalers called the Nuggets, Nugget Point takes its name*

▲Fossilised trunks and
stumps of ancient trees
related to the kauri
and the Norfolk Island
pine are visible at low
tide at Curio Bay

The Catlins is thought, because of archaeological discoveries at Papatowai, on the south bank of the Tahakopa River, to have been one of the last places in New Zealand where the giant flightless moa lived. The moas died out more than 200 years ago, but the Catlins forest remains rich in other birds. Attentive visitors are likely to see and hear the New Zealand pigeon, tui, kaka, bellbird, rifleman, yellow-breasted tit and yellowhead as well as more common bush birds.

South of Papatowai, Florence Hill gives a view of one of the glories of the New Zealand coast—the golden curve of Tautuku Bay. A dense forest, possessed of many fine rimu, miro, totara and rata trees, is separated from the sand by only the thinnest intervening zone of scrub. Access to the beach is from the northern end of Tautuku Bay, off which lies a tiny island called Rainbow Island. It has a blowhole whose spray produces rainbow effects in sunlight.

Behind the middle of the beach there is a short track from the highway to a lookout above a beautiful pool set in deep bush. Although the pool, called Lake Wilkie, is a few hundred metres from the sea and has no surface outlet, it rises and falls with the tides, it is said. Opposite the Lake Wilkie signpost on the highway there is access to the Tautuku Forest Reserve, 550 hectares of marvellous

forest, preserved in its original state by the Royal Forest and Bird Protection Society of New Zealand.

The forest in this part of the Catlins is true rainforest, where gigantic moss-hung emergent trees intermittently soar above a canopy so thick that very little light reaches the forest floor. At the edges the growth is so dense that the highway seems to pass between two towering green walls.

The species of trees and other plants growing together in the Catlins rainforest create an impression of overwhelming richness and diversity. But for the swooping and darting and the chiming and piping of the ever-present birds, all is stillness and silence.

One of the few side roads that branch off into the forest goes to the Waipati Beach Scenic Reserve. From the end of the road it is 20 minutes' walk to the Cathedral Caves. These caves, so called because of their arched roofs and reverberant acoustics, are more than 30 m high and stretch more than 100 m into the richly coloured cliffs.

The headland at the opposite end of Waipati Beach is called Chasland's Mistake. Chasland was a part-Aboriginal Australian whaler named Tommy Chasland, but the nature of his mistake is unknown. After a craggy extinct volcano called Samson, the road again passes through a long stretch of

Living and stony forests

forest, perhaps the finest of the whole route. Highway 92 becomes a sealed road after crossing the Waikawa River, but it is worth turning south along the broad estuary of Waikawa Harbour and the curving beach of Porpoise Bay to see the so-called petrified forest at Curio Bay. A subtropical forest growing there 160 million years ago was overwhelmed by sand. Over the ages the sediment turned to sandstone, and silica replaced the woody structure of the trees in the buried forest. Later the action of the sea cut away the sandstone, exposing the fossilised floor of that ancient forest. Low tide reveals stony stumps and fallen trunks, up to 30 m long, of trees related to the kauri and the Norfolk Island pine.

◄*The sea has cut arches and caverns in the cliffs at many points along the Catlins coast. This arch is near Jacks Bay*

▼*Products of forest decay darken the beds of Catlins rivers, and the waters themselves take on a sinister, swarthy aspect*

Stewart Island

By far the least populous and least known of the three main islands of New Zealand, Stewart Island has remained largely a wilderness. Those who would explore its forests, coasts or bleak heights must do so on foot

Captain Cook, after sailing round the east, south and west coasts of Stewart Island in March 1770, believed that 'there was little reason to suppose it an island'. So he called the region South Cape and on his chart he linked it with dotted lines to the South Island. More than 30 years later, in 1804, an American sealer named Owen Folger Smith, showed that it was indeed an island by sailing through the strait. Smith's Strait it was called for a few years, until it was named after Governor Foveaux of New South Wales.

Smith also began a sealing boom which brought temporary European settlers to the island. It was on a sealing mission that William Stewart, first officer of the vessel *Pegasus*, came to the island that now carries his name.

The Maoris, there for centuries, called it *Rakiura*—'island of the glowing skies'.

The Polynesian ancestors of the modern Maoris possibly skirted the Stewart Island coast in their twin-hulled canoes as early as 1200. It is unlikely that they ever settled Stewart Island in large numbers, but in later prehistoric times a small permanent village existed on The Neck, a narrow peninsula at the entrance to Paterson Inlet. Its presence is recorded by middens of bones and shells.

Settlements have come and gone on the island, and now there is only Oban at Halfmoon Bay. The 500 inhabitants of the town have two stores, a hotel, television and more than 30 000 visitors a year.

In shape, the island is a ragged triangle. Its west coast, 60 km long from Rugged Point in the north to South West Cape, faces the unceasing rollers of the Tasman Sea. The southeast coast, from South West Cape to East Cape, is scarcely less rugged or exposed, but it has good harbours at Port Pegasus, Lords River and Port Adventure. Beyond East Cape the coast faces northeast. This is the milder, sheltered aspect where the bush is at its most luxuriant.

Into this northeast coast Paterson Inlet penetrates deeply, half the width of the island. Beyond, the valley of the Freshwater River and its tributaries continues to the northwest, through swampy flats and low sandy hummocks, almost to the west coast. The inlet and the valley effectively divide the island into two greatly dissected massifs. To the north is Mt Anglem, at 980 m the highest point on the island. The larger southern massif presents several summits over 700 m high.

The island is part of the roof of a large intrusive granite mass lying mainly beneath the sea south of the South Island. It emerges to form part of Fiordland, Stewart Island, the Snares Islands and some of the subantarctic rocks and islets. Some 70 million years ago an almost flat land surface stretched over the whole region. Much later, it was warped and tilted and much of it was submerged. Stewart Island is part of an eastward-tilted segment, so that all the major rivers on the island run to the east.

Valleys eroded when sea-level was lower during the ice ages were flooded as the oceans rose in post-glacial times, forming deep bays like Paterson Inlet and Port Pegasus.

▶Bush crowds down to the edge of the water along Paterson Inlet's convoluted shore

Foveaux Strait
Rugged Point
Codfish I.
Mt Anglem
Christmas Village Bay
Ruggedy Mtns
Port William
Lee Bay
Horseshoe Bay
Halfmoon Bay
Tasman Sea
Mason Bay
Paterson Inlet
The Neck
Doughboy Bay
East Cape
Port Adventure
Mt Allen
Tin Range
Fraser Peaks
Muttonbird Is
Port Pegasus
South West Cape

▲Stewart Island has no highways, but there are launches to take visitors to some of the wild places

Vast waterway with many arms and islands

In the mid-1870s the first boatload of organised sightseers arrived at Halfmoon Bay from Bluff. Some of their descendants have been making regular voyages or flights across Foveaux Strait ever since.

Many visitors prefer the 20-minute flight from Invercargill to the two-hour ferry voyage from Bluff across the often-turbulent strait. South Air operates four flights daily. The ferry *Acheron* sails from Bluff at 9 a.m., Mondays, Wednesdays and Fridays, and leaves Halfmoon Bay at 2 p.m. There is enough time between for a minibus tour, but Stewart Island deserves a longer stay.

Scientists have said that virtually every type of vegetation on Stewart Island differs significantly from its counterpart on the South Island. The distinctive plant life is a product of the island's soils, geology and climate, plus modification during nearly 10 000 years of isolation.

Many of Stewart Island's special plants can be seen in a scenic reserve called Moturau Moana ('islands of bush above the sea'), near Halfmoon Bay, between Butterfield Beach and Bragg Bay. It was given to the Government in 1940 by Noeline Baker, who had gathered many plants on field trips throughout Stewart Island. The reserve has an arboretum and a picnic area.

Part of the settlement at Halfmoon Bay spills over to Paterson Inlet at Golden Bay, near Iona Island. There is a commanding view of the vast waterway from Observation Rock, above Golden Bay, and tracks lead along its northern flanks. But the best way to see the bush-ringed, many-armed inlet is from the sea, and launches can be chartered at Halfmoon Bay.

The mouth of Paterson Inlet, between Native Island and The Neck, is reached after a half-hour trip round Ackers Point. A little white-painted wooden lighthouse and a dilapidated stone house stand upon the point. The latter was built in 1834–36 by Lewis Acker, an American sealer. He found the local stone unsuitable, so he brought rocks across Foveaux Strait. The house, which is one of the most historic monuments on Stewart Island and old by any New Zealand standard, can be reached by walking from Halfmoon Bay.

Immediately inside Paterson Inlet is Ulva Island, 4 km long and much the largest of the many islands in the harbour. For 51 years until 1923 it had a post office—it was Stewart Island's first—from which visitors used to send a kind of natural postcard. They would write a message on the underside of a big leaf of the shrub puharetaiko and have it stamped and posted.

Now Ulva Island is a nature reserve and visitors enjoy its rich natural vegetation and

◄*The crescent of sand is Horseshoe Bay beach. The next Bay is Halfmoon Bay, site of the only town on Stewart Island. On the opposite side of the entrance to Paterson Inlet is a peninsula called The Neck, the site of an earlier settlement*

bird life. The larger trees have never been cut and rimu, miro, totara and kamahi are abundant. In summer the red flowers of southern rata glow against the darker bush. The birds include red-crowned and yellow-crowned parakeets, tuis, bellbirds and pigeons.

The Forest Service has made a nature trail, along which numbered markers indicate various types of vegetation. Orchids are to be found along the trail, including the silver orchid, or excited dancer orchid. It has a heart-shaped leaf, green with silver underneath, which takes on purple veining in midsummer, and a wine-coloured flower with long tendril-like lateral sepals and petals. Ferns are also to be seen in great variety on the trail, which can be visited on a round trip to Sydney Cove, not far from the wharf. There are several other walks on Ulva Island.

South from Ulva, a scattering of islets shelter the entrances to Big Glory Bay and Glory Cove, both perfect bush-ringed anchorages. Deeper in, on the northern side, is historic Prices Inlet, a scene of early sawmills and a whaler's refitting base established in 1865 by C. E. Price, a shipwright. Then in the 1920s a Norwegian whaling company chose to have its fleet, which hunted whales in the Ross Sea, serviced there. But by 1939 most of the equipment had been removed and all that remains now are a few rusting propellors and the skeletons of the buildings.

Westward of Prices Inlet is the flat swampy valley of the Freshwater River, flanked by the many-summitted Ruggedy Range to the

▲*Paterson Inlet, seen here from Golden Bay at dusk, is a huge, many-armed harbour which reaches halfway across the island*

▼*Diorite, an igneous rock, at Halfmoon Bay. Weathering has caused the elliptical pattern of fractures*

north and the conspicuous cone of Mt Rakeahua rising to the south. Towards the head of Paterson Inlet the water shoals quickly and at low tide there are large expanses of mudflat where oystercatchers, dotterels and godwits feed. Westerly gales can howl across this bleak western limit of the inlet, which has branching arms to north and south.

The South West Arm, 7 km long, leads to the Rakeahua River, which starts its journey not far from Doughboy Bay on the far west coast. Tracks to Doughboy Bay, Mason Bay and the rough country of Pegasus II Reserve start at the head of South West Arm.

Another track to Mason Bay runs from the Freshwater valley. Tracks from the head of Paterson Inlet and Halfmoon Bay converge at a boat landing on the Freshwater River. The Mason Bay track leads off to the southwest. Another track continues on a circuit of the northern part of the island, up the Freshwater Valley and Ruggedy Flat to East Ruggedy Beach, and from there around the coast back to Halfmoon Bay. This northern circuit, which takes 10–12 days, is becoming a 'recognised stop on the migration of young people around the world', according to the authors of a study of land management on Stewart Island.

Nevertheless, all these tracks are only for the fit and experienced who can carry their own supplies and equipment for days away from civilisation. Trampers wanting to walk the northern route must sign in with Halfmoon Bay Department of Conservation.

▶*Mt Anglem, the highest peak on Stewart Island, dominates the horizon in this view of the northeast coast from above Horseshoe Point*

▼*As stark as its name suggests, Ruggedy Point juts into the Tasman Sea. Near here walkers on the northern track head inland to return to Paterson Inlet*

The mildest climate, the most luxuriant bush and some of the loveliest coast on Stewart Island are between Halfmoon Bay and Saddle Point, 20 km to the northwest. There is a good coastal track which trampers of moderate fitness and experience, properly equipped, could spend five or six days exploring. Department of Conservation has three huts, all small, along the way.

The road from Halfmoon Bay ends at Lee Bay, 4 km to the north. The track, initially wide and gently-graded, passes through dense bush, with occasional views of the sea, before coming down to the long white sweep of Maori Beach. This forms the southern side of a considerable bay called Port William, one of the historic places of Stewart Island.

In prehistoric and early historic times there was a small Maori settlement there. Later sealers and whalers came, for the northern part of the bay is an all-weather anchorage, and it was close to the sealing coasts and the Solander whaling ground. They were followed by gold-seekers.

In 1869 five prospectors cut a track from Ruggedy, on the northwest corner of the island, to the east coast 7 km north of Port William. They cut 30 km of track in 19 days but, because of lack of food and the impenetrable nature of the bush, they were unable to join up with a track cut from Port William by a policeman.

The bush has reclaimed their trail just as it has reclaimed traces of an attempt to settle immigrants at Port William. In a grandiose scheme for settling 1000 families along the northeast coast to build up an oyster industry, a barracks for 150 people was built. The only immigrants who ever came were 24 Shetlanders in 1873. They soon left. There is nothing at Port William now but a Department of Conservation hut and an old wharf.

Beyond Port William the track runs inland, rising and falling over bushed ridges before going down to the sea and another hut

Coastal walk passing sites of vanished settlements

at Big Bungaree Beach. North of there is the long stretch of Murray Beach and the Murray River. 'Came about noon to Murrays River,' Bishop Selwyn recorded in 1844. 'Found a pretty little settlement . . . large potato gardens . . . 4 Englishmen living with native women; a very respectable, industrious body.' Murrays River is long deserted.

The track continues north across the base of Garden Point and another 4 km to the hut at Christmas Village Bay. The track is more difficult beyond Christmas Village Bay. It continues around the coast to Ruggedy Point and then down the Freshwater valley to Paterson Inlet.

▲*Coastal view on the track between Horseshoe Bay and Port William*

▼*Lee Bay, north of Halfmoon Bay. The road ends here and the coastal track begins. It follows the coast to Ruggedy Point, then crosses the island to Paterson Inlet*

A sheltered coast reclaimed by nature

◄*The rocky coast between The Neck and East Cape is fringed with bull kelp.*

On the east, Paterson Inlet is protected by a northward-jutting peninsula, nearly an island. At one point the higher land to each side is linked only by a strip of sand some 100 m across. From this tenuous strand the peninsula takes its name—The Neck. Launches from Oban travelling to the wildlife sanctuary of Ulva Island, just inside the inlet, pass close to The Neck. There is little to tell the traveller who looks across the dark water that the reef-fringed peninsula is one of the most historic parts of the island.

From the first years of the 19th century, sealers out of Sydney, spurred by the thought of profit, crept around this coast, disproving Captain Cook's peninsula and encountering, not always happily, the Maoris who knew it so well. From the 1820s sealers and later shore-whalers from the Fiordland coast, looking for a haven and rest after the rigours of a hunting season, settled at The Neck. Like all the northeastern coast of the island, The Neck is rather sheltered from the westerly gales, and has a milder and more equable climate than the southland coast, only 20 km away on the northern horizon.

In 1844, Bishop Selwyn noted 13 European men resident at The Neck, all with Maori wives and a total of 56 children. Some Stewart Island families proudly trace back their lineage to this group. For the next few decades The Neck remained the hub of human activity on Stewart Island. However, when Stewart Island was sold to the Crown by the southern Maoris in 1863, The Neck was largely set aside for allotment to those of mixed blood. Thereafter Europeans had to look elsewhere for land, and gradually settlement shifted to Halfmoon Bay, 6 km north across the mouth of Paterson Inlet. A school on The Neck closed in 1915, after which the peninsula became deserted.

Now long grass grows amid the encroaching bush, where a score of houses once stood. 'Mutton-bird scrub', *Senecio reinoldii*, with its distinctive, white-undersurfaced leaves, runs down to the kelp-fringed reefs of the shoreline. Ashore, many flocks of silvereyes move through the low vegetation. Fantails, bellbirds, native pigeons, and the inevitable introduced blackbirds. On the shore the long-beaked, short-legged pied oystercatchers fuss for food in sand and crevices. White-faced herons elegantly flap their smoky blue wings

▲*Ferns and tree ferns flourish in the mild climate of the sheltered northeast coast of Stewart Island*

▼*One of the few beaches between The Neck and East Cape. Human feet rarely tread these beaches*

above the shore, uttering a harsh cry that seems unfitted to their appearance. Occasionally a little blue penguin may dive at the approach of the launch, returning to the surface many metres away. Most magnificent of all the birds is the mollymawk, a small albatross with black-backed wings contrasting with the startlingly white feathers of the undersurface, and a bill edged with bright yellow.

The commonest birds frequenting these southern waters are four or five species of petrels. One is the sooty shearwater, darkest grey with a fleck of white under its wings as it flies, and more commonly known as the muttonbird or *titi*. The birds nest in burrows on some of the islets lying off Stewart Island after their long migration south across the Pacific in the spring. In the autumn the young are taken and preserved in hundreds of thousands. The right to take them is confined to the descendants of the southern Maoris who lived when Stewart Island was sold.

Most of the islets where the *titi* nest lie to the southwest. But less than a kilometre off the tip of The Neck lies tiny Whero Island, where the ornithologist Dr L. E. Richdale spent several seasons meticulously recording the habits of the *titi*.

Five or six kilometres further north is the squat shape of Herekopare, where an earlier ornithologist, Herbert Guthrie-Smith, studied them. Early this century he wrote: 'All muttonbirds, I was told, lay on Nov-

ember 25th, and such as cannot reach land at that date drop their eggs during flight, or whilst at rest on the water. Statements so remarkable, and repeated on all hands, certainly whetted my desire to know more of these members of the Petrel tribe . . .' Months later he concluded: 'I should say therefore, that far from the egg of each Mutton Bird being laid on November 25th, either on land or on water, that eggs are obtainable during the months of November, December, January, and February, probably also earlier and probably later.'

From The Neck the coast tends slightly east of south for some 10 km to East Cape. There are a few beaches but it is largely a very rocky coast fringed with bull kelp. The Maoris used to slit pockets into portions of the giant fronds of this kelp to store the preserved muttonbirds in them. The bush beyond the shore still contains some of the finer, larger native trees that have long since disappeared from The Neck. Rimu, with its fine prickly leaves; the related miro; totara with even sharper leaves; and kamahi with white-blotched trunk, saw-toothed leaves, and an attractive red flower in the spring, all thrive there.

East Cape marks the limit of the milder northeast coast, for the southeast faces wilder seas and winds. Even The Neck can be wild enough when the westerly gales funnel down Paterson Inlet and the spume flies across the narrow waist of sand.

Areas of protected land on Stewart Island include the 67 440 hectares of the Pegasus Nature Reserve. This reserve extends from South West Cape nearly to the shore of Paterson Inlet. There are also the 17 000 hectares of Mt Anglem Nature Reserve for the preservation of wildlife and Codfish Island Reserve, a sanctuary for endangered birds.

Many of the islands girdling the main island are scenic reserves. There is a nest of them at Port Pegasus on the southern coast. Port Pegasus was where British sovereignty over Stewart Island was declared in 1840.

Ten years later Captain J. L. Stokes visited Port Pegasus in HMS *Acheron* and recorded that there did not seem 'soil enough to nourish a potato'. But later in the century gold brought a population boom to Port Pegasus. The southeast coast gave quite rich returns between 1889 and 1894, although some miners who sought tin did better than the gold miners. Until late last century Port Pegasus was the scene of a thriving fishing industry at Burial Cove.

It was at Port Pegasus in 1905 that white-tailed deer were first released on Stewart Island. Now descendants of the original nine white-tailed deer are plentiful in many parts of the island. Despite their efforts, the hunters have been unable to reduce the deer population to a level desirable for forest regeneration.

The coast from Port Pegasus to Port Adventure is a rugged assortment of rocky headlands and equally rocky bays. Windswept scrub clings to the promontories, reflecting the southerly aspect of the coast. Behind Toitoi Bay is Toitoi Flat, a large swampy clearing set in terrain which is either heavily forested or covered with impenetrable scrub.

In 1850, HMS *Acheron* also called at Lords River, not far from Port Adventure, and this comment was left in the ship's journal: 'An utter solitude . . . no human beings besides ourselves . . . for an obvious reason . . . the eye looks in vain for a single foot of soil . . . nought but rock, rock, rock, rock.' It is much the same today, but in compensation Lords River is one place in New Zealand where the sound of birds can still be almost deafening at times. Parakeets dart across the river, pigeons soar in flocks of 30, 40 or more. Wekas forage

▲*Lords River, broad and navigable by small boats in its lower reaches, runs through impenetrable country*

on the rocky shore, and the large red-brown Stewart Island subspecies of brown kiwi thrives there. Pied shags and blue shags work the edge of the water.

Lords River is accessible only by sea, for the old coastal track, passing from The Neck to Port Pegasus, is now overgrown and impassable. Owen Island and a number of islets protect the entrance of the river. Within is calm water and shelter for fishing boats for a kilometre or more inland. Beyond, a dinghy can explore for 5–6 km, up a dark waterway between rocky shores and thick bush. Then the river swings north through tangled, impenetrable country, another 20 km to its source on Bald Hill.

Port Adventure attracts interest because of its fine bays and headlands and because of the colour and clarity of its water. One of the bays of this harbour is called Abraham's Bosom, one of the many fanciful names in which this coast abounds.

◄*The bole of an ancient rata on Stewart Island. Scarlet rata blossom decorates the forests in summer*

▲*The muttonbird breeds on offshore islands. Thousands of young birds are taken every autumn for food*

▼*The south arm of Port Pegasus, with the Fraser Peaks beyond. This area has seen settlers come and go*

▲The granite-strewn slopes of Table Hill look westward to the inlet of Doughboy Bay

▼Looking toward Little Hellfire Beach, so called because it is a dangerous lee shore. In the distance is the line of Mason Bay

Mt Allen, 749 m above sea level and the highest point of the southern massif of Stewart Island, is also the centre of the Pegasus II wildlife reserve. This wilderness, scarcely touched by man, may only be entered with permission from the Department of Conservation in Invercargill, but in any case is not an area to attract the casual visitor. The bush is less luxuriant than on the northeast coast,

the major trees—rimu, miro and kamahi—are stunted and soon give way with altitude to almost impenetrable subalpine scrub.

Even the white-tailed deer tend to shun the central part of this reserve, preferring the milder coast with its more palatable growth. Their impact on the native vegetation has been severe, and in some of the milder eastern coastal regions it is becoming serious. The thinned bush is being replaced by grassland.

If the introduction of deer was an error, Stewart Island has still been more fortunate in its dealing with European man than has most of the country. Rabbits were never introduced, and were therefore not followed by their supposed predator, the stoat.

To this is probably owed the recent exciting discovery in Pegasus II Reserve, of 11 kakapo. The rare native ground parrot had previously been thought to live only in Fiordland.

Westward from Mt Allen is a view of the deep inlet of Doughboy Bay, and farther north the great sweep of Mason Bay. This is a superb, 10 km crescent of white sand on which the rollers of the Tasman perpetually break. Behind the beach, huge sand dunes and creeping vegetation fight for supremacy. The highest dunes stand at 150 m and are 1500 m from the sea. The fragile plant communities that strive to stabilise the dunes include a small mat-forming plant found nowhere else in the world. Mason Bay also

Barren expanses of a highland wilderness

◄ *The white-tailed deer, so called because the underside of its tail is white, has done serious damage to coastal bush on Stewart Island*

has one of the island's few sheep runs.

Mason Bay is accessible by track from the head of Paterson Inlet, and to those who are prepared for wet feet and a chance of gales, it is an invigorating place. 'Blown sands, clean seas, Heaven's vault above, and space illimitable, these are the features of the bay,' wrote the naturalist H. Guthrie-Smith, and in 70 years Mason Bay has not changed.

▼ *The bleak heights of Table Hill and Mt Allen (in the background) lie at the heart of the Pegasus II wildlife reserve. Entry to the reserve is only for those with permits*

Peaks of the northern and southern massifs

In March 1770 Captain Cook's *Endeavour* hauled round the southern extremity of Stewart Island. 'By noon we were near the land which was uncommonly barren,' Sir Joseph Banks wrote. 'The few flat places we saw seemingly produced little or nothing, and the rest was all bare rocks which were amazingly full of large veins, and patches of some mineral that shone as if it had been polished, or rather looked as if the rocks were really paved with glass; what it was I could not at all guess, but it was certainly some mineral, and seemed to argue by its immense abundance a country abounding in minerals . . . .'. Banks could only have been describing the heights now called the Fraser Peaks, and their two most conspicuous summits, Gog and Magog. The granite of these domes was polished by the glaciers of the last ice age. The metallic gleam of the smooth granite—probably due to feldspar crystals—is a deception, for Gog and Magog have never yielded any worthwhile mineral. This southern extremity of Stewart Island is untracked wilderness. The upper slopes of the peaks hold little soil and support little vegetation. The sour swampland fringing them supports only grasses, sedges and *Dracophyllum*, known as grass-tree or, for its ability to burn, turpen-

▼*Gog and Magog in the Fraser Peaks, were named after legendary giants associated with London. Magog is the sharper peak*

tine scrub, The fernbird thrives there and an occasional white-tail deer is seen. Closer to the coast and facing the subantarctic seas, bog pine and muttonbird scrub dominate the windswept vegetation.

The wind-buffetted south coast was the scene of a massacre in 1810, when sealers rowed ashore near South Cape on a hunting expedition. Maoris from the far side of Foveaux Strait attacked them and killed all but 16-year-old James Caddell. For the next 12 years he adopted Maori manners and costume, marrying the daughter of the chief whose tribe had killed his companions.

In 1823 a newspaper explained that Caddell's life had been spared because in his fright he ran to an old chief and touched his mat. '. . . his person was then held sacred,' the newspaper said. 'Subsequently Caddell lost his language as well as European customs and soon became transformed from an English sailorboy into a dauntless and terrifying New Zealand chief.'

The Fraser Peaks look across the North Arm of Port Pegasus to the Tin Range, a remnant of the original crust of Stewart Island. Tin and gold have been mined there intermittently during the last 100 years. Northwest of the Tin Range is Mt Allen, at 749 m the highest peak in the southern massif. It was named after one of the first men to make an overland crossing from Port Pegasus to Paterson Inlet.

In the northern part of the island the outstanding heights are the Ruggedy Mountains and the Anglem highlands. Mt Anglem, the highest peak on Stewart Island at 980 m, is reached by track from Christmas Village Bay on the northeast coast. It is a three-hour climb to the summit. The bush is soon left behind and the track passes through leatherwood scrub and then tussock land where mountain daisies and other wildflowers bloom in summer.

The view from the rocky summit is superb—east to the flat outline of Ruapuke Island in Foveaux Strait, south across the Freshwater Valley and Paterson Inlet to the

▲*Granite knobs, made round and smooth by glacial action, lie a few kilometres south of Mt Allen, the highest peak of the Tin Range*

crumpled southern massif, west to Codfish Island lying beyond the Ruggedy Range and north to the Solander Islands and the hazy bulk of Fiordland.

The Solander Islands, 60 km off Stewart Island, are part of Fiordland National Park, but an old Maori legend attaches them to Foveaux Strait. It tells of a great whale which chewed through the great blocks of land until the strait was formed. Some of the small isles are crumbs that dropped from its prodigious jaws; some of the bigger islands were left because the whale did not like their taste. Gaining the open sea, the whale kept swimming westward, but the vigorous chewing had loosened some of its teeth. One tooth fell out and became Solander Island. The island, the largest of the group, rises precipitously to a sharp 351 m high summit. It was named by Captain Cook after a Swedish botanist.

Touring and walking

in wild New Zealand

This part of the book gives practical guidance on visiting the regions described and depicted in the second part. It tells how each region can be reached by air, rail and road, and the kinds of accommodation available.

The New Zealand climate is extremely varied. There are places with an annual rainfall of less than 380 mm only 100 km away from places that are drenched by more than 7600 mm. Monthly average rainfalls and maximum and minimum temperatures are provided for one or more places in each or near region to give guidance on the best times for visits.

The landscape is experienced most intensely by walking through it, so this part of the book gives details of some walks, ranging from short strolls to trips of several days, in most regions. The locations and details of all established sections of that ambitious and imaginative scheme, the New Zealand Walkway, are also given here.

Walking in the wilderness is not without dangers, but these are minimised if the basic rules for safety and survival are followed.

Visiting the wild regions

At least the fringes of all the wild landscape regions in the North and South Islands of New Zealand can be reached by road. In many regions sealed highways run through the dramatic scenery.

This section of the book outlines the main access roads to the regions described in Part 2. There are two classes of highway in New Zealand — national state highways, numbered from 1 to 5, and provincial state highways, numbered from 10 to 99. Generally the national highways are superior and they are almost entirely sealed.

Many of the regions can be reached by aircraft, train or bus, but schedules can change, so intending travellers should check. Accommodation available in the regions ranges widely in comfort, from first-class hotels to youth hostels.

New Zealand's climate is temperate, but varies considerably from region to region, influenced by the topography of the land and its isolated position in the Pacific Ocean. Westerly winds prevail throughout the year.

On the other hand, many wild regions of New Zealand are rainforest country where rain falls hard and often at any time of the year. The tables that follow give average rainfall over a 30-year period at selected weather stations and will give some guidance on when fine weather is most likely. The temperature figures are daily averages for each month.

Arthur's Pass National Park

Transport The *Tranz-Alpine* Express train runs daily to Arthur's Pass and Otira from Christchurch and Greymouth.
Road Access From Greymouth, go south on Highway 6 to Kumara Junction. Turn east onto Highway 73 and go to Otira and then over the mountains to Arthur's Pass township. From Christchurch, access is by Highway 73. Travelling distance from Christchurch is 153 km and 95 km from Greymouth.
Accommodation Arthur's Pass township has a motel, a guest house and a youth hostel. Otira has a hotel and there are mountain huts throughout the park.
Climate There are long periods of unsettled weather, often with gusty westerly winds.

Arthur's Pass

	J	F	M	A	M	J	J	A	S	O	N	D
mm	331	327	291	356	346	271	256	288	319	443	398	342
max	18.5	18.5	16.7	13.7	10.0	7.1	6.1	8.1	10.8	13.4	15.2	17.1
min	3.6	6.6	5.0	2.5	-1.0	-3.5	-4.0	-2.4	0.0	2.4	3.9	3.7

Auckland's West Coast

Transport Air New Zealand, Ansett New Zealand, Mount Cook Airlines and Air Nelson fly to Auckland daily from the main centres. The *Northerner Express* train travels nightly, Sunday to Friday, north and southbound on the Wellington–Auckland line. The *Silver Fern* train travels daily, Monday to Saturday, on the same route. Both stop at Te Kuiti from where there are connecting Intercity buses through to Waitomo Caves. Intercity coaches travel daily to Waitomo from Auckland and Rotorua.
Road Access The Waitakere Ranges are 30 km, via Henderson, from Auckland. The approach to Raglan is by Highway 22 from Auckland, connecting with Highway 23 from Hamilton.
Accommodation Auckland has all types of accommodation, from luxurious to budget, including two youth hostels. Otorohanga, Raglan, Kawhia, Te Kuiti and Waitomo have hotels and motels. Otorohanga has a youth hostel and Waitomo a budget hostel.
Climate Moderate temperatures with heavy rain in the north-east.

Whatawhata

	J	F	M	A	M	J	J	A	S	O	N	D
mm	81	112	109	135	150	191	163	157	127	150	119	114
max	23.0	23.7	22.1	19.4	16.2	13.8	13.1	14.2	15.7	17.2	18.9	21.3
min	12.8	13.4	12.0	9.7	7.5	5.5	4.4	5.6	6.9	8.7	10.2	12.0

Te Kuiti

	J	F	M	A	M	J	J	A	S	O	N	D
mm	91	94	99	114	142	168	155	150	127	152	119	119
max	24.1	24.6	22.8	19.8	16.4	13.7	13.2	14.3	16.1	17.9	20.0	22.3
min	12.6	12.8	11.6	8.7	6.2	3.8	3.0	4.6	6.4	8.1	9.8	11.5

Banks Peninsula

Transport Air New Zealand, Ansett New Zealand, Mount Cook Airlines and Air Nelson fly to Christchurch daily from the main centres. The *Coastal Express* train runs daily from Picton to Christchurch and vice versa. The *Southerner Express* runs Monday to Saturday, north and south bound, on the Christchurch–Invercargill line, and the *Tranz–Alpine* runs daily from Christchurch to Greymouth and back. There are bus services to Christchurch from Queenstown, Milford Sound, Mount Cook, Dunedin (Intercity and Mount Cook Landline, daily), Invercargill (Intercity and Mount Cook Landline, Sunday to Friday), Fox and Franz Josef Glaciers, Greymouth (Intercity, daily) and other centres. An Intercity bus runs daily to Akaroa from Christchurch Railway Station and local buses run from the centre of Christchurch to Lyttleton.
Road Access The main approach to Banks Peninsula is Highway 75 from Christchurch, but there are two other spectacular routes. The Summit Road from Christchurch to Gebbies Pass and then from Hill Top to Akaroa has superb views as it winds around the rims of the volcanic craters. The second route leaves the highway at Little River and climbs around Mt Bossu before it descends to the harbour at Wainui.
Accommodation Christchurch has a range of accommodation, from the luxurious to budget. At Akaroa there are hotels, motels, motor camps, cabins and an associate youth hostel. Camping sites are located at Akaroa, Le Bons Bay and Duvauchelle.

Akaroa

	J	F	M	A	M	J	J	A	S	O	N	D
mm	64	58	74	102	124	99	112	89	66	58	66	81
max	22.0	22.1	20.1	17.1	13.9	11.3	10.4	11.9	14.6	17.0	19.1	20.5
min	12.1	12.2	11.0	8.9	6.7	4.4	3.6	4.3	6.0	7.6	9.1	10.9

The Catlins

Transport Air New Zealand flies daily from the main centres to Invercargill. The *Southerner Express* train runs Monday to Saturday on the Christchurch–Invercargill line and includes a stop at Balclutha. There is a daily Intercity bus service to Invercargill from

on the Christchurch–Invercargill line and includes a stop at Balclutha. There is a daily Intercity bus service to Invercargill from Christchurch, Timaru and Dunedin, and a weekday Cook Landline bus service from Queenstown, Te Anau and Wanaka. There is a service to Picton, Monday to Saturday.

Road Access The main approaches to the Catlins are Highway 92 from Invercargill to Balclutha and Highway 1 from Edendale.

Accommodation There are hotels, motels and motor camps at Invercargill and Balclutha. Invercargill has a youth hostel. Owaka has a motor lodge and motel, and there is a motor camp at Pounawea, 4 km from Owaka.

Climate The Catlins has a variable climate, sheltered by the Southern Alps. There is a low rainfall and fairly constant sunshine in summer and winter storms bring snow and sleet to lower levels.

Finegand, Balclutha

	J	F	M	A	M	J	J	A	S	O	N	D
mm	55	41	57	62	69	55	41	38	52	58	60	64
max	19.8	20.1	18.6	15.4	11.9	9.4	8.9	11.0	13.7	15.3	16.9	18.9
min	9.7	9.3	8.8	5.7	3.5	1.5	0.4	1.5	3.5	5.1	6.8	8.4

Central Otago

Transport Air New Zealand, Ansett New Zealand and Mount Cook Airlines fly daily into Queenstown from Auckland, Mount Cook, Christchurch, Rotorua and Wellington. There are frequent flights between other main centres. Mount Cook Landline and Intercity buses run daily to Queenstown and Wanaka from Christchurch, Fox and Franz Josef Glaciers and Mount Cook. Intercity buses run Monday to Saturday and Mount Cook Landline buses run Sunday to Friday to Queenstown and Wanaka from Dunedin. Mount Cook Landline buses run from Invercargill to Queenstown Monday to Thursday, and to Wanaka on weekdays.

Road Access Highways 6 and 8 traverse Central Otago. Wanaka is linked with Queenstown by Highway 6 and by Highway 89 over the Crown Range, which may be closed during winter. Highway 89 is unsealed and comparatively difficult but offers magnificent views. It is used during the ski season as an access from Queenstown to the Cardrona and Treble Cone fields.

Accommodation There are hotels, motels and camping facilities at Queenstown, Wanaka, Cromwell and Frankton. Youth hostels are at Queenstown and Wanaka.

Climate Central Otago has an extreme climate, with hot summers and cold winters. Rainfall is the lowest in the country.

Cromwell

	J	F	M	A	M	J	J	A	S	O	N	D
mm	43	36	41	33	36	28	23	23	28	33	36	36
max	24.5	24.2	21.4	17.1	12.0	8.1	7.6	10.8	15.1	18.0	20.4	23.1
min	11.1	10.8	8.7	4.7	1.2	−1.2	−1.9	−0.6	2.8	5.4	7.4	9.6

Tapanui

	J	F	M	A	M	J	J	A	S	O	N	D
mm	89	71	84	79	84	89	66	51	56	74	81	79
max	28.8	27.8	26.7	21.9	18.4	14.6	14.5	16.8	19.8	22.9	25.4	27.1
min	2.9	2.6	1.7	−0.3	−2.3	−3.4	−4.6	−3.3	−2.4	−0.8	0.3	1.9

Coromandel Peninsula

Transport Air Coromandel operates daily flights between Auckland and the Coromandel Peninsula. Intercity buses operate an excursion trip from Auckland through Coromandel to Whitianga,

Sunday to Friday. There is a weekday Whangamata Buses service from Waihi to Whangamata.

Road Access Highway 25 winds around the Coromandel Peninsula from Thames on the west coast to Waihi in the east. Rough, hilly and winding roads cross the peninsula.

Accommodation There are hotels, motels and camping facilities at Thames, Coromandel, Whitianga, Whangamata and Waihi. There are camping grounds at many bays along the peninsula. There is a youth hostel at Opoutere.

Climate A moderate climate with heavy rain in winter.

Thames

	J	F	M	A	M	J	J	A	S	O	N	D
mm	66	94	97	114	122	135	127	124	102	109	94	94
max	23.8	24.2	22.7	20.0	17.3	14.8	14.3	15.0	16.6	18.4	20.3	22.1
min	14.8	15.3	14.0	11.5	9.1	6.9	6.1	6.9	8.6	10.7	12.2	13.8

East Cape

Transport Air New Zealand flies daily to Gisborne from the main centres and Eagle Air flies daily to Gisborne from Auckland and Napier. The *Bay Express* train runs daily from Wellington to Napier and vice versa, with a connecting bus on the Napier–Gisborne sector. There is an Intercity bus service daily between Auckland and Gisborne via Rotorua and between Wellington and Gisborne, Sunday to Friday.

Road Access Two roads give access to the East Cape region from the north. Highway 2 from Opotiki crosses the hills by the Waioeka Gorge. The longer but more picturesque Highway 35 follows the coast around the cape. This road winds through rugged country and it is not recommended in wet weather. Access from Napier is north on Highway 2. There is an alternative route on Highway 36 from Wairoa.

Accommodation There are hotels, motels and camping facilities in most settlements along the East Cape road. There is a youth hostel in Gisborne.

Climate The East Cape has a mild and sunny climate, with peak rainfall in August.

Ruatoria

	J	F	M	A	M	J	J	A	S	O	N	D
mm	127	135	152	173	206	193	211	218	142	142	114	119
max	24.3	24.3	22.8	20.4	17.7	15.1	14.3	15.0	17.0	19.3	21.2	22.8
min	13.7	13.7	12.5	10.0	7.6	5.3	4.8	5.9	7.0	8.7	10.3	12.3

Egmont National Park

Transport Air New Zealand flies daily into New Plymouth from the main centres. There are weekday Intercity and Newmans bus services to New Plymouth from Auckland, Hamilton, Tauranga and Wellington.

Road Access There are three approaches to Mt Egmont from Highway 3, which runs between New Plymouth and Hawera. Access to Dawson Falls Tourist Lodge is via Eltham, west to Kaponga and then north for 14.5 km. Stratford Mountain House is 14.5 km from Stratford via Pembroke Road. North Egmont Chalet is accessible from Egmont Village, 16 km west along Egmont Road.

Accommodation Dawson Falls Tourist Lodge and Stratford Mountain House have motel and bunk accommodation. At Dawson Falls there is also a chalet-style accommodation building called

'Konini', similar to North Egmont Chalet, which has bunk accommodation and camping facilities. There are motor camps in Stratford and Eltham and huts on the mountain. There are hotels, motels, a motor camp and a youth hostel in New Plymouth. Hawara has hotels, motels and a camping ground.

Climate Weather can change with unexpected rapidity in Egmont National Park, bringing a sudden drop in temperature, high winds, rain and poor visibility.

Stratford Mountain House

	J	F	M	A	M	J	J	A	S	O	N	D
mm	417	437	429	488	655	696	711	648	561	615	513	505
max	18.2	18.6	16.6	13.1	10.1	7.7	6.7	7.7	9.7	11.9	14.1	16.4
min	7.9	8.6	7.7	5.6	3.7	1.5	0.7	1.4	2.6	3.4	5.3	6.6

Fiordland National Park

Transport Mount Cook Airlines fly to Te Anau from Queenstown and Christchurch. Intercity and Mount Cook Landline buses run daily from Queenstown to Te Anau and Milford.

Road Access The Milford Road from Te Anau is the only main road into the park. For 125 km it winds through river flats and canyons. There may be delays of up to 25 minutes at the Homer Tunnel.

Accommodation Accommodation in Te Anau and Manapouri ranges from camping grounds to a first-class hotel. A youth hostel is situated on the Milford Road, 1.6 km from Te Anau. There are also camping sites along this road between Te Anau and the Eglinton Valley. At Milford there is a first class hotel, which may be subject to closure during the winter months, and a hostel. Te Anau Downs and Cascade Creek have motor lodges.

Climate Milford Sound is one of the wettest places in the country. The weather is unpredictable at all times.

Milford Sound

	J	F	M	A	M	J	J	A	S	O	N	D
mm	531	569	630	526	483	419	378	424	538	546	638	554
max	18.4	18.4	17.4	15.0	12.2	9.4	9.3	11.0	12.6	14.1	15.4	17.3
min	10.3	10.4	9.3	6.9	4.3	2.0	1.5	2.4	4.2	6.1	7.5	9.6

Te Anau

	J	F	M	A	M	J	J	A	S	O	N	D
mm	89	84	99	99	99	109	89	86	94	102	97	89
max	20.3	21.5	19.1	15.0	11.3	8.5	7.9	9.9	12.9	14.4	16.3	19.4
min	7.9	7.9	7.5	4.6	1.7	−0.2	−0.2	0.6	2.4	3.9	5.4	7.0

Golden Bay

Transport Air New Zealand, Mount Cook Airlines and Air Nelson fly daily to Nelson from the main centres, and there are commuter airlines operating. Newmans buses run daily to Nelson from Picton and Christchurch. There is a daily Intercity bus between the Glaciers, Greymouth and Nelson.

Road Access The approach to Golden Bay and Abel Tasman National Park is by Highway 60 from Nelson and Highway 6 from Westport. Park headquarters are at Totaranui, 32 km by metalled road from Takaka.

Accommodation There are hotels and motels at Takaka and Motueka, as well as motor camps and camping sites in the area, including the Totaranui Beach Camp in Abel Tasman National Park. There are summer youth hostels in Motueka and Takaka and an all-year-round youth hostel in Nelson. Tramping huts are

scattered throughout the Abel Tasman National Park.

Climate Golden Bay has a sunny, mild climate with little wind. Abel Tasman National Park has higher rainfall and lower temperatures than the plains.

Riwaka, Motueka

	J	F	M	A	M	J	J	A	S	O	N	D
mm	74	99	104	127	155	119	145	140	117	112	89	91
max	23.2	23.3	21.6	18.8	15.7	13.5	12.5	13.7	15.5	17.9	19.8	21.8
min	11.6	11.7	10.6	7.3	4.5	1.7	1.3	2.5	4.6	6.6	8.5	10.7

Farewell Spit

	J	F	M	A	M	J	J	A	S	O	N	D
mm	74	79	84	102	142	117	130	117	91	117	84	89
max	22.5	22.9	21.0	18.9	16.3	13.7	13.0	13.7	15.6	16.8	18.5	20.8
min	12.9	13.8	12.6	10.4	8.1	5.6	5.4	6.1	7.6	8.8	10.8	11.9

Hauraki Gulf

Transport Ferries run from Princes Wharf, Auckland, to Rangitoto Island and Waiheke Island. A ferry service also operates from Sandspit (north of Auckland, near Warkworth) to Kawau Island. Tourist aircraft, hydrofoil and charter boats operate to almost all the islands of the gulf. To land on some of the islands a permit is required, which can be obtained in writing from the Secretary of the Hauraki Gulf Maritime Park Board, P.O. Box 5249, Auckland 1.

Accommodation On Waiheke Island, Onetangi has a hotel, motels, a youth hostel and guest houses. There are camping areas at North Harbour, Kawau Island, and on Motutapu Island.

Climate The Hauraki Gulf has a modified Mediterranean climate with wet and cool winters and hot, dry summers.

Port Fitzroy, Great Barrier Island

	J	F	M	A	M	J	J	A	S	O	N	D
mm	94	130	135	160	185	211	201	213	147	135	127	114
max	23.4	23.9	22.9	20.6	18.2	16.2	15.4	15.9	17.0	18.4	20.2	21.9
min	15.0	15.3	14.9	13.0	10.9	9.0	8.1	8.6	9.6	10.7	12.3	14.0

Otara, Auckland

	J	F	M	A	M	J	J	A	S	O	N	D
mm	64	97	86	107	119	130	132	135	91	99	81	79
max	23.0	23.8	22.4	19.9	17.2	14.9	14.0	14.8	16.1	17.7	19.5	21.5
min	13.9	14.5	13.3	10.7	8.6	6.4	5.0	6.3	7.4	9.4	11.0	13.0

Hawke's Bay and Wairarapa coast

Transport *Daily Bay Express* rail services link Napier and Wellington. Intercity buses travel between Napier and Hastings, Sunday to Friday. Bus and rail services run daily between Wellington and Masterton.

Road Access Excursions to Cape Kidnappers run from Summerlee Station 20 km south of Hastings; the journey by four-wheel drive vehicle is 18 km return and takes three hours. The Cape can also be reached along the beach at low tide in tractor trailers run from Haumoana, 10 km northeast of Hastings. This excursion takes four hours.

Accommodation There is plentiful accommodation in the main centres on Highway 2. There are motor camps at Te Awanga and Clifton, near Cape Kidnappers, and a camping area at Mt Holdsworth, with hotels and camping areas at Carterton and Masterton.

Lake Ferry has a hotel and a motor camp. There is also a youth hostel at Kaitoki, near Upper Hutt.
Climate In the north, around Hastings and Napier, the climate is generally warm. The south coast, however, is exposed to winds, fog and sudden weather changes.

Hastings

	J	F	M	A	M	J	J	A	S	O	N	D
mm	58	58	61	56	79	84	79	86	48	51	46	61
max	25.4	25.1	23.1	20.4	16.8	14.3	13.4	14.7	16.9	19.7	22.0	23.9
min	12.4	12.6	10.6	7.9	5.1	2.6	2.4	3.4	4.8	7.0	8.9	11.1

Waingawa, Masterton

	J	F	M	A	M	J	J	A	S	O	N	D
mm	64	58	76	71	102	107	102	91	74	74	69	76
max	23.5	23.7	21.6	18.2	14.8	12.4	11.8	12.8	15.2	17.3	19.3	21.7
min	10.7	11.0	9.6	7.2	5.3	2.9	2.3	3.4	4.7	6.3	7.7	9.7

Kaikouras

Transport The main line between Picton and Christchurch runs along the Kaikoura coast. There are daily trains and several coachlines operate daily between these two centres.
Road Access The main approach to Kaikoura is by Highway 1, from both Picton and Christchurch. Highways 7 and 70 provide an alternative route between Kaikoura and Waipara, but both of these roads are unsealed.
Accommodation There are hotels, motels, a motor camp and a youth hostel in Kaikoura. Further north along the coast, there are camping facilities at Seddon.
Climate Winds are light in the Kaikouras, although the coast experiences the full effect of the winter squalls.

Kaikoura

	J	F	M	A	M	J	J	A	S	O	N	D
mm	69	64	76	74	102	66	81	81	51	61	66	74
max	19.9	20.1	19.2	16.5	13.7	11.4	10.7	11.4	13.6	15.4	17.0	18.7
min	12.5	12.6	12.0	9.5	7.3	5.2	4.6	5.1	6.6	7.8	9.4	11.2

Lake Taupo

Transport Air New Zealand and Mount Cook Airlines fly to Taupo daily from the main and resort centres. Newmans and Intercity coaches run daily from Auckland, Rotorua and Wellington and Napier to Taupo.
Road Access Taupo is on Highway 1, 153 km from Hamilton. From Rotorua to Taupo on Highway 5 is 84 km. From Napier, Taupo is 143 km northwest on Highway 5.
Accommodation Taupo has hotels, motels, motor camps, cabins and a summer youth hostel. There is a first-class hotel at Wairakei. Most bays around the lake have camping grounds and there are some huts in the Kaimanawa Forest Park.
Climate Taupo has a stable climate. Summers at Taupo are usually pleasantly warm but winters can be cold when the winds blow from the lake and the nearby mountains.

Taupo

	J	F	M	A	M	J	J	A	S	O	N	D
mm	81	94	76	91	109	122	117	109	102	102	84	112
max	23.4	23.3	21.3	17.8	14.3	11.7	10.9	12.2	14.5	16.9	19.1	21.4
min	10.8	11.3	9.9	7.2	4.9	2.8	1.7	2.6	4.1	6.0	7.8	9.8

Marlborough Sounds

Transport Air New Zealand flies daily to Blenheim from most main centres. The inter-island ferry runs daily and *Skyferry* operates six flights daily between Wellington and Picton. There is a daily train from Christchurch. Newmans buses travel daily to Picton from Nelson. Pelorus and Queen Charlotte Sounds are accessible by launch from Havelock and Picton respectively.
Road Access Little of the coast in the Marlborough Sounds is accessible by road. Havelock is approached from Nelson or Blenheim via Highway 6, and Picton from Blenheim via Highway 1. A minor road winds between Picton and Havelock.
Accommodation There are hotels, motels and camping grounds at Picton and Havelock. There is also a youth hostel at Havelock and an associate hostel at Picton. There is also accommodation on Kenepuru, Pelorus and Queen Charlotte Sounds.
Climate Fine weather during spring and summer with rapid changes. Strong gusty winds are felt in some areas.

Blenheim

	J	F	M	A	M	J	J	A	S	O	N	D
mm	51	43	51	53	76	58	66	61	53	53	48	51
max	23.7	23.5	21.8	18.8	15.5	12.9	12.3	13.5	15.8	18.0	20.3	22.4
min	11.9	12.1	10.3	7.6	4.6	1.8	1.4	2.9	4.9	7.0	8.7	10.9

Mt Aspiring National Park

Transport Mount Cook Airlines and Ansett New Zealand fly daily to Queenstown from Christchurch. Mount Cook Landline and Intercity coaches run daily from Christchurch to Queenstown and Wanaka. Buses also run daily to Wanaka from Fox and Franz Josef Glaciers, Dunedin and Mount Cook.
Road Access The approach from Omarama is southward on Highway 8 to Tarras, then westward on Highways 8A and 6. Access to Wanaka from Haast is through Mt Aspiring National Park, via the Haast Pass, on Highway 6.
Accommodation There are hotels, motels and motor camps in Queenstown, Wanaka and Hawea (15 km north of Wanaka on Highway 6). There are youth hostels at Queenstown and Wanaka and tramping huts throughout the park.
Climate If the weather is overcast in Queenstown or Wanaka, it will probably be raining in most parts of the park.

Lake Hawea

	J	F	M	A	M	J	J	A	S	O	N	D
mm	69	61	71	58	71	58	58	58	71	66	71	58
max	22.8	22.7	19.9	16.1	11.4	8.3	7.5	10.3	13.1	16.1	17.8	21.3
min	11.7	11.2	9.4	6.3	3.1	0.4	-0.3	1.1	3.6	6.0	7.9	10.3

Queenstown

	J	F	M	A	M	J	J	A	S	O	N	D
mm	74	66	76	71	79	66	64	61	76	76	76	64
max	21.7	21.6	19.3	15.3	11.3	8.2	7.7	10.0	13.1	15.8	17.9	20.4
min	9.9	10.0	8.4	5.8	2.7	0.3	-0.5	0.8	3.1	5.1	6.8	8.8

Mt Cook National Park

Transport Mount Cook Airlines fly daily to the Hermitage from Christchurch, Queenstown and Rotorua. Intercity and Mount Cook Landline buses run daily from Christchurch and Queenstown to Mt Cook village.

Road Access The usual approach to the park is by Highway 80 from Lake Pukaki. Drive northwest on Highway 8 from Omarama, or southwest on Highway 8 from Timaru, to Lake Pukaki. Access to Lake Pukaki from Christchurch is by Highway 1 to the Geraldine turnoff, by Highway 79 to Fairlie and then on to Lake Pukaki by Highway 8.

Accommodation The Hermitage, Glencoe Lodge and Mt Cook Motel provide first class accommodation in the Mt Cook village, but there are comfortable motels and chalets at lower tariffs. There is a youth hostel and an informal camping ground. There are also mountain huts in the park.

Climate The weather is changeable and summer rainstorms are common. Wind squalls, low cloud and a rapid fall in temperature accompany heavy rain.

Twizel

	J	F	M	A	M	J	J	A	S	O	N	D
mm	43	41	52	59	50	41	45	56	88	65	46	43
max	22.4	23.2	19.7	15.7	10.7	6.4	6.0	8.0	12.9	15.2	18.8	21.2
min	10.3	10.2	8.6	5.8	2.0	−1.0	−1.6	−0.4	2.9	4.5	7.1	8.8

The Hermitage, Mt Cook

	J	F	M	A	M	J	J	A	S	O	N	D
mm	401	391	353	340	323	251	244	282	330	371	399	386
max	19.2	19.3	17.8	14.0	9.8	7.2	6.0	8.1	11.2	14.0	15.7	18.2
min	8.0	8.1	6.8	4.0	0.6	−1.6	−2.7	−1.1	1.2	3.4	5.2	7.2

Nelson Lakes National Park

Transport Air New Zealand flies daily to Nelson from the main centres. Several commuter airlines fly to Nelson, from Blenheim, Palmerston North, Auckland, Wellington, Paraparaumu and Masterton. Newmans buses run daily to Nelson from Picton and Christchurch. A bus service operates from Nelson and Blenheim to St Arnaud township, three times a week.

Road Access Park headquarters are at St Arnaud on Lake Rotoiti. Approach from Nelson is southwest on Highway 6, then southeast on Highway 63 (102 km). From Westport, go east on Highway 6 and Highway 63 (101 km).

Accommodation Murchison has a hotel, motels, motor camps, cabins and a youth hostel (open from December to March, inclusive). St Arnaud has a guesthouse/motel, an alpine lodge and a motor camp. There is also a lodge and a guesthouse at Rotoroa. Camping areas are at Kerr Bay, Rotoroa and West Bay. Huts for trampers are positioned throughout the park.

Climate Rainfall is greater in the west than in the east of the park, with spells of unsettled weather in spring and early summer.

Lake Rotoiti

	J	F	M	A	M	J	J	A	S	O	N	D
mm	97	107	122	142	173	142	157	150	132	132	124	117
max	20.8	21.6	18.9	14.8	11.4	8.8	8.2	9.8	11.9	14.2	16.6	19.2
min	8.6	8.7	7.9	4.6	1.6	−2.0	−2.2	−0.6	1.7	3.4	5.5	7.6

Northland

Transport Eagle Air flies daily to Kaitaia and Whangarei from Auckland. Mount Cook Airlines fly daily to the Bay of Islands and Monday to Saturday to Kerikeri from Auckland, Christchurch, Rotorua, Mt Cook and Queenstown. Daily Intercity coach services connect Auckland and Whangarei through to Kaitaia and weekday Clarks Northerner Coachlines service operates from Auckland to Whangarei and Paihia. Amphibian flights can be arranged from Mechanics Bay in Auckland. There is a passenger ferry from Paihia to Russell and a car ferry operates from Opua (5 km south of Paihia) to Okiato Point (8 km from Russell). For a voyage around the islands, there is the Cream Trip, departing from Paihia every morning.

Road Access The main approach to Northland and the Bay of Islands is by Highway 1 from Auckland. The highway passes through Warkworth (66 km), Wellsford (85 km), Kaiwaka (103 km), Whangarei (174 km) to Kaitaia. The metalled road from north of Kaitaia to Cape Reinga is inclined to deteriorate during the holiday season.

Just before Cape Reinga an all-weather road gives access to Tapotupotu Bay. Access to Ninety-Mile Beach is from Ahipara (west of Kaitaia) and Waipapakauri (north of Kaitaia) by partly sealed roads. Bus tours up Ninety-Mile Beach to the cape are available from Kaitaia and Paihia.

The west coast route, Highway 12 through Dargaville and the Waipoua Kauri Forest to Kaikohe, is longer and is unsealed for a stretch. Highway 12 branches off Highway 1 at Brynderwyn, 112 km north of Auckland.

Accommodation There are numerous hotels in the Paihia–Waitangi area, including the THC Waitangi, a first-class resort hotel in Waitangi. There are hotels, motels and camping grounds in most towns throughout the region. There are youth hostels at Dargaville, Kaitaia, Kerikeri, Opononi and Whangarei. In the far north, there are camping grounds at Tapotupotu Bay and at Spirits Bay, just east of Cape Reinga. The most northerly hotels are at Waipapakauri and Houhora. There is no form of accommodation at Cape Reinga.

Climate Northland is characterised by a warm, humid summer, relatively mild winters and plentiful rainfall. Floods may occur.

Cape Reinga

	J	F	M	A	M	J	J	A	S	O	N	D
mm	61	58	69	97	107	112	119	122	81	71	61	58
max	20.9	21.7	20.7	18.8	16.6	14.9	14.0	14.3	15.2	16.4	17.9	19.5
min	15.9	16.6	15.8	14.5	12.8	10.9	9.8	10.0	10.6	11.5	12.7	14.4

Kaitaia

	J	F	M	A	M	J	J	A	S	O	N	D
mm	79	94	84	119	152	157	150	165	122	112	102	94
max	23.6	24.3	23.0	20.5	18.0	15.9	15.1	15.5	16.7	18.2	19.9	22.0
min	14.8	15.9	14.8	12.9	11.2	9.5	8.2	8.6	9.3	10.8	12.1	13.7

Waipoua Forest

	J	F	M	A	M	J	J	A	S	O	N	D
mm	79	112	107	150	178	198	178	191	137	150	114	102
max	22.4	23.1	22.1	20.0	17.4	15.4	14.5	15.1	16.2	17.7	19.2	21.2
min	12.6	13.1	12.2	10.8	8.5	6.9	5.7	6.2	7.0	8.6	10.0	11.3

Rotorua

Transport Air New Zealand, Ansett New Zealand, Mount Cook Airlines and Nelson Air fly daily from the main centres to Rotorua. There are daily Intercity, Mount Cook Landline and Newmans bus services from the main North Island centres.

Road Access From Hamilton, Highway 1 joins Highway 5 at Tirau. The route winds east for 110 km through the Waikato Valley and the Mamaku Ranges to Rotorua. The approach from Taupo is north through the Tahorakuri Forest for 84 km. Access from Tauranga is south for 92 km on Highway 33 and from Whakatane, southwest for 92 km on Highway 30.

Accommodation Rotorua has a wide variety of accommodation, including first-class hotels, motels, guesthouses and motor camps, as well as a youth hostel.

Climate Rotorua has a stable climate.

Whakarewarewa

	J	F	M	A	M	J	J	A	S	O	N	D
mm	99	114	117	117	150	150	142	137	127	122	104	132
max	22.7	22.9	21.2	18.3	15.0	12.6	11.8	13.0	15.0	17.1	19.2	21.1
min	12.0	12.7	11.1	8.2	5.7	3.5	2.6	3.7	5.3	7.2	8.9	11.1

Stewart Island

Transport The ferry *Acheron* sails from Bluff to Halfmoon Bay at 9 a.m. and returns at 2 p.m., Mondays, Wednesdays and Fridays. There is a connecting bus from Invercargill. South Air operates four flights daily from Invercargill to Halfmoon Bay. There is a mini-bus tour of the island from the bay.

Accommodation Oban in Halfmoon Bay has a hotel, motel units, a lodge, motor camp and a caravan park, as well as an associate youth hostel.

Climate The weather is very changeable. Brilliant sunshine may be followed by pouring rain.

Invercargill

	J	F	M	A	M	J	J	A	S	O	N	D
mm	89	79	94	104	91	107	69	66	74	86	94	89
max	18.4	18.5	17.2	14.7	12.0	9.5	9.4	11.1	13.1	14.8	16.1	17.4
min	8.9	8.5	7.5	5.3	2.6	1.5	0.5	1.2	3.3	5.3	6.4	8.1

Tongariro National Park

Transport The *Silver Fern* train runs Monday to Saturday from Auckland and Wellington, through the National Park. From National Park township there is a connection to the Chateau and Whakapapa on Mt Ruapehu. The *Northerner Express* runs nightly on the same route. Buses run regularly from Auckland and Wellington to National Park township. There are similar connections to Ohakune. Mountain transport is available from Ohakune to Turoa skifield.

Road Access From Taumarunui, 38 km south along Highway 4 to the settlement of National Park. The main road to Whakapapa village is Highway 48. The turnoff is signposted 9 km along Highway 47 from National Park. From Turangi travel south on Highway 1 to the Rangipo turnoff of Highway 47A. Travel the length of 47A until it joins Highway 47 and continue on to the turnoff of Highway 48. Access from Ohakune is by Highway 49A and National Park, or by the Ohakune Mountain Road.

Accommodation There is a variety of accommodation at National Park and Turoa skifield is serviced by the mountain village of Ohakune. There is a youth hostel at Ohakune.

Climate Weather in the park can change quickly, bringing rain and high winds.

The Chateau, Tongariro

	J	F	M	A	M	J	J	A	S	O	N	D
mm	188	206	178	224	257	292	269	251	244	279	262	264
max	16.7	16.8	15.2	12.1	9.0	6.5	5.8	6.7	8.6	10.7	12.7	15.1
min	6.6	7.4	6.1	3.9	1.6	−0.3	−1.3	−0.5	0.5	1.9	3.5	5.3

Urewera National Park

Transport Buses run twice a week to Aniwaniwa from Rotorua and Wairoa.

Road Access Aniwaniwa is accessible from both Rotorua and from Wairoa by Highway 38. This road includes a long unsealed stretch on which care needs to be taken.

Accommodation There are motels, chalets, cabins, a motor camp and camping areas at Waikaremoana and a motel at Ruatahuna. There are camping sites with basic facilities at Mokau and Hopuruahine, and huts throughout the park for which fees are payable for overnight stays.

Climate The Urewera National Park is characterised by frequent steady rain. Occasional gale-force winds accompany torrential rainstorms, particularly in summer.

Lake Waikaremoana

	J	F	M	A	M	J	J	A	S	O	N	D
mm	150	140	168	180	211	188	198	226	150	150	147	152
max	20.4	20.4	18.6	15.3	12.2	9.7	8.9	10.0	12.1	14.7	16.7	18.9
min	11.3	11.7	10.5	8.4	6.0	3.8	3.0	3.5	4.6	6.4	8.0	10.0

Westland National Park

Transport Air Nelson has daily flights from both Christchurch and Nelson to Hokitika. Intercity buses travel daily to Christchurch, Greymouth, Fox Glacier and Franz Josef Glacier. There is an Intercity bus service which runs daily from Queenstown and Wanaka to Fox and Franz Josef Glaciers.

Road Access Highway 6 crosses the park, giving good access from both north and south. The 24 km of highway between Franz Josef and Fox Glacier townships winds and climbs steeply.

Accommodation There are hotels, motels and camping facilities at Franz Josef and Fox Glaciers. Accommodation is available in the Westland National Park at Harihari, Whataroa, Lake Paringa, Lake Moeraki and Haast. There is a youth hostel at Franz Josef and a shelter hostel at Okarito.

Climate Westland National Park is rainforest, with periods of heavy rain, particularly during spring and early summer. Changes in wind, weather, temperature and visibility can occur quickly on the mountains.

Franz Josef

	J	F	M	A	M	J	J	A	S	O	N	D
mm	457	495	450	401	411	297	343	381	439	488	513	455
max	19.8	20.0	18.9	16.5	14.1	11.5	11.4	12.5	13.6	14.8	16.1	18.9
min	10.2	10.4	9.8	7.2	5.2	2.7	2.0	3.1	4.7	6.2	7.4	9.3

Walking in the wild regions

Arthur's Pass National Park

Avalanche Peak
There are two all-day walks in summer. The easier is Scott's Track, signposted 400 m north of Arthur's Pass village. A side track 8 km up Scott's Track leads to Avalanche Peak with views of the Upper Bealey Valley and Arthur's Pass. The more difficult walk is a steep track starting behind the chapel at Avalanche Creek. The track emerges above the bushline and goes along the ridge to Avalanche Peak.

Bridal Veil Falls
The walk up the east side of the valley to the Bridal Veil lookout takes half-day from Arthur's Pass village. The walk begins at the car park at the northern end of the village.

Dobson Nature Walk
An easy self-guided nature walk on the summit of Arthur's Pass, 5 km north of the village. Pamphlets are available at the national park headquarters. The track crosses bog and tussock areas before climbing onto a ridge overlooking the Otira Valley. A right turn at the junction of the Otira Valley track leads back to the highway.

Mt Bealey
An all-day trip. The track climbs through the forest to emerge in open tussock country and follow the crest of the ridge to Mt Bealey. It starts 300 m south of Arthur's Pass village, just over Rough Creek.

Bealey Valley Track
An easy half-day return walk starts from the highway, 2.6 km north of Arthur's Pass village. A footbridge crosses the Bealey River. There are fine views of Mt Rolleston. The track then follows the river, to the gorge where avalanche debris from the mountains collects.

Auckland's West Coast

Bridal Veil Falls
The walk starts from the Raglan–Kawhia road near the Pakoka River bridge. A wide track follows the stream through unspoiled bush to the top of the falls. A steep track continues down to an even more spectacular vantage point at the foot of the falls.

Te Puia Beach
A one-hour walk around Kawhia Heads, starting from Karewa Beach, leads to hot springs at Te Puia Beach. The springs are in front of the first white shellbank. The best time for a visit is when the tide has turned. Allow half a day.

Waitakere Ranges
There are more than 130 km of well-kept walking tracks in the Waitakere Ranges. Information on the walks is available from the information office in the park. From Piha Beach a steep climb from the top of Gander Road leads to Maungaroa trig, which has a superb view. Another popular walk is from the end of Glen Esk Road to Kitekite Falls. Allow 45 minutes.

Banks Peninsula

Coronation Hill Walk
From the Sign of the Kiwi to Kennedy's Bush. The round trip takes five hours.

Crater Rim
Panoramic views can be enjoyed on a walk from Brides Path to Coopers Knob, with a side extension from the Sign of Kiwi to the Sign of Takahe. It parallels the Summit Road Scenic Drive.

Godley Head Walkway
There are two walks from Godley Head Park, the Tunnel Route (2 km, 1 hour) and the Taylor's Mistake (6 km, 3 hours).

Mt Brazenose
A stiff climb with fine views of Banks Peninsula, the Canterbury Plains and the Southern Alps. Access is from Akaroa, 7 km along Lighthouse Road to Flea Bay summit.

Mt Herbert
The 20 km track starts at Orton-Bradley Farm Park and goes up to the summit of Mt Herbert. From the top of the mountain three arms diverge, one back to Orton-Bradley Farm, one to Diamond Harbour and one to Little River–Port Levy Saddle.

Central Otago

Mt Iron
A track to the summit is signposted 1.3 km east of Wanaka on Highway 6. Allow 90 minutes for the walk to the top and back.

Queenstown Hill
A leisurely climb to the summit of Queenstown Hill gives wide views. The track begins in Kent Street. Allow about three hours for the round trip. A more spectacular view is from Ben Lomond, reached by a track starting in Lomond Terrace. Allow six hours for the walk there and back. Another breathtaking view over the town, lake and mountains is from Bob's Peak. Access to the track is from Brecon Street. There are many routes to the top of the Remarkables, varying in difficulty. All are full-day walks.

Coromandel Peninsula

Castle Rock
Access is southeast of Coromandel, on the Whitianga Road. Allow an hour and a half.

Coromandel Walkway
Access is from the end of the eastern coastal road, 7 km beyond Port Jackson, or from the end of the western coastal road, 10 km from Port Charles at Stony Bay. The walk takes three hours one way and goes from Fletchers Bay to Stony Bay.

Kauaeranga Valley
There are many fine tracks in the Kauaeranga Valley. Further information is available from the visitor centre, 12 km into the valley. The turnoff is from Highway 26, 1.5 km south of Thames.

Mt Moehau
An all-day climb to the summit provides spectacular panoramic views. Access to the track is from Te Hope Stream, 35 km north of Coromandel township.

Wentworth Valley Track
The access road is signposted 2.7 km south of Whangamata Post Office. The walk to the Wentworth Falls begins 1 km past the picnic ground, follows the stream, crosses it in places and ascends a ridge to the top of the falls. There is a view down Wentworth Valley out to sea. An intersecting track descends to the lagoon. Allow three hours.

East Cape

Anaura Bay
The two-hour walk begins at the Anaura Bay Recreation Reserves, crossing into the Waipare Farm Settlement Block. There are magnificent views of the coastline.

Cooks Cove
An easy family walk to Cook's landing place at Tolaga Bay, 52 km north of Gisborne. The return trip takes about 2½ hours.

Egmont National Park

There are more than 300 km of walking tracks in Egmont National Park. Further information about the various walks is available from the visitors' centres at North Egmont and Dawson Falls.

Fiordland National Park

Hollyford Track
The track begins at Cascade Creek in the Eglinton Valley. Public transport is available to Hollyford Road from Te Anau. The only way back from the end of the track at Long Reef is on foot or by chartered plane. See also pp. 270–1.

Lake Hauroko
A camping ground at Lake Hauroko, 31 km west of Clifden, is the starting point for

some walks in the southern part of the park. A walk from the lake to Lookout Bluff takes about two and a half hours for the round trip.

Lake Monowai

Tracks lead to Rodger Inlet (three hours and a half) and on to Clark Hut on the Grebe River via Green Lake (nine hours).

Milford

Along the Milford Road from Te Anau there are walks signposted at 82 km. Allow two and a half hours for the walk to and from Key Summit. At the head of Milford Sound, where Tutoko and Cleddau Rivers meet, a tough four-hour track leads to Mt Tutoko. From the Doughboy Landing, reached by boat from Milford, there is a 90-minute walk to Giant Gate Falls.

Milford Track

A motor launch takes walkers from Te Anau across the lake to the start of the track. Another launch collects them at the end of the track and travels on to Milford. Buses run from Milford to Te Anau. Walks begin three days a week from December to April. See also pp.262–5.

Golden Bay

Cape Farewell Walk

Magnificent views of Farewell Spit on a one-hour walk. The start of the walk is signposted 26 km from Collingwood on the road to Wharariki Beach.

Gibbs Hill Track

Views over Golden Bay and Tasman Bay. The track is signposted on the road to Totaranui from Takaka. Allow half a day.

Heaphy Track

A five-day walk from Bainham, over the Tasman Mountains to the Kohaihai River, 15 km north of Karamea, on the west coast. There are huts along the track for which fees are payable for overnight stays.

Marahau/Whariwaharangi Bay

A three-day coastal walk begins at the car park at Marahau, which is reached by formed road either via Kaiteriteri or over Sandy Bay Hill. The track crosses lagoons and estuaries. There are huts for which fees are payable for overnight stays.

Takaka Hill Walk

Through beech forest to a rocky canyon on a one-hour walk starting 14 km west of Riwaka on Highway 60.

Totaranui

The Headland Track climbs through the forest to a point overlooking Totaranui. Access to the track is across the tidal inlet from the Totaranui camping ground. Allow one hour. A slightly longer walk is along a track from Awaroa Road, 1 km from the Totaranui turnoff, to the beach.

Hauraki Gulf

Motutapu Farm Walkway

There are magnificent views of the Hauraki Gulf islands on this 3.5 km route on Motutapu Island. Access is by launch from Princess Wharf steps, Auckland. The round trip takes two to three hours. The Walkway is closed from 1 July to 30 September during the lambing season.

Rangitoto Island

The most interesting of many walks over the island is the 4 km walk from Rangitoto Wharf to the summit of the volcano. There are magnificent views of the Hauraki Gulf, the Waitemata Harbour and Auckland City.

Hawkes Bay/Wairarapa

Cape Kidnappers

An 8 km walk along the beach from Clifton, 21 km east of Hastings, leads to the gannet sanctuary at Cape Kidnappers. A permit from the ranger at Clifton is needed for the visit. The sanctuary is closed from July to November. The walk, which takes about two hours each way, should be made only at low tide—starting no earlier than three hours after high tide and beginning the return no later than an hour and a half after low tide. Watch for poisonous katipo spiders in the driftwood above the high tide line.

Putangirua Pinnacles

An hour's walk from Lake Ferry to Cape Palliser leads to the pinnacles. The access is signposted 17 km along the road from the Lake Ferry Road turnoff.

Kaikouras

Kaikoura Peninsula

The 4.5 km walkway provides several coastal walks around the Kaikoura Peninsula across pastoral lands. There are views of the Kaikoura Ranges and also seal and tern colonies. The walk takes about 1½ hours.

Lake Taupo

Taupo Walkway

There are parking areas at both ends of the two-and-a-half-hour walk. Water is released through the Aratiatia Rapids at 10 a.m. and 2.30 p.m. daily for an hour and a half. The walk passes through a scenic reserve and also gives views of the Huka Falls and the Wairakei Geothermal Power Station.

Kaimanawa Forest Park

There are numerous walking tracks in the Park. Access to the park is by Clements

Mill Road, Kiko Road, Kaimanawa Road, Waipakahi Road and by Desert Road.

Mt Tauhara

There are superb views over Lake Taupo and the Kiangaroa Plains from the summit of Mt Tauhara. Access to the start of the track is on Mountain Road, 6 km along Highway 5. Allow three hours for the return climb.

Marlborough Sounds

Anakiwa Walkway

Six-and-a-half-hour walk following the foreshore of Queen Charlotte Sound before climbing through bush to Te Mahia on Kenepuru Sound then to Torea Bay. Access is by road from Linkwater or by boat from Picton.

Endeavour–Resolution Walkway

Seven-hour track in Queen Charlotte Sound, leading from Endeavour Inlet through Resolution Bay to Ship Cove.

Pelorus Walkway

A 22 km track, with views of the lower Pelorus and Kenepuru Sounds, from Kaiuma Bay, north of Havelock. It climbs through bush to the Kaiuma Saddle, then descends to Nydia Bay, climbs to Nydia Saddle and ends at Elaine Bay. Allow three days.

Wither Hills Walk

A circular walk of two-and-a-half hours offering excellent views over Blenheim, the Wairau Valley, and Cook Strait. It climbs through farmland to a 240 m lookout, where a loop track allows the less energetic to return to the start. Further along the walk, Taylor Valley and dam come into view.

Mt Aspiring National Park

Glacier Burn

An attractive short walk up the Matukituki Valley from the old Aspiring homestead into the upper basin of the Glacier Burn takes about half an hour.

Greenstone Track

An hour's walk from Elfin Bay on the shore of Lake Wakatipu leads to the start of the track at Rere Lake. The 40 km walk to Lake Howden is usually spread over two days. The track joins the Routeburn Track at Lake Howden. Access to Elfin Bay is by boat from Queenstown or Glenorchy.

Rees-Dart Track

A four-day or five-day round trip from the Glenorchy–Paradise Road on Lake Wakatipu. See pp.230–1.

Routeburn Track

This four-day track is professionally managed. Information is available at the Glenorchy ranger station, 49 km along the shore of Lake Wakatipu from Queenstown. During summer, buses run from Queenstown to the Route Burn end of the track, and regularly along the Milford–Te Anau road at the other end. See also pp.232–3.

Mt Cook National Park

Bowen Bush
The Bowen Bush ten-minute walk starts on the south side of Glencoe Stream. It passes through dense subalpine scrub to a vantage point with excellent views up the Hooker Valley to Mt Cook.

Governors Bush
Through some of the last stands of silver beech in the Hooker Valley on a one-hour return walk. The signposted track starts near the post office. The highest point overlooks Mt Sebastopol.

Hooker Valley
A half-day walk, crossing two swing-bridges, to magnificent views from Sefton Stream.

Kea Point Track
This half-day track starts in front of the Hermitage, in Mt Cook village, and ends at a point overlooking the Mueller Glacier, with views of the ice face of Mt Sefton, the Hooker Valley and Mt Cook. Allow one and a half hours, one way, from the village.

Red Tarns
Outstanding views of the Mt Cook Range on a day's walk. The track leaves the highway south of the national park headquarters, crosses Black Birch Stream and zigzags steeply to the three small Red Tarns. A climb to the top of Mt Sebastopol provides a wider panorama of peaks, glaciated valleys and river flats.

Wakefield Track
An interesting half-day walk with creeks, waterfalls, and views of Mt Sefton and the Sealy Range. The track, which passes between Hooker River and the base of the Mt Cook Range, can be reached from Mt Cook village by following the Hooker Track to the first swing-bridge and turning right.

Nelson Lakes

Lake Head Track
A full-day's walk around the shore of Lake Rotoiti. A track from Kerr Bay follows the beach where a well-formed track leads to the head of the lake. Return is along the western shore beneath the Robert Ridge.

Paddy's Track
An all-day walk on a track winding up over the exposed northern slopes of Mt Robert and turning west to link with the Pinchgut Track and return to the Mt Robert Lookout.

Peninsula Walk
Two-hour walk from Kerr Bay along the western shore of Lake Rotoiti to West Bay. Return by View Road which leads to Rotoiri Lodge and back to St Arnaud.

Pinchgut Track
The track, starting from the car park at Paddy's Hut, zigzags through beech forest to the snowfields on Mt Robert. Allow three hours for the round trip.

Porika Track
A half-day walk from the Lake Rotoroa car park leads up over the ridge between Rotoroa Peak and Hodgson Peak. From the lookout above the forest line there is a view to the lake head, with Mt Misery behind.

Rotoroa Track
Along the eastern shore to the Sabine Hut at the head of the lake. It is a full day's walk to this point, from which experienced trampers can follow marked tracks eastward and up the Sabine Valley.

St Arnaud Range
Magnificent views of Lake Rotoiti and both sides of the Main Divide on a full-day walk. The track starts near the motorcamp at Kerr Bay and zigzags up through the bush to emerge at Parachute Rocks.

Northland

Cape Reinga/Ninety-Mile Beach Walkway
The 100 km marked route starts at Cape Reinga and leads by way of Te Werahi and Twilight beaches to the top of Ninety-Mile Beach. Allow at least seven hours to Te Paki Station Road. The route continues along the beach as far as Ahipara but returns to the road at marked points.

Cape Reinga/Spirits Bay Walkway
Walk begins at Cape Reinga car park and passes through Sandy Bay to Tapotupotu Bay (two hours). The route continues to Te Paki trig (three hours and a half) and on to Pandora Beach and Spirits Bay (five hours). There is vehicle access from the main road at Tapotupotu Bay, Te Paki trig and Spirits Bay.

Dome Forest Walkway
Starts from Highway 1, 7 km north of Warkworth. A steep climb through native bush leads up to a hill with views of the Hauraki Gulf. The walk continues to Waiwhiu Kauri Grove and back to the car park. The round trip takes about two hours.

Kaitaia Walkway
There are views of the northern peninsula, the Okahu Falls, Diggers Valley and Takahue Valley from various places on the walk, which takes three-and-a-half hours. Access is 3 km south of Kaitaia on Highway 1. Turn right at Larmers Road and follow the metalled track to Kiwanis Club Bush Camp hut.

Mangawhai Cliffs Walkway
Begins 2 km along Mangawhai Beach, east of Kaiwaka. A farm track on top of the cliffs gives extensive views inland and of the islands of the Hauraki Gulf. A shag colony may be viewed. Return along the foreshore is not advised at high tide or when the sea is rough. Allow about four hours for the return walk. The walkway is closed from 1 July to 30 September.

Maungatapere Walkway
Panoramic views from the main ridge line. Allow an hour and a half. Turn left into Pukeatua Road 13 km west of Whangarei on Highway 14.

Moirs Hill Walkway
Starts near Redwoods Depot, 6 km south of Warkworth on Highway 1. Passes through Pohuehue Scenic Reserve to a forest road with views of the Hauraki Gulf. The walk ends at Moirs Hill Lookout. Allow three-and-a-half hours to Moirs Hill.

Mt Auckland Walkway
Walk through native forest in Ataunui Forest to the Summit of Mt Auckland, which has panoramic views in all directions. The unsealed, steep, winding Glorit-Kaipara Hills road, off Highway 16, 22 km north of Kaukapakapa, leads to the start of the walkway. Allow three to four hours each way for the walk.

Russell Walkway
The track passes through the Ngaiotonga Scenic Reserve and Russell Forest. There are excellent views from two summits. Access is from the Russell–Whangaruru road, 20 km east of Russell. Eight hours should be allowed.

Rotorua

In the thermal areas around the Rotorua region many of the walking tracks have admission fees. Most of the walking tracks not in the thermal areas are free.

Mokoia Island
There are 4 km of walks through regenerating bush on this island on Lake Rotorua. Wekas and other native birds live freely on this predator-free island. A launch leaves Rotorua twice daily.

Tikitere (Hell's Gate)
This very interesting walk leads past boiling pools, mud pools, a thermal waterfall and a crater lake. Allow one hour.

Eastern and Western Okataina Walkways
The two tracks pass through rolling volcanic country. The Eastern track is 8 km long and takes two and a half hours, beginning at the end of Okataina Road along the eastern shoreline of Lake Okataina and ending on the shores of Lake Tarawera.

Another track continues on from this point to the Tarawera Falls. The Western track passes through Lake Okataina Scenic Reserve, with views of Mt Tarawera, the Bay of Plenty and the Rotorua Lakes. The walk, which can be broken into shorter walks, is 22.5 km long and takes six hours. It begins at Ruato Bay, Lake Rotoiti, 22 km northeast of Rotorua on Highway 30 and ends at Lake Okareka. Buses run from Rotorua and a tourist launch goes to Ruato from Okere Falls. There is no public transport at the end of the walk.

Waimangu

The track leads down the thermal valley to the shore of Lake Rotomahana and a direct view of the ragged crater ridge of Mt Tarawera. There are launch trips available.

Whakarewarewa Thermal Reserve

This interesting walk includes Pohutu Geyser, the Prince of Wales Feathers Geyser, boiling pools, mud pools, silica terraces and a replica of a Maori village. Allow one hour.

Whakarewarewa Forest Park

Many of the walks in this park are outlined at the Redwood Grove Information Centre, Rotorua. A short walk through tall redwood forest starts at the Redwood Grove. A two-hour walk around the Blue Lake passes through bush shrublands and pine forest. Access to the start of the track at the northwest corner of the lake is by Tarawera Road, off Highway 30. The eight-hour Forest Park Walk passes the Blue and Green Lakes and the Waipa Mill before returning to the starting point at the Redwood Grove.

Tongariro National Park

Ketetahi Springs

A well-defined track leads to a fascinating thermal valley. The start is signposted on Highway 47, 6.4 km east of the junction with the Pihanga Saddle route to Turangi. It is a walk of two-and-a-half hours to the springs from the Ketetahi car park.

Mt Ruapehu

Several tracks start from the Mt Tongariro National Park headquarters at Whakapapa Village on Mt Ruapehu. Most of the tracks can be walked only in summer.

The two-hour Whakapapanui Track follows the Whakapapanui Stream through the bush and passes the Golden Rapids. The round trip to Silica Springs takes half a day.

The full-day walk to the Whakapapanui gorge follows the road above Chateau Tongariro to the bridge across the Whakapapanui Stream. From there it follows the stream to the gorge.

The return climb to the Mt Ruapehu crater lake is an easy one-day walk for the fit.

Taranaki Falls

There is a good view of Mts Ngauruhoe and Ruapehu from the bridge above the Taranaki Falls. The 3 km track passes through tussock and beech as it follows the river to the falls. The circular walk takes about three hours. The track continues to the Tama crater lakes. Take warm clothing for the walk and allow six hours for the round trip.

Tongariro Track

It takes three to four days for a round trip from the park headquarters, taking in the craters of Mt Tongariro and Mt Ngauruhoe. There are three huts along the track.

Urewera National Park

Ngamoko Track

A steep half-day walk to the summit of the Ngamoko Range. There are views over Lake Waikaremoana and out to the coast. The track starts at Whaitiri Point.

Lake Ruapani Track

This easy track, which links with Lake Waikareiti Track, reaches Lake Ruapani by Waipai Swamp, noted for its orchids. From the park headquarters and back allow six to seven hours.

Lake Waikareiti

An easy walk, starting at the park headquarters, leads to the lake. The return walk takes three hours.

Lake Waikaremoana

From the car park at the Onepoto entrance to the lake, 10 km from Aniwaniwa, a track leads up Panekiri Bluff to a panorama of the lake. The return journey to this point takes four and a half hours. The track descends to the lake, following it around to Hopuruahine Landing. There are six huts along the 62 km route, which takes three or more days. Access to both ends of the track is from Highway 38.

Mt Manuoha Track

This track leads to the highest point in the Urewera National Park (1402 m), from which there are views over Poverty Bay and as far as Lake Taupo and Mt Ruapehu. Allow two days, return. The track starts from the Waiotukapuna Stream bridge.

Mt Whakataka

Magnificent views from the summit of Mt Whakataka are the reward for a day's walk to and from Hopuruahine Landing.

Westland National Park

Alex Knob

The most impressive view of Franz Josef Glacier is from Alex Knob. A kilometre along the access road to the glacier a well-graded track through varied rainforest climbs gradually for 10 km. There are superb views of the entire length of the glacier, the peaks at its head and the coast from Greymouth in the north to Knights Point in the south. The walk there and back takes about seven hours.

Canavans Knob

Magnificent views of the Franz Josef Glacier and some of the peaks of the Main Divide from the end of this steep track, near the top of the knob. There are several views of the coast along the track. It begins at the highway less than 3 km south of Franz Josef township. Allow 30 minutes each way.

Copland Track

The track crosses the Main Divide at the Copland Pass and goes into Mt Cook National Park. Only experienced trampers should continue past the first stage, an all-day walk to Welcome Flat. Access is from Highway 6, some 26 km south of Fox Glacier.

Fox Glacier

The terminal face walk starts at the end of the access road, south of Fox Glacier township on Highway 6. The walk to Cone Rock offers the most impressive views of the glacier, but it can be steep in parts. It begins on Glacier View Road and takes 40 minutes one way. There are also fine views of the glacier and mountains from Mt Fox.

Franz Josef Glacier

It is inadvisable to walk on the glacier without a guide, but there are walking tracks in the vicinity. The glacier terminal is approached from the end of the access road. Allow 40 minutes for the walk over ice-scoured rock to the face.

Gillespies Beach

There are mountain and coastal views from a trig point reached by a track from the bridge near the mouth of the lagoon, 21 km from Fox Glacier.

Greens Beach

Home of a seal colony, 2 km north of Lake Ianthe. Allow 90 minutes each way.

Lake Matheson

It is a two-hour walk around the lake. A track branches off to Lake Gault. From Lake Matheson to Lake Gault and back takes four hours. Access to the Lake Matheson track is from the car park off the Gillespies Beach road, 3 km from Fox Glacier.

Lake Wombat

This track follows the Alex Knob Track for 1.5 km from its start before it descends a short distance to Lake Wombat. Allow two hours for the round trip.

Okarito Trig

Magnificent views of the Southern Alps on a clear day. The 45-minute track to the trig starts 200 m from the town memorial at Okarito, reached by a road off Highway 6, 23 km northwest of Franz Josef Glacier.

New Zealand Walkway system

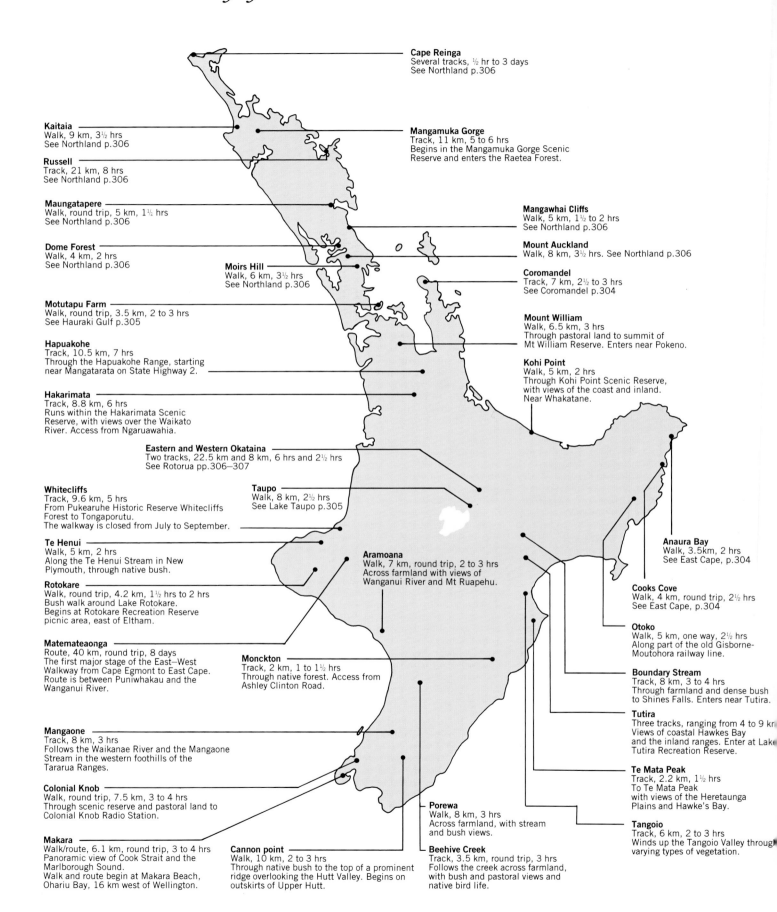

Cape Reinga
Several tracks, ½ hr to 3 days
See Northland p.306

Kaitaia
Walk, 9 km, 3½ hrs
See Northland p.306

Russell
Track, 21 km, 8 hrs
See Northland p.306

Maungatapere
Walk, round trip, 5 km, 1½ hrs
See Northland p.306

Dome Forest
Walk, 4 km, 2 hrs
See Northland p.306

Moirs Hill
Walk, 6 km, 3½ hrs
See Northland p.306

Motutapu Farm
Walk, round trip, 3.5 km, 2 to 3 hrs
See Hauraki Gulf p.305

Hapuakohe
Track, 10.5 km, 7 hrs
Through the Hapuakohe Range, starting
near Mangatarata on State Highway 2.

Hakarimata
Track, 8.8 km, 6 hrs
Runs within the Hakarimata Scenic
Reserve, with views over the Waikato
River. Access from Ngaruawahia.

Eastern and Western Okataina
Two tracks, 22.5 km and 8 km, 6 hrs and 2½ hrs
See Rotorua pp.306–307

Whitecliffs
Track, 9.6 km, 5 hrs
From Pukearuhe Historic Reserve Whitecliffs
Forest to Tongaporutu.
The walkway is closed from July to September.

Te Henui
Walk, 5 km, 2 hrs
Along the Te Henui Stream in New
Plymouth, through native bush.

Rotokare
Walk, round trip, 4.2 km, 1½ hrs to 2 hrs
Bush walk around Lake Rotokare.
Begins at Rotokare Recreation Reserve
picnic area, east of Eltham.

Matemateaonga
Route, 40 km, round trip, 8 days
The first major stage of the East–West
Walkway from Cape Egmont to East Cape.
Route is between Puniwhakau and the
Wanganui River.

Mangaone
Track, 8 km, 3 hrs
Follows the Waikanae River and the Mangaone
Stream in the western foothills of the
Tararua Ranges.

Colonial Knob
Walk, round trip, 7.5 km, 3 to 4 hrs
Through scenic reserve and pastoral land to
Colonial Knob Radio Station.

Makara
Walk/route, 6.1 km, round trip, 3 to 4 hrs
Panoramic view of Cook Strait and the
Marlborough Sound.
Walk and route begin at Makara Beach,
Ohariu Bay, 16 km west of Wellington.

Mangamuka Gorge
Track, 11 km, 5 to 6 hrs
Begins in the Mangamuka Gorge Scenic
Reserve and enters the Raetea Forest.

Mangawhai Cliffs
Walk, 5 km, 1½ to 2 hrs
See Northland p.306

Mount Auckland
Walk, 8 km, 3½ hrs. See Northland p.306

Coromandel
Track, 7 km, 2½ to 3 hrs
See Coromandel p.304

Mount William
Walk, 6.5 km, 3 hrs
Through pastoral land to summit of
Mt William Reserve. Enters near Pokeno.

Kohi Point
Walk, 5 km, 2 hrs
Through Kohi Point Scenic Reserve,
with views of the coast and inland.
Near Whakatane.

Taupo
Walk, 8 km, 2½ hrs
See Lake Taupo p.305

Aramoana
Walk, 7 km, round trip, 2 to 3 hrs
Across farmland with views of
Wanganui River and Mt Ruapehu.

Monckton
Track, 2 km, 1 to 1½ hrs
Through native forest. Access from
Ashley Clinton Road.

Porewa
Walk, 8 km, 3 hrs
Across farmland, with stream
and bush views.

Cannon point
Walk, 10 km, 2 to 3 hrs
Through native bush to the top of a prominent
ridge overlooking the Hutt Valley. Begins on
outskirts of Upper Hutt.

Beehive Creek
Track, 3.5 km, round trip, 3 hrs
Follows the creek across farmland,
with bush and pastoral views and
native bird life.

Anaura Bay
Walk, 3.5km, 2 hrs
See East Cape, p.304

Cooks Cove
Walk, 4 km, round trip, 2½ hrs
See East Cape, p.304

Otoko
Walk, 5 km, one way, 2½ hrs
Along part of the old Gisborne-
Moutohora railway line.

Boundary Stream
Track, 8 km, 3 to 4 hrs
Through farmland and dense bush
to Shines Falls. Enters near Tutira.

Tutira
Three tracks, ranging from 4 to 9 km
Views of coastal Hawkes Bay
and the inland ranges. Enter at Lake
Tutira Recreation Reserve.

Te Mata Peak
Track, 2.2 km, 1½ hrs
To Te Mata Peak
with views of the Heretaunga
Plains and Hawke's Bay.

Tangoio
Track, 6 km, 2 to 3 hrs
Winds up the Tangoio Valley through
varying types of vegetation.

Three grades of track

The New Zealand Walkway is a growing net-work of tracks of varying difficulty which will eventually make it possible to travel on foot from Cape Reinga, at the north of the North Island, to Bluff at the south of the South Island. It is still in its early stages, but the Walkway Commission has already establish-ed tracks over both public and private land, usually close to cities and towns, and for all types of walkers.

Wherever possible the walkways go across public land—public reserves, national parks and state forest parks—but when they cross private property to achieve a continuous route, the walkway system relies on co-operation between landowners and walkers.

Most of the present tracks are suitable for families, but other parts of the Walkway will be opened and graded in three degrees of difficulty:

walk: well formed track, suitable for the av-erage family.

track: a well defined walking track, suitable for people of good average physical fitness.

route: a lightly marked track for use only by the well-equipped and experienced tramper.

The sections shown are already in use.

Wither Hills
Walk, round trip, 6 km, 2½ hrs
Crosses pastoral land, to climb ridges and reach lookout. South of Blenheim.

Dun Mountain
Walk, 9.5 km, 2½ to 3 hrs
Through native bush and open grass areas along the Brook Valley south of Nelson.

Lyell
Track, 3 km, 1 to 1½ hrs
Begins at an historic reserve and passes an old cemetery on its way to Croesus Gold Battery. Begins northeast of Inangahua.

Charming Creek
Walk, 5.5 km, 1½ to 2 hrs
Through native forest along the route of an old coal company's railway, to the Mangatini Falls.

Denniston
Walk, 5 km, 1 to 1½ hrs
Between Waimangaroa and Denniston, along an old bridle track.

Point Elizabeth
Walk, 5 km, 2 hrs
In the Rapahoe Range Scenic Reserve, with views of sea and coast. North of Greymouth.

St James
Track, 66 km, 4 to 5 days
The area is subalpine and the track is partly in the Lewis Pass National Reserve, passing through diverse scenery and vegetation.

Marlborough Sounds
Tracks, 11 to 22 km, 1 to 2 days
See Marlborough Sound p.305

Picton
Walk, 2 km, 1 hr
Through Picton Scenic Reserve.

Kaikoura Peninsula
Walks, 1 to 4.5 km, 20 mins to 1½ hrs
See Kaikouras p.305

Quail Island
Walk, 4.5 km, 2 hrs
Around Quail Island past several interesting historical features. The island can be reached by ferry from Lyttelton.

Mt Herbert
Track, 20 km, 10½ hrs
See Banks Peninsula p.304

Crater Rim
Walk, 12 km, 4 hrs
See Banks Peninsula p.304

Godley Head
Walk, round trip, 8 km, 4 hrs
See Banks Peninsula p.304

Pegasus Bay
Walk, 11 km, 3 to 4 hrs
Follows the Kaiapoi and Waimakariri rivers to coast and Waimakariri Beach.

Methven
Walk, 14 km, 3 hrs
Passes through a plantation and farmland to the Ashburton River. Begins near Methven Racecourse.

Opihi River
Walk, 26 km, one way, 10 hrs
Three sections: Fairlie (3 km, one way, 40 min.), Opihi Gorge (13 km, one way, 6 hrs) and Arowhanua to Tengawai Bridge (13 km, one way, 3 hrs).

Pareora
Walk/track, 5 km, round trip, 3 hrs
Commences at Evens Crossing and then follows Pareora River up the side of a gully to a lookout.

Waimate
Track, 3 km, round trip, 2.5 hrs
From the Te Kiteroa Rest Home, through pasture and bush. Finishes at the White Horse monument.

Mahinapua
Walk, 5.5 km, 2 hrs
Through the Lake Mahinapua Scenic Reserve and freehold land, and around Lake Mahinapua. South of Hokitika.

Ross Historic Goldfields
Two walks, 1 km and 1.5 km, ½ hr and 1 hr
Through a former goldmining area. From Ross township.

Queenstown Hill
Walk, 4.5 km, 3 hrs
See Central Otago, p.304
Ben Lomond
Track, 10 km, 5 to 6 hrs
See Central Otago, p.304
Frankton-Queenstown
Walk, 5 km, 2½ hrs
Along Frankton Arm.
One Mile Creek
Walk, 2.5 km, 50 mins
A stream walk through native forest.

Pourakino
Walk, 8.5 km, 3 hrs
Follows the Pourakino River. Northeast of Invercargill.

Pineapple-Flagstaff
Walk, 5 km, 2 hrs
Through native bush and open tussock land to Flagstaff summit.

Croydon Bush
Walks, 5.7 km, 3½ hrs
Three possible walks through native bush. Entered at Colamore Park, northwest of Gore.

Foveaux-Bluff
Walk/track, 8 km, 2½ hrs
Fine views from coast across Foveaux Strait to Stewart Island. The Glory track passes through native bush.

Waihopal Embankment
Walk, 3.8 m, 1 hr
Along the Waihopai River in the city of Invercargill, with diverse views.

Mt Cargill-Bethunes Gully
Walk, 4 km, round trip, 3½ hrs
In North East Valley, Dunedin to the top of Mt Cargill.

Safety and survival in the bush

New Zealand's many walking tracks have opened up national parks, forests, scenic reserves, public domains and some private land for the recreation of a growing number of holidaymakers. These unspoilt regions are fragile, limited in their ability to withstand the visitor. They must be protected. Therefore, take from the bush only photographs and memories, leave nothing behind but footprints, and carry out what you carry in.

Careful planning can overcome many problems that might spoil a walking trip. Tramping can be dangerous for the inexperienced, requiring special skills such as a knowledge of the bush, first aid experience and an ability to read maps.

Clothing
A sturdy pair of light boots or ankle-length sandshoes with heavy soles are good for short walks. Heavier boots are needed to protect feet and support ankles when walking over rough terrain. Leather soles can be slippery when wet, therefore, treaded rubber or synthetic soles are safer. New footwear should be broken in before a walk, otherwise blisters will develop.

Light, loose-fitting clothes allow circulating air to carry away excess body heat. Natural fabrics such as wool or cotton absorb moisture, which permits air to circulate more effectively than nylon and other synthetics. Most synthetics are wind-resistant so it makes good sense to wear natural fibres next to the skin and synthetic garments on the outside. Remove an article of clothing when you become hot and add one when you become cold.

A wide-brimmed hat provides good protection from the sun and rain. To prevent heat loss in colder weather, wear a woollen beanie.

Camping equipment
BACKPACK On longer, overnight walks a backpack is necessary to carry equipment. If there are no huts along the route, a tent and a portable stove will be needed. The frameless pack is best for loads of up to 9 kg, and a frame pack for heavier loads.

Choose a pack of lightweight, durable, waterproof material such as treated canvas or nylon. Plenty of outside pockets on a pack are practical. Wide shoulder straps with thick pads are recommended. A waist belt transfers weight from the shoulders to the hips. A backpack frame should be light and sturdy, with rounded corners and canvas or nylon webbing. What goes into the pack should be selected as carefully as the pack itself.

SLEEPING BAG A sleeping bag should be warm, lightweight and not too bulky. Warmth depends on the type of insulation. Down filling is considered to be the best; it is more expensive than the bulkier synthetic filling.

TENT The tramper should consider a tent weighing less than 2.5 kg. The best is a double-skin nylon tent, which is waterproof and airtight. Condensation will form inside a single-skin nylon tent unless it is properly ventilated which defeats its effectiveness.

COOKING UTENSILS A compact nest of aluminium pots and a combination frying pan with a detachable handle will serve as cooking utensils and take up little space.

SURVIVAL KIT No one should venture into the bush without a survival kit. It should include a whistle, compass, knife, waterproof matches, water purification tablets, a pencil and paper for leaving messages, fishing line, hooks and lures, and solid fuel capsules.

FIRST AID KIT A first aid kit can be easily assembled and should include antiseptic and sunburn cream, aspirin, razor blades, bandages, bandaid and insect repellent.

Food
Trampers should maintain a balanced diet, eating well and regularly throughout the trip. Freeze-dried foods, although light and nonperishable, are not as palatable as fresh foods. Therefore, a mixture of fresh, freeze-dried and dehydrated foods is recommended. Be sure to take along more sugar than you would normally use. Sugar, honey and chocolate provide energy quickly. Heavy tinned goods or breakable glass containers should not be carried.

Safety
Before setting off into the bush, always tell a reliable person where you are going and your estimated time of return. Be specific. Point out your route and destination on a map and make it clear that any delay after a certain time means trouble. Fill in intention books where these are displayed and leave notes in the log books at huts.

As you walk, follow the trail markers and take note of major landmarks. Allow more time than you estimated to ensure getting to your destination before dark.

Unless you are experienced do not travel alone or at night. On any lengthy walk, a party should consist of at least three people. If someone is injured, one of the party can stay with that person while another goes back for help, leaving a clearly defined trail for the rescue party to follow.

A fast start usually means a poor finish. Start slowly and build up to a steady pace. Strive for rhythm, not speed. When travelling in a group, do not drop out at erratic intervals as this disrupts pace and rhythm. The slowest members of the group should be near the front, and an experienced tramper should bring up the rear. If one of the group feels tired, stop.

Do not attempt to cross a river unless you are sure you can cross it safely. Moving water is often dangerous. If the river is in flood, camp and wait for the water to drop. Drowning is the most common cause of death in the New Zealand outdoors.

Weather
Before setting out on a walk, make a point of listening to weather forecasts. Enquiries can be made at national park headquarters. Local weather changes can be sudden, and trampers should turn back immediately or descend to lower levels if the weather deteriorates. Creeks and rivers can become flooded after a few hours of rain, cutting off retreat.

The weather can be forecast with reasonable accuracy by learning to interpret the many clues in cloud patterns, wind direction and temperature changes.

Frequent changes in cloud patterns often precede a storm. Wispy cirrus clouds warn of rain within 48 hours. The clouds form layers, become denser and darken shortly before rain falls. Cumulus clouds are piled and fluffy and indicate continuing fine weather. A halo around the sun or moon means that rain is on the way. The sunset gives a hint of conditions to be expected the following day. There is truth in the ancient rhyme, 'Red sky at dawning, shepherds' warning. Red sky at night, shepherds' delight.'

Survival
Common sense and safety precautions on the track can minimise the chances of accidents or of getting lost, and can help you through the experience unscathed if it happens.

If you do become lost or separated from your group, stop and take stock of the situation. Do not panic. Backtrack, if possible, to the area where you last saw other members of the party, marking the route as you go. If you cannot find your way back, then look for a sheltered camp site and make a fire. Do not wander aimlessly or attempt to walk at night.

A smoky fire, three shouts, three whistle blasts, three mirror or torch flashes, or any other three signals given together at regularly spaced intervals, are the standard signals for distress.

When signalling aircraft, use the code of international emergency symbols. Brightly-coloured fabric, wood or stones can be laid out to make the symbols and should be about 2.5 metres long and contrast with the background.

EMERGENCY SIGNALS

MESSAGE	SYMBOL	MESSAGE	SYMBOL
Require doctor, serious injuries	**I**	Probably safe to land here	**△**
Require medical supplies	**II**	Require fuel	**L**
Unable to proceed	**✕**	All well	**LL**
Require food and hot water	**F**	No	**N**
Require map and compass	**☐**	Yes	**Y**
Indicate direction to proceed	**K**	Not understood	**⌐L**
Am proceeding in this direction	**↑**	(If in doubt in an emergency, use international symbols)	**SOS**

FINDING WATER A healthy adult can survive for two or three weeks without food, but water and protection from extreme weather is essential.

Dehydration is caused by lack of water and can be fatal. The symptoms include loss of appetite, sleepiness, nausea, dizziness, headache, impaired speech and inability to walk.

Water is the only treatment for dehydration. Fast-running water in isolated areas is likely to be safe to drink. Water may also be found by digging into low-lying moist ground. In rocky areas, it can be found near clumps of lush vegetation, dark stains on rock walls and seepages in cracks and caves. Other sources of water are rain and dew on plants.

Stagnant water can be purified by filtering it through cloth and adding water purification tablets. If these are not available, boil the filtered water for at least 15 minutes. Oxygen can be restored by shaking the water in a closed container, or by pouring it from one vessel to another.

MAKING A SOLAR STILL

Dig a hole a little smaller than an available piece of plastic or groundsheet. Place leaves, twigs or any other moist material in the hole with a water container, such as a billy, in the centre. Anchor the plastic with the earth you have dug out of the hole, and place a small stone in the centre over the container. The sun's heat will cause water to condense from the soil and plants where it will collect on the underside of the plastic and drip into the container.

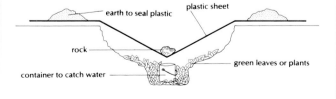

EXPOSURE Any person involved in strenuous activity and exposed to cold, wind and rain, may die unless treated immediately. Signs of exposure, also known as hypothermia, are not easily recognised and can be confused with fatigue. The victim may feel very tired, behave irrationally, lose control over the limbs and fall repeatedly.

Make no attempt to move the victim. Provide shelter from the wind and keep warm. Do not give massage or apply any form of direct heat. Re-warming may take up to 24 hours. Sweet and warm drinks, but not alcohol, may be given after recovery.

Route finding

The most practical way to determine direction is by means of a compass. A good compass is sensitive, accurate and sturdily made. Take care that the presence of metal, a belt buckle or knife does not create a wrong reading. Learn how to determine true north from the magnetic north indicated by a compass needle.

FINDING YOUR WAY BY THE SUN Never rely solely on a map or compass. The natural features of a terrain, the sun and the stars, are also easy guides to follow. You can also determine north with a watch. Hold the watch level, with the 12 on the dial pointing towards the sun. If you are on daylight-saving time, turn the watch back one hour to standard time. A line half way between the hour hand and the 12 will point to north.

FINDING YOUR WAY BY THE STARS At night your position can be checked by the Southern Cross, the most distinctive constellation in the Southern Hemisphere. Locate the five stars in the pattern of the cross and the pointers—the two bright stars closest to the cross. Do not confuse the Southern Cross with the False Crosses. They are less bright and their stars more widely spaced. Draw an imaginary line through the long axis of the cross. Join the two bright stars near the cross, called The Pointers, with an imaginary line. Bisect this at right angles. The South Celestial Pole (CS) is near the point of intersection with the line through the cross. True south can be found with the Southern Cross and The Pointers in different positions.

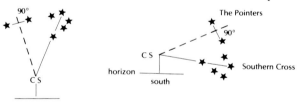

TRAMPER'S ETIQUETTE

- Keep your group small. Larger parties tend to damage the environment.
- Plan your trip to minimise litter.
- Carry out all non-burnable rubbish. Leave your camp site clean and tidy.
- Keep to tracks where provided. Taking short cuts can cause erosion.
- Avoid polluting streams and lakes with detergent, washing water or scraps.
- Use a portable stove rather than an open fire.
- If you do use a wood fire use only dead wood, completely extinguish fires after use and bury the ashes. Replenish wood supplies before leaving a camp area.
- Ask permission to cross private property and leave gates as you find them.

Index

Page numbers in *italics* refer to illustrations

A

Abel Tasman National Park *128*, 130-131
Acclimatisation societies 23
Acheron, HMS 266
Acker, Lewis 284
Adventure, Port 290
Aiguilles Island *45*
Aiguilles Rouge, Mt 193
Akaroa 168, 175
Akaroa Harbour *175*, 175
Akaroa Head *168*
Alabaster, Lake *271*
Aladdin's Cave 75
Alarm, Mt 151
Alba, Mt 224
Alderman Islands 55
Alexandrina Lake 198
Alex Knob track 307
Allen, Mt 292-293
Alpine Fault 13-14, *13*, 136, 140, 271
Anakiwa Walkway 305
Anaura Bay walkway 304
Andesite 56-57, 62, 78, 82, 108
Angelus Hut *141*
Angelus, Lake 141
Anglem, Mt 282, *286*
Animals *22*, 22-23
  introduced 23, 118
Anistome haastii 232
Antarctica 13
Aorangi Mountains 113, 117, 118
Aramoana Walkway 308
Arapawa Island 120, 122
Aratiata River 74-75
Arawa Tribe 59
Arawata River *234*, 234-235, *235*
Arrowtown 249
Arthur River *265*, 265
Arthur Valley 264, *264*
Arthur's Pass 164
Arthur's Pass National Park 156-167, *165*, 298
  walkways 304
Aspiring, Mt 184, 223, *226*, 226-227
Astrolabe, corvette 126
Auckland 29, 43
  West Coast of 46-51, 298
    walkways 304
Avalanche Peak *164*, 165
  walkways 304
Awaroa *130*
Awatere Fault 147
Awatere River *148*, 148

B

Balloon, Mt *263*, 264
Banks Peninsula 15, 168-177, *175*, 298
  walkways 304
Banks, Sir Joseph 168, 294
Bannockburn 244
Bark Bay *131*
Barrington, Alphonse 234
Bat 38
Bay of Islands *28*, 28-29
Bealey, Mt track 304
Bealey Valley 164-165
Bealey Valley Track 304
Beeby's Knob 140
Beech *19*, 19, 20, 21, *105, 142, 143, 156, 160, 165*, 204, 254
  black 19
  hard 19
  mountain 19, 229, 231
  red 19, 231, *233*
  silver 19, *105*, 220, 221, 224, *225, 228*, 229, 231
Beehive Creek Track 308
Bellbird 43
Benmore, Lake 178, 200
Bethell's Beach 49
Bethell's Swamp 49
Bevan, Mt *229*
Birley, Harry 230, 232
Blackhead 116
Black Hill 138-139
Blue Cliffs Ridge 144
Blue Lake (North Island)
  see Tikitapu, Lake
Blue Lake (South Island) *142, 143*, 143
Boulder Lake *133*
Boundary Stream Walkway 308
Bowen Bush walkway 306
Bowen Falls 267, *269*
Brazenose, Mt walkway 304
Bridal Veil Falls:
  North Island *46, 50*, 51, 69
    walkway 304
  South Island *271*, 304
    walkway 304
Brothers Islands *127*, 127
Browns Island *40*, 41
Buckland, James 31
Buller, Charles 144
Buller River *138*, 138, *144*, 144-145, *145*
Burke, Michael John 196
Burke Pass 196
Burnett Mountains *201*
Bush Island *54*
Butler, Samuel 180

C

Cabbage tree *97*
Callender–Hamilton Bridge 217
Cameron, Charles 220
Camping equipment 310
Canavans Knob track 307
Cannibal Bay *278*, 278
Cannibal Gorge 141
Cannon Point Walkway 308
Cape Farewell Walk 305
Cape Maria van Diemen 31
Cape Reinga Walkway 306
Caples, Patrick 230, 232, *270*, 270
Cardrona Valley 250
Cargill, Mt – Bethunes Gully Walkway 309
Carrot, wild *232*
Castle Hill *159*, 159
Castle Hill Peak *159*
Castle Mountain 264
Castle Rock walkway 304
Castor, Mt 224
Cat, feral 43
Cathedral Caves 280
Cathedral Cove Reserve *55*
Cathedral Rocks *67*
Catlins, Lake 278
Catlin Forest Park 274
Catlins, The 274-279, 298-299
Cattlin, Edward 274
Caves *51*, 51, 256
Celmisia 19, 21
Central Otago *16*, 299
Chalmers, Nathaniel 222, 245
Chamois 188, 189, *198*
Champagne Pool *68*, 69
Charming Creek Walkway 309
Chasland, Tommy 280
Chetwode, Lieutenant Phillip 124
Chetwode Islands 127
Church of the Good Shepherd *198*
Clarence Gorge 153
Clarence River 147, 148, *150*, 151, *152*
Climate 298-303
Clinton Canyon 263
Cloudy Bay 122
Clutha River *223, 240*, 240-241
Cobb and Company 159
Cobb River *131*
Cockayne, Leonard 18
Colonial Knob Walkway 308

Buttercup:
  Mountain *202*, 209
  Mt Cook lily *202*, 202
  New Zealand *267*

Colville Channel 44
Cone Rock 212
Cone, The 51
Conifers, Northern Hemisphere 76
Conservation 259
Constance, Lake 142-143
Continental drift 13, 20
Continental shelf 12
Cook, Captain 22, 28, 95, *96*, 98, 106, 113, 114, 116-117, 120, 122, 125, 148, 168, 181, 260, 282
Cook, Mt *180, 181, 182, 183*, 180-185, 192, 193
Cook River *185*
Cook Strait 20, 126
Cooks Cove walkway 304
Copland Pass *194*
Copland River 214
Copland Shelter 194, *195*
Copland Track 214, *214*, 307
Coprosma 21
Coromandel Farm Park 55
Coromandel Forest Park *53*, 53, 56
Coromandel Peninsula 53-57, 299
  walkways 304
Coromandel Range *57*, 57
Coromandel Walkway 304
Coronation Hill Walk 304
Craigieburn Forest Park 160
Craigieburn Range *158*, 160
Crater Rim walkway 304
Craters:
  Central *88*, 90
  Christmas 99
  Echo *66*, 66, 67
  Inferno 66, *67*
  Ngawha 60
  North 89
  Red *89*, 89, 90
  South *89*, 90, *91*
  Southern *66*, 66, 67
Crayfish 155, 261
  Chatham Islands 22
Cretaceous Period 14, 15
Criffel Range *251*
Cromwell Gorge *240, 241*
Crow River *162*
Croydon Bush Walkway 309
Cuckoo, long-tailed (koekoea) 212
Curio Bay 281
Cuvier Island 55

D

Daisy:
  everlasting *195*
  mountain 202
Dart Valley 230-231

Darwin, Charles 29
Dawson Falls *111*
Deer:
   red 77, 143, 253, 256-257
   white-tailed 290, *293*
Deer farming 257
Dehydration 311
Denniston Walkway 309
Department of Conservation 44, 72,
   118, 160, 285, 286, 292
Devil's Punchbowl Falls 166, *167*
Devonian period 14
Dieffenbach, Ernst 106
Diorite 233, *285*
Disappear, Lake 51
Distress signals 310-311
Dobson, Arthur 156
Dobson, Edward 156
Dobson Nature Walk 304
Dog, Polynesian 22
Dome Forest Walkway 306
Dome Islands *257*
Dome Lakes *257*
Dotterel, banded 158-159
Double Cone 248
Doubtful Sound 259, 260, *261*
Doughboy Bay 285, *292*
Douglas, Charles 224, 234, 235
Duck, blue mountain *80*, 81
Du Faur, Freda 183, 189, 193
Dun Mountain Walkway 309
Dunstan Mountains 242, *243*
D'Urville Island *126*, 126
d'Urville, Sébastien César Dumont
   125, 126
Dusky Sound 260

E

Earle, Augustus 32
Earle, L.M. 193
Earle's Ridge 193
Earnslaw, lake steamer 232
Earnslaw, Mt *230*
Earthquakes 119, 144, 164
East Cape *92*, 92, 299
   walkways 304
Eastern Okataina Walkway 306–307
Edelweiss, New Zealand *202*
Edgecumbe, Mt 64
Edwards River 164
Edwards Valley 164
Egmont, Mt 15, *106*, 106, *108*,
   108-111, *109*
Egmont National Park 106-111, *110*,
   299-300
   Board 106
   walkways 304

Elie de Beaumont, Mt *190*, 190, 206
Ellesmere, Lake 172-173, *173*
Emerald Lakes *89*, 90
Endeavour, HMS 260
Endeavour Inlet 122
Endeavour–Resolution Walkway
   305
Epiphytes 18
Erosion 15,16, *17*, 17, 44, *151*, 160,
   161, 196
Exposure 311
Eyebright 19

F

Faerie Queene Peak 140, 141
Falcon, New Zealand 252
Fantham, Fanny 108
Fanthams Peak *106*, 108
Farewell Spit *132*, 132
Faur, Freda du 183, 189, 193
Feather star *37*
Feraud, Jean Désiré 243
Ferns 38, *56*, 105, 204, 210, *216*,
   289
   crown 19
   kidney *41*
   king *77*
   Polystichum cystostegia 111
   prickly shield 19
   Prince of Wales feathers 84
   Tmesipteris elongata 110
Ferry, Lake 119
Fiordland 16, 254
Fiordland National Park 233,
   254-273, 300, 304-305
   walkways 304
First aid 310
Firth of Thames 38, 39
Fishing 73, 142, 155, 160, 172, 240
Fitzgerald, Edward 183
Flax 210
   milling 220
Folding 16
Footstool 214
Forget-me-not 141
Forsyth, Lake *173*, 173
Fossils *280*, 281
Four Peaks 222
Four Sisters *34*
Foveaux–Bluff Walkway 309
Fox Glacier 204, 208, *212*, 212, *213*
   glacier terminal walk 307
Foxglove, mountain 228
Fox, Mt 212
Fox River 212
Fox, William 139, 249
Frankton–Queenstown Walkway 309

Franz Josef Glacier 207, *208*,
   208–209
   glacier terminal walk 307
Frenchman Bay *130*
French Pass *126*, 126
Freshwater Basin 266
Fresne, Marion du *29*
Frog:
   Archey's *57*
   Hamilton's 125
Frog Pond *60*
Frying Pan Flat 67
Frying Pan Lake 67
Fyfe, Tom 184, 192

G

Gannet (takapu) 45, 99, *113*, 113,
   114-115, *115*
Gas, natural 97
Gault, Lake 210
Gecko 37
Geikie snowfields *208*
Gentian 19, 135, *203*
Geysers 60, *61*, 74, 77
   eruptions 67
   Great Wairakei 70
   Lady Knox 69
   Pohutu *60*
   Prince of Wales Feathers 60
   Waikorohihi 60
   Waimangu (Black Water) 67
Giant Gate Falls 265
Gibbs Hill Track 305
Gillespies Beach 210
   track *307*
Gillespies Point 210
Glaciation 16, *17, 20*, 20, 21, 108,
   132, 138, 139, 156, 162, 204,
   208, 212, *213*, 262
Glacier Burn walkway 305
Gloriana Peak 140
Glow worms *51*
Gneiss 16
Goats 122
Godley Head *170*, 170
   Walkway 304
Godwit *30*
   eastern bar-tailed (kuaka) 31, 132
Gog and Magog Mountains *294*,
   294–295
Gold 44, 144, 206, 210, 238, 240,
   241, 242, 244, 249, 250, 253,
   261, 290
Golden Bay 128, 300
   walkways 305
Golden Fleece Terrace *75*, 75
Goldney Glacier *166*

Gondwanaland 13, 20, 22
Goose Bay 155
Gouland Downs *135*, 135
Governors Bush walkway 306
Gowan River 144
Graham, Peter 192, 193
Granite 14, 16, 282, *295*
Graptolites 14
Grasmere, Lake 161
Grassland 19
Great Barrier Island 39, 44-45, *45*
Great Mercury Island 55
Grebe, crested 160-161, *207*, 210
Green Lake 63
   see Rotokakahi, Lake
Green, Rev. William Spotswood 182,
   185, 230
Greens Beach walk 307
Greenstone 15, 141, 222, 233, 266,
   267
Greenstone Track 305
Grey, Sir George 23, 38, 41
Greywacke 14, 16
Grono, John 266
Gull, black-backed (karoro) 40
Gum diggers 44
Guthrie-Smith, Herbert 289
Gunn, Davy 273

H

Haast, Julius von 139, 180
Haast Pass 220–221
Haast River 220, *221*, 221
Haidinger, Mt 193
Hakarimata Walkway 308
Halfmoon Bay 284
Hapuakohe Walkway 308
Harper, Arthur Paul 163, 192
Harper, Mt *163*, 163
Harrier (hawk) *252*
Harris, Lake 233
Harwoods Hole 131
Hauhungatahi Wilderness Area 84
Hauraki Gulf 38-45, 300, 305
Hauraki Gulf Maritime Park *38*, 53,
   55
   Board 40, 42
Hauraki Plains 38
Haurangi Forest Park 118
Hauroko, Lake walkways 304-305
Hawai Beach *94*
Hawaiki 30, 97
Hawea, Lake 222, *223*, 223
Hawkdun Range *242*
Hawke's Bay 113-117, 300-301
   walkways 305
Hayes, 'Bully' 249

Hayes, Lake 249
Haywards Point *279*
Head, Major Bernard 230
Heaphy, Charles 134, 142
Heaphy River *129*
Heaphy Track 132, *134*, 134–135, 305
Hebe 19, 21, 165, 203
    subalpina *231*
Heberly, James 106
Hector, James 228, *229*
Hen and Chickens Islands 21, 36, 38
Henry, Richard 261
Herbert, Mt track 304, 309
Hermitage, The 194
Heron:
    reef (matuku-moana) 155
    white (kotuku) *207*, 216
    white-faced *118*
Hicks Bay *96*, 96
Hicks, Lieutenant Zacchary *96*
Hidden Falls *270*, 270
High Valley Walk 212
Hikurangi, Mt 92, 97
Hillary, Edmund 183
Hill, Henry 114
Hinahina Island 278
Hinepouri Tarn *141*
Hingaia Point *43*
Hirakimata, Mt 45
Hobson, Governor 29
Hobson, Mt 44
Hochstetter Icefall *187*, 187
Hodder River *151*
Hokianga 32, 33–34
Hokianga Harbour *32*, 32, 33
Hole in the Rock *28*
Holloway, J. T. 234
Hollyford River 269, *270*
Hollyford Track 270-272, 304
Homer Tunnel 269
Homer, W. H. 269
Hooker Glacier 183, 214
Hooker Valley walkway 306
Hope Arm *258*
Horahora Kakahu 122
Horseshoe Bay *284*
Hot springs 60, 97, 164
Howard Forest 144
Howden, Lake 233
Huka Falls *74*, 74
Hunting 22, 143, 290
Hydro-electricity 200-201, 259

I

Ianthe, Lake 17, 204, 206
Ice ages *16*, 17, *20*, 20, 21, 26, 46,
    108, 138, 166, 168, 254

Ignimbrite 15, 16, 70, 72
    Kaingaroa-Tangitaiki 76
    Taupo 70
Ihenga, Chief 59
Indian-Australian plate *12*, 12, *13*,
    13, 16, 70
Inferno Crater 67
Iron, Mt track 304
Ironsands 46, 48, 49
Ironside, Samuel 122

J

Jacks Bay 278-279
Jack's Blowhole 278
Jackson Bay *235*
Jamestown 272
Jamestown Bay 273
Johnson, Mt 192
Johnson, P. H. 192

K

Kahikatea 18, 204, *206*, 206, 210,
    216, 220
Kaikawaka 109, 110
Kaikoura Mountains *16*
Kaikoura Peninsula 147, 153,
    154, 155, 154-155, 301
    walkway 305
Kaikoura Ranges 16
Kaikouras:
    Inland 147-151
    Seaward *147*, 147-153
Kaimanawa Forest Park 76, *77*,
    76-77
    walkways 305
Kaingaroa 76-77
Kaitaia Walkway 306
Kaitake Range 108
Kaitorete Spit 173
Kaka 43, 210
Kaka beak (koehai-ngutu-kaka) 105
Kakahi Falls 64
Kakanui Mountains 238
Kakapo 267, *269*, 292
Kamahi 18, 20, 212, 214
Karaka 19
Karangahake Gorge 56
Karangahape Cliffs 72
Karangarua River 214
Karapiti 'blowhole' 74
Karekare 48
Kauaeranga Valley walkways 304
Kauri 18-19, 20, 21, 22, 26, 29, 32,
    33, *34*, 34, *36*, 44, *56*, 56

grass 18
logging 56
milling 34
Kauri Timber Company 44
Kawarau Gorge 244-245, *245*
Kawarau River 244-245, *245*
Kawhai 210
Kawau Island 38, 41
Kea *163*, 163, *266*
Kea Point Track 306
Kenepuru Sound 125
Ketetahi Springs 89
Ketetahi Track 90, 307
Key Summit 233
Kidnappers, Cape *112, 114*,
    114-115, 305
    walk 305
Kiwi:
    brown 43, 84, *85*, 204
    great spotted 76
Klondyke Corner 161
Knights Point 216
Knot, eastern 132
Kohekohe 19
Kohi Point Walkway 308
Kokako (wattled 'crow') 51
    grey 45
    North Island 53
Korokoro Falls *103*
Kuaka
    see Godwit, eastern bar-tailed
Kupe the navigator 113, 117

L

Lake Head Track 306
Lake Ruapani Track 307
Lammerlaw Range 238
Lammermoor Range 238, *239*
Lava 86, 88, *126*, 138
Leaning Peak 258
Lee Bay *287*
Legends
    see Maoris, legends
Lewis Pass 140, 141
Lindis Pass *252*, 252-253
Lion Rock *48*, 49
Little Barrier Island 38, 42-43, *42*
Little Hellfire Beach 292
Logging 18, 56
Lord Howe Rise 12, 20
Lords River *290*, 290
Lottin Point *97*
Lower Buller Gorge 145
Luncheon Cove 260
Lyell Walkway 309
Lyndon Lake 158
Lyttelton Harbour *170*

M

MacAndrew, James 272
Macaulay River *198*
Mackay, James 134
Mackenzie Country 196-197, *197*
Mackenzie Pass *196*
Mackenzie, Sir Thomas 232, 262, 263
Mackinnon, Quintin 263-264, *264*
MacRae, Lake 148
Madeline, Mt *271*
Magma 12, 13, 60, 70
Mahinapua Walkway 309
Main Divide 178
Makara Walkway 308
Makarora River 220, 222, 224
Makarora Scenic Reserve 220
Malte Brun, Mt *190, 192*, 192, 193
Mamaku Ignimbrite 60
Manaia Sanctuary 56
Manapouri, Lake 258-259, *258, 259*
Mangamaunu Beach 152, 153
Mangamuka Gorge Walkway 308
Mangaone Walkway 308
Mangapohue Natural Bridge 51
Mangatepopo 89, *90*, 90-91
Mangatepopo Stream *91*
Mangawhai Cliffs Walkway 306
Mangroves 19, 26, *29, 33*, 33, 50
Mannering, George 182
Manuka 148, 162, 210
Manukau Harbour 50
Maori Leap Caves *155*, 155
Maoris 22, 29, 30, 33, 37, 42, 43,
    80, 89, 92, 96, 102, 114, 120,
    124, 128, 134, 148, 154, 155,
    159, 216, 222, 233, 260, 266,
    268, 278, 282, 288, 289, 295
    legends *30*, 31, 32, 59, 64, 72, 78,
    92, 95, 98, 102, 106, 113, 114,
    117, 127, 154, 181, 198, 222,
    228, 239, 242, 246, *260*, 295
    sacred ground 72, 80
Mapourika, Lake *206*, 206, *207*, 207
Marahau/Whariwaharangi Bay
    walkway 305
Maraunui Bay *122*
Markham, Edward 32
Marlborough Sounds 120-127, 301
    walkways 305
Marokopa Falls *50*
Maroro 116
Marsden, Samuel 29
Martins Bay *272, 273*, 272-273
Mason Bay 293
Matagouri *160, 247*
Matai 206, 212, 220
Matakitaki 144
Matakitaki Falls 144

Matakitaki River 144
Matemateaonga Walkway 308
Matheson, Lake 17, *210*, 210-211
   track 307
Matukituki River 222, 228-229
Maungatapere Walkway 306
McKenzie, Michael John 196-197
McKerrow, James 228, 230, 232
McKerrow, Lake *271*, 271, 272
McLean, John 253
Mercury Islands 38
Methven Walkway 309
Milford Road 232, 262, 305
Milford Sound 265, 266-269, *268*
Milford Track 262-265, *263*, 268, 305
Mineshafts 54, 56
Minarets, The *193*
Mining:
   copper 44
   gold 44, 55, 145, 242, 244, 295
   ironsand 75
   quartz 230, 238, 243, 244
   silver 44
   sulphur *98*, 98-99
   tin 295
Minehaha Stream 212
Minehaha Track 212
Mintaro, Lake 263
Miocene era 20
Miranda 39
Missionaries 100, 122
Mistletoe, red 105
Mitchell, Ernest 263
Mitre Peak:
   Fiordland *266*, 266, *267*
   Kaikouras 151
Moa 22, 118, 151, 256, 280
Moehau, Mt *55*
   track 304
Moehau Range 57
Moeraki 216
Moeraki, Lake 216
Moirs Hill Walkway 306
Mokau Falls 102
Mokoia Island 60, 64
   walkways 306
Mollymawk 289
Monckton Walkway 308
Monowai, Lake *259*
   tracks 305
Morepork (ruru) 212
Moss 40, *166*
Motuarika Island *199*
Motu Falls 94, *95*
Motukaramarama *54*
Motupia Island *30*
Moturau Moana 284
Motu River 92, 95
Motutaiko Island 72
Motutapu Farm Walkway 305

Mount Anglem Nature Reserve 290
Mount Arthur Tableland 132
Mount Aspiring National Park
   218-227, 233, 301
   walkways 305-306
Mount Auckland Walkway 306
Mount Cargill–Bethunes Gully
   Walkway 309
Mount Cook National Park
   178-203, 301-302
   walkways 306
Mount Herbert Walkway 304
Mount Manuoha Track 307
Mount William Walkway 308
Mud pools 60, *61, 65*, 69, 74, 78
Mueller Glacier *195*
Murchison 144
Murchison Mountains 256
Muriwai Beach 49
Muttonbird 289, *291*

N

Nairn, Charles 258
Native genetian *135*
Neck, The *222*, 282, 288-289
Nelson Lakes National Park *136*,
   136-145, 302
   walkways 306
Nephrite
   see Greenstone
New Zealand Forest Service 44
Ngaiotonga Scenic Reserve *36*
Ngakoro, Lake 69
Ngamoko Track 307
Ngapouri Fault 68
Ngati-Poru Tribe 92, 96-97
Ngauruhoe, Mt 15, *79*
   eruptions *86, 87*, 86-87
Nikau palm *134*
Ninety-Mile Beach *27, 31*
   Walkway 306
Nohuroa, Chief 122
Norfolk Ridge 12, 20
Northland 26-37, 302
   walkways 306
Northwest Forest Park *128*
Nugget Point 276, *277*
Nydia Walkway 305

O

Oban 282
Ocean Beach 116
Ohakuri Dam 75
Ohau, Lake *197*, 199, 201

Okarito Trig track 307
Okataina, Lake 63, 64
   walkways 306-307
Old Man of the Buller *144*
Old Man Range 242, *243*
Old Man Rock 242
O'Leary, William 230
Oligocene era 20
Olivine Ice Plateau 234
Olivine Range 234
Onawe Peninsula *175*, 175
One Mile Creek Walkway 309
Onetapu Desert
   see Rangipo Desert
Onoke, Lake 118-119
Opihi River Walkway 309
Opo, (dolphin) 32
Opononi *32*, 32
Opotiki 94
Orakei 46
Orakei Korako *75*, 75
Orchid, silver 285
Otehake Wilderness 164
Otoko Walkway 308
Ourisia 19
Oystercatcher *132*, 158

P

Pa, Maungapohatu 102
Pacific plate *13*, 13, 16, 70
Paddy's Track 306
Palliser Bay 118-119
Palliser, Cape 117
Palms, nikau *133, 134*
Panekiri Bluff *102*, 102
Papa 17
Papakorito Falls *100*, 102
Parakeet, Red-crowned 43
Parengarenga Harbour *31*
Pareora Walkway 309
Paringa, Lake 216, 217
Paterson Inlet *280*, 282, 284-285, *285*,
   288
Pearson, Joseph 160
Pearson, Lake 160-161, *161*
Peel Range *133*
Pegasus II Reserve 290, 292, *293*
Pegasus Bay Walkway 309
Pegasus Port 282, 290, *291*
Pelorus, HMS 124
Pelorus Jack (dolphin) 126
Pelorus Sound 120, *124, 125*,
   124-125
Pelorus Walkway 305
Penguins:
   blue 289
   Fiordland crested *261*

   yellow-eyed 276
Peninsula Walk 306
Pérouse, La 214
Perry Saddle *135*
Peter's Pool *209*, 209
Petrel 38, 43
   black 43, 45
   Buller's shearwater 37
   Cook's 43
   dove 127
Picton Walkway 309
Piercy Island *28*
Pig, and Pigeon Islands *247*
Pigeon, New Zealand 210
Piha 48
Piha Beach *48*
Pihanga, Mt *80*, 81
Pinchgut Track 306
Pine:
   pygmy 19
   radiata 59
   silver 210
Pineapple-Flagstaff Walkway 309
Pink and White Terraces *62*, 63
Pinnacle Ridge *83*
Pioneer Hut *217*
Pipit, New Zealand (pihoihoi) 85
Pirongia, Mt 51
Pirongia Forest Park 51
Pisa, Mt 250, *251*
Pisa Range 250, *251*
Plate movement 12-13, *13*, 16
Podocarps 18, 21, 22
Pohutukawa 31, 40, 43, *54, 94*, 95,
   97, *98*, 99
   Te Waho o Rerekohu 19, 97
Point Elizabeth Walkway 309
Pollux, Mt 224
Polynesian 22
Poor Knights Islands *36*, 36-37, 38
Poor Knights lily 37
Porangahau River 116
Porika Track 142, 306
Porters Pass 158-159
Port Fitzroy *44*
Port Hills 170-171
Possum, brushtail 77, 84
Pouakai Range 106, 108, 109
Pounawea 278
Pourakino Walkway 309
Powell, Paul 229
Preservation Inlet 261
Price Range 206
Providence 260
Puhipuhi Forest 21
Puka *20*, 21
Pukaki, Lake 17, 178, 181, 185, 199,
   200, 200-201
Pukeko (swamp hen) 173
Pumice 70, *71*

Pupuke 46
Purakaunui Falls Reserve 278
Purakaunui River 278
Puriri:
    moth 32
    tree 19, 96
Putangirua Pinnacles *119*, 119
    walkway 305

Q

Quail Island Walkway 309
Queen Charlotte Sound 120, *122*, 122
Queenstown 246, 247
    walkways 304, 309
Quicksand 224
Quill, Lake *265*
Quill, Will 264-265

R

Rabbits 243
Raggedy Range *239*
Raglan 298
Rainbow Island 280
Rainbow Mountain 68
Rainforest 18, 52, 56, *104*, 110, 134,
    274, 280
Rangipo Desert *81*, 81
Rangitoto *39*, 38
Rangitoto Island 39, *40*, 40
    walkways 305
Ranunculus 21
Rat. Polynesian (kiore) 22, 43, 99
Rata 20, 166, 204, 210, 214, *215*, 291
    Northern 19, *57*
    Southern 221
Raukumara Range 92, 94-95, 96
Raumahanga River 118
Red Tarns track 306
Rees-Dart Track *231*, 231, 305
Rees Saddle *230*, 230-231
Rees Valley *231*
Reinga, Cape *31*, 31
    Walkway 306
Reko, Chief 222
Remarkables, The 248-249, *248*, *249*
Rerewhakaaitu, Lake 63
Resolution, HMS 260
Resolution Island 261
Resolution Walkway 305
Rewarewa 20
Rhyolite 62, 70, 72
Richardson Mountains *246*
Rifleman, green 210
Rimu 18, 19, 20, *77*, 204, 210

Roaring Billy 221
Roaring Meg River *244*, 245
Rob Roy Peak *229*
Roberts, Mt *1, 9*, 139
Roberts Point Track 209
Rolleston, Mt 162, 166
Ross Historic Goldfields Walkway 309
Rotoehu, Lake 64
Rotoiti Breccia 64
Rotoiti, Lake:
    North Island 59, 64
    South Island 138-139, 142
Rotokakahi, Lake 63
Rotokare Walkway 308
Rotoma, Lake 64
Rotomahana, Lake *58*, 63, *64*, 66
Rotopounamu, Lake 81
Rotoroa, Lake *137*, 142-143, *143*
Rotoroa Track 142, 143, 306
Rotorua *59*, 59-60, 302-303
    walkways 306–307
Route Burn 232
Routeburn Falls *232*
Routeburn Gorge *233*
Routeburn Track 232-233, 305-306
Royal Forest and Bird Society of New
    Zealand 280
Rua Kenana 102
Ruamoko's Throat *67*
Ruapehu, Mt 80, 82-85, *109*
    crater lake, *82*, 82-83
    eruptions 82-83, *83*, *84*
    walkways 307
Ruatahuna 102
Ruatapu (sacred cave) 75
Ruera River 214
Ruggedy Point *286*
Runaway, Cape 95
Russell 29
Russell, Lord John 29
Russell Walkway 306

S

Sabine River 142, *143*
St Arnaud 139
St Arnaud Peak 140
St Arnaud Range *140,* 140
    track 306
St James Walkway 309
Salmon, quinnat 241
Sandhills 50
Savannah Range *160*
Scaup, New Zealand 142
Schist 12, 14, 16, *220*, 221, 236, 250
Seals *118*, *154,* 155, 210
    elephant 22
    New Zealand fur 22

New Zealand sea lion 22
    southern fur 260, *277*
Sealers, sealing 22, 260-261, 274,
    282, 286, 288
Sealy Range *192*
Sefton, Mt *190,* 190, 191
Selwyn, Bishop 287, 288
Sentinel Rock 209
Shag, spotted 171, *276*
Shelduck 224
Shipbuilders 33
Ship Cove 122
Shotover Gorge 251
Shotover River *250,* 250
Sign of the Takehe 171
Silberhorn, Mt *189,* *191,* 191
Silica springs *83*
Sinbad Gully 267, *268*
Skink 37
    spotted *239*
Smith, Owen Folger 282
Skippers road *251*
Snail, native bush 132
    Placostylus ambagiosus 31
Snowberry *203*
Soda Springs 90
Solander Island 295
Solar still *311,* 311
Southern Alps 15, 178, 193
Spaniard 19, 244
Spencer Mountains 140
Spirits Bay Walkway 306
Spoonbill, royal *207*
Spider wood 20
Steel industry 75
Stephens Island 126-127, *127*
Stephen, W. H. 258
Steward Island 282-295, 303
Stitchbird 42
Stokes, Captain J. L. 261, 266, 290
Strauchon Glacier 214
Summit Road 171
Survival 310-311
    kit 310
Sutherland, Donald 264, 266-267
Sutherland Falls 264, *265,* 266
Swallow *23*
Swan, black *23,* 173

T

Table Hill 292
Table Mountain Rising 56
Tahakopa Bay 279
Tahakopa River *279,* 279
Takahe *256,* 256
Takaka Hill 128, *130*
    Walk 305

Takano Glacier 214
Tane Mahuta 34, *35*
Tane Nui 56
Tangoio Walkway 308
Taniwa 32
Tapuaenui Bay *103*
Tapuaenuku, Mt 151
Taranaki 106
Taranaki Falls track 307
Tarawera, Mt 62-63
    eruption *62,* 63, 66
Tasman, Abel 106
Tasman Glacier *184,* 186-187, *186,*
    187
Tasman, Mt *184, 188,* 188-189
Tasman Pulp and Paper Company
    77
Tasman Valley *17*
Tauhara, Mt *72,* 73
    track 305
Taupo, Lake *70,* 70-73, *71,* *72,* 74,
    301
Taupo Volcanic Zone 13, 70
Taupo Walkway 305
Tautuku Bay 280
Tautuku Forest Reserve 280
Tawa 18, 20
Teal, brown 45
Te Anau 256
Te Anau, Lake 222, 256-257
Te Araroa 96-97
Tea-tree 20
Teazle *242*
Tecomanthe speciosa 21, 21
Te Henga
    see Bethell's Beach
Te Henui Walkway 308
Tekapo, Lake 178, 181, *198,* 198-199,
    199
Te Kaukau Point 116
Te Kooti, rebel leader 92, 100
Te Mata Peak Walkway 308
Te Matua Ngahere *34*
Te Paki Stream *30*
Tephra 70, 76
    Mangatawai 86
Te Puia Beach walk 304
Te Puia hot springs *51*
Tertiary Period 20
Te Titoki Point *43,* 43
Te Wairoa 67
Thermal activity 60, 64, *65,* 68, 74,
    75
    eruptions 60, 67
Thomson, John Turnbull 227, 252
Three Kings Islands 21, 31
Thunder Creek Falls 221
Tikitapu, Lake (Blue Lake) 63
Tikitere (Hell's Gate) 64, *65*
    walkway 306

Timber 34
  milling 220, 274
Timutimu Head *169*
Tiritiri Matangi Island 39
Tit, yellow-breasted 210
Tmesipteris tannensis 209
Toheroa 31, 116
Tokaanu 73
Tolaga Bay *93, 96*
Tongariro, Mt 79, 88-89, 90
Tongariro National Park *78,* 78-81,
  80, 88, 303
  walkways 307
Tongariro River 73
Tongariro Track 307
Torlesse, Charles Obins *158,* 159
Torlesse Range *158,* 159
Tora *117*
Totara 18, *105*
  Hall's *177*
Totaranui walkways 305
Travers River 138, *140,* 141
Tree daisy 18, 19
Tree fern, dwarf 18
Trout:
  brown 223, 224
  hatcheries 72-73
  rainbow 223, 224
Tuatara *23,* 31, 37, *126,* 127
Tuhoe Tribe 100, 105
Turakirae Head *118*
Turner, Samuel 270
Tutira Walkway 308
Tutoko, Mt *271*
Twin Falls 228

U

Ulva Island 284-285
Urchin, scarlet *37*
Urewera National Park *100,*
  100-105, 303

walkways 307
Urquhart, Doreen 185

V

Venison 257
Volcanic:
  activity: *15,* 15, *16,* 21, 46, 54, 60,
    62-63, 64, 66, *71,* 76, 78, 82,
    83, *86,* 86, 98, 99, 108-109, 168
  cores *29*
  craters 59, 63, 64, 66-67, 88-89
  debris 14, 15, 70
  islands 36, *53*
  plugs *53*
Volcanism 13, *15,* 15, *29,* 40, 41, 46,
   57, 62-63, 72, *78,* 78, 82, 86, *86,*
   98, 108, 168

W

Wahapo, Lake 206
Waiapu River 92, *97*
Waiatoto River 235
Waiau River 259
Waiau Valley *56*
Waiatoto Valley *235*
Waiho Loop 208
Waihopai Embankment Walkway 309
Waiho River *208,* 208
Waikareiti, Lake 102
  walkway 307
Waikaremoana, Lake 102
  track 307
Waikato River 46, 50, *73,* 74-75, *74*
Waimakariri River 161, 162-163, *163*
Waimakariri Valley 162
Waimangu track 307
Waimangu Cauldron
  see Frying Pan Lake

Waimangu Thermal Valley 66-67
Waimate Track 309
Waioeka Scenic Highway 94
Waiora Valley 74
Waiotapu thermal area *68,* 68-69
Waipapa Point *280*
Waipoua Forest 34
Wairakei thermal scheme 74
Wairakei Tourist Park 74
Wairarapa coast 113, 116-119,
  300-301
Wairarapa, Lake 118
Wairau Arm *103*
Wairau River 147
Waitakere Ranges 46, 48, 298
  walkways 304
Waitaki River 200
Waitangi, 29
  Treaty of 122
Waitangitaona, Lake 206
Waitara River 108
Waitomo Caves *51,* 51
Wakatipu, Lake 222, *246,* 246-247
Wakefield Track 306
Walkway system 308-309
Wallaby, dama (tammar) 41
Wanaka, Lake 220, 222-223, 240
Wanganui River 89
Wapiti 256
Warbrick Terrace *66*
Waro Limestone Reserve *37*
Water, finding 311
Weather forecasts 310
Weka 46, 159, *161*
Welcome Flat 214
Wentworth Valley Track 304
Western Okataina Walkway
  306-307
Westland National Park *204,*
  204-217, *209,* 303
  walkways 307
Weta *32,* 38
Whakamaru Ignimbrite 70, 73
Whakapapaiti Stream *84*

Whakapapaiti Valley *85*
Whakarewarewa 60
  Thermal Reserve walkway 307
Whakarewarewa Forest Park 63
  walkways 307
Whakataka, Mt walkway 307
Whales 29
  blue 22
  hump back 22, 45
  sperm 22
Whalers, whaling 22, 261, 274, 286
Whaling stations 45, 122
Whangamata Bluffs *73*
Wanganella 259
Whanganui Inlet *132*
Whangaparapara 45
Whangaparaoa Bay 95
Whangaroa *29*
Whataroa, Lake 206
Whirinaki Forest *18*
Whitebait, inanga 145
White Beach *49*
Whitecliffs Walkway 308
Whitehead 43
White Island 98-99, *98, 99*
White Rock *116*
Whymper Glacier 206
Wigley, Harry 187
Wilkies Pools *111*
Wilkin Valley 224, *224*
William, Port 286-287
Windbag Creek *217*
Wingbag Valley 216
Wine 243
Wither Hills Walk 305
Wombat, Lake 209
  track 307
Worsley Arm *257*

Z

Zurbriggen, Mattias 183, 185

Acknowledgments

Many people and organisations assisted in the preparation of this book. The publishers wish to thank them all, particularly the following:
Automobile Association (Auckland) Inc.
Department of Conservation
Department of Transport
Hamish Keith
Lands and Survey Department
Mount Cook Airlines, Sydney
New Zealand Consulate-General, Sydney
New Zealand Forestry Corporation
New Zealand Meteorological Service
New Zealand Tourist and Publicity Office, Sydney and Wellington
New Zealand Walkway Commission

Sources of Reference
The publishers also acknowledge their indebtedness to the following books which were consulted for reference: *Aorangi* by Jim Wilson (Whitcombe & Tombs); *Auckland and the Central North Island* edited by Warren Moran and Michael J. Taylor (Longman); *Beneath New Zealand Seas* by Wade Doak (Reed); *The Cliff Dwellers* Wade Doak (Hodder & Stoughton); *Common Insects in New Zealand* by David Miller (Reed); *The Companion Guide to the South Island of New Zealand* Errol Brathwaite (Collins); *The Companion Guide to the North Island of New Zealand* Errol Brathwaite (Collins); *Coromandel Walks* Graeme Foster (Wilson & Horton); *The Cultivation of New Zealand Trees and Shrubs* L. J. Metcalf (Reed); *A Dictonary of the Maori Language* H. W. Williams (NZ Government Printer); *The Encyclopaedia of New Zealand* (NZ Government Printer); *Fishes in the New Zealand Region* Wade Doak (Hodder & Stoughton); *Forest Wildlife* (Wildlife Service & NZ Forest Service); *Gazetteer of New Zealand Place Names* (Department of Lands and Survey); *The Geology of New Zealand* (NZ Government Printer); *Geology of Whakarewarewa Hot springs* E. F. Lloyd (N.Z. Geological Survey); *Glaciers of Westland National Park* W. A. Sara (NZ Government Printer); *The High Alps of New Zealand* W. S. Green (MacMillan); *In Search of Birds in New Zealand* Ross McKenzie (Reed); *Legends in the Rocks — An Outline of New Zealand Geology* M. Gage (Whitcoulls); *Mobil New Zealand Travel Guide: North Island,* and *South Island* Diana and Jeremy Pope (Reed); *National Parks:* Abel Tasman, Arthur's Pass, Egmont, Fiordland, Mount Aspiring, Mount Cook, Nelson Lakes, Tongariro, Urewera, and Westland, from the *Microtone Colour Book Series* (Bascands); and the *Handbooks* issued by the relevant Park Boards; *New Zealand* edited by K. B. Cumberland (Kummerly & Frey, Switzerland); *New Zealand Atlas* (NZ Government Printer); *New Zealand in Maps* A. Grant Anderson (Hodder & Stoughton); *Rakiura* (Reed); *Rugged Landscape* G. R. Stevens (Reed); *Scenic Reserves of Canterbury, Hawke's Bay, Nelson, Otago, South Auckland, Southland* and *Westland,* L. W. McCazcill (The Department of Lands and Survey); *Shell Guide to New Zealand* Maurice Shadbolt (Whitcombe and Tombs); *Small Land Animals of New Zealand* R. R. and L. M. Forster (John McIndoe); *The Southern Alps of New Zealand* Philip Temple (Whitcoulls); *Transactions of the Royal Society of New Zealand*: Volume Two, 1963, a paper by R. P. Suggate; *The Tuatara Lizards and Frogs of New Zealand* Richard Sharell (Collins); *Volcanoes of Tongariro National Park* D. R. Gregg (New Zealand Department of Scientific and Industrial Research); *Ways to the Wilderness* Philip Temple (Whitcoulls); *Wild Animals in New Zealand* A. L. Poole (Reed); *Wises New Zealand Guide* (Wises Publications).

Photographs
Photographers are listed in the order the pictures appear from left to right from the top of the page unless otherwise indicated.
Cover (Purakaunui Falls) Gordon Roberts. Back cover (Coromandel bush) Dennis Beytagh. 17: all by G. R. Roberts. 18: F. J. Newhook. 19: Brian Enting. 20: F. J. Newhook. 21: A. F. Billing. 23: top, bottom, G. J. H. Moon; Walter Imber. 27: Robin Smith. 28: AF Photographic Library. 30: Philip Temple; G. J. H. Moon; Philip Temple. 32: Philip Temple. 33: Brian Enting; A. F. Billing; Brian Enting; Philip Temple. 34: Brian Enting; bottom left, right, Philip Temple. 35: Philip Temple. 37: top left, top right, Wade Doak. 38-45: all by Robin Morrison. 48: bottom, Susanna Burton. 49: J. Robb; NZ Wildlife Service; G. R. Roberts; Robin Smith; J. ten Broeke. 50: bottom left, Andris Apse; bottom right, J. ten Broeke. 51: J. ten Broeke; bottom left, bottom right, Robin Smith. 52: Gordon Roberts. 54: G. J. H. Moon; Andris Apse. 55: bottom, Gordon Ell, Bush Films. 56: Andris Apse; G. R. Roberts. 57: G. J. H. Moon; J. Robb; John Johns; NZ Forest Service. 58-9: Robin Smith. 60: Robin Smith. 60-1: Brian Enting. 61: top left, Brian Enting; top right, Robin Smith. 63: Robin Smith. 64: G. J. H. Moon; top right, bottom, Brian Enting. 65: Andris Apse. 66: Fritz Prenzel; Robin Smith. 67: G. J. H. Moon; Robin Smith. 68: NZ Geological Survey; National Publicity Studios. 69: G. R. Roberts. 71, 72, 73: all by G. R. Roberts. 74: bottom, Fritz Prenzel. 75: Robin Smith; Philip Temple. 76: National Publicity Studios. 77: Martin Barriball. 78: NZ Geological Survey. 78-9: Robin Smith. 80: A. F. Billing; National Publicity Studios; Philip Temple. 81: Brian Enting. 82: NZ Geological Survey. 83: David Moore; Philip Temple. 84: NZ Geological Survey; Philip Temple; Brian Enting. 85: Brian Enting; G. J. H. Moon; bottom left and right, Philip Temple. 86: Bob Mossel; Robin Smith. 87: Walter Imber; Robin Smith; Philip Temple. 88: Philip Temple; Brian Enting. 89: Philip Temple; Conon Fraser. 90: Philip Temple. 91: Philip Temple; Conon Fraser. 94: top right, Brian Enting. 95: Ray Knox; J. Kenny; NZ Geological Survey. 98: G. R. Roberts; Warren Jacobs/Robin Smith Photography. 99: Warren Jacobs/Robin Smith Photography. 100-1: G. J. H. Moon. 102, 103: Philip Temple. 104: Australian Picture Library. 105: F. J. Newhook; G. J. H. Moon. 106-7: G. R. Roberts. 108: G. R. Roberts. 109: Walter Imber; G. R. Roberts; John Rundle. 110: G. R. Roberts; Conon Fraser; G. J. H. Moon. 111: Richard Silcock; Greig Royle. 112: Robin Smith. 114: Geoff Mason. 115: Warren Jacobs/Robin Smith Photography. 116: NZ Geological Survey; G. R. Roberts; Martin Barriball. 117: J. ten Broeke; Geoff Mason. 118: Conon Fraser; G. J. H. Moon; NZ Geological Survey. 119: Richard Silcock; Conon Fraser; Ray Knox. 120-1: Philip Temple. 122: Philip Temple; Walter Imber. 123: Warren Jacobs/Robin Smith Photography. 124: Brian Enting. 125: Fritz Prenzel; PhilipTemple. 126: G. R. Roberts; NZ Geological Survey; G. R. Roberts; Walter Imber. 127: top left and right, bottom left, John Johns; Richard Silcock. 129: Philip Temple. 130: left, Greig Royle; Conon Fraser; G. R. Roberts. 131: Greig Royle; Martin Barriball. 132: NZ Wildlife Service; G. J. H. Moon; Richard Silcock. 133: Walter Imber; NZ Geological Survey; M. Bennetts. 134: Geoff Mason; Guy Mannering; Philip Temple; Guy Mannering. 135: Philip Temple. 136-7: Walter Imber. 138: Philip Temple. 139: Dennis Beytagh. 140: Walter Imber; Brian Enting. 141: Brian Enting; Derek Fraser; Philip Temple. 142: Brian Enting. 143: John Rundle; both bottom, Brian Enting. 144: Philip Temple; Warren Jacobs/Robin Smith Photography. 145: top left and right, Philip Temple; NZ Geological Survey. 146-7: G. J. H. Moon. 148: J. Braggins; NZ Geological Survey. 149: Philip Temple. 150: John Rundle. 151: John Rundle; Philip Temple. 152: Geoff Mason; Greig Royle. 153: K. & J. Bigwood; Andris Apse. 155: top left, Robin Smith; top right, G. R. Roberts. 156-7: Walter Imber. 160: top and centre, Philip Temple; Geoff Mason. 162: Philip Temple. 163: A. F. Billing; top, right, and bottom, Philip Temple. 164, 165: all by Philip Temple. 166: Walter Imber; Philip Temple. 167: Philip Temple. 168-9: Philip Temple. 170: bottom, Conon Fraser. 172: Philip Temple; G. J. H. Moon. 173: A. F. Billing; G. J. H. Moon; Photographic Library of Australia. 174: Guy Harris. 175: bottom, Philip Temple. 176, 177: Philip Temple. 178-9: AF Photo Library. 180: Warren Jacobs/Robin Smith Photography; top right, bottom right, Philip Temple. 181: G. J. H. Moon. 182: Philip Temple. 183: Walter Imber; Philip Temple. 184, 185, 186: all by Philip Temple. 187: Bob Mossel; top right, bottom, Philip Temple. 188-195: all by Philip Temple. 196: top left, bottom, Philip Temple; Philip Temple. 197: top left and right, Philip Temple; M. Bennetts. 198: Gordon Roberts; top right, bottom, Philip Temple. 199: Philip Temple. 200: M. Bennetts; Philip Temple. 201: Philip Temple. 202: top, bottom left, bottom centre, Philip Temple; A. F. Billing. 203: Philip Temple. 204-5: Warren Jacobs/Robin Smith Photography. 206: John Johns; NZ Forest Service. 207: G. J. H. Moon; John Johns; Fritz Prenzel. 208: Philip Temple; Walter Imber. 209: Walter Imber; Philip Temple. 210: J. Kenny. 210-11: Fritz Prenzel. 212: M. Bennetts; Philip Temple. 213: Denise Kuhne; Fritz Prenzel. 214, 215: Philip Temple. 216: Walter Imber; Philip Temple. 217: J. Kenny; M. Bennetts; Walter Imber. 218-19: Fritz Prenzel. 220: Philip Temple; Walter Imber. 221: J. Kenny; Philip Temple. 223: Walter Imber; Philip Temple. 224: Greig Royle. 225: Philip Temple. 227: Warren Jacobs/Robin Smith Photography; John Rundle. 228, 229, 230: all by Philip Temple. 231: John Johns; F. J. Newhook; Philip Temple. 232: Philip Temple. 233: Philip Temple; Greig Royle. 234, 235: Philip Temple. 236-7: M. Bennetts/Fritz Prenzel Library. 238: Robin Morrison; Philip Temple. 239: top, bottom, Philip Temple; G. R. Roberts. 240: Robin Morrison; Philip Temple. 241: Robin Morrison; Philip Temple. 242: top, Robin Morrison. 243: Robin Morrison; M. Bennetts. 244: Philip Temple; J. Flux. 245: bottom, G. R. Roberts. 246: Andris Apse; Philip Temple. 246-7: Guy Mannering. 247: Philip Temple; Brian Enting. 248: Philip Temple; Photographic Library of Australia. 249, 250: Robin Morrison. 251: centre, Walter Imber; bottom, Warren Jacobs/Robin Smith Photography. 252: G. R. Roberts; Brian Enting; Philip Temple. 252-3: Guy Mannering. 254-5: Fritz Prenzel. 256: G. R. Roberts; Walter Imber. 257, 258, 259: all by Philip Temple. 260: Australian Picture Library; Philip Temple; John Johns. 261: P. Drewitt-Smith; NZ Wildlife Service; Walter Imber. 262: Philip Temple. 263: top left and right, Philip Temple; Warren Jacobs/Robin Smith Photography. 264: Philip Temple. 265: top and centre right, Philip Temple; Walter Imber. 266: Walter Imber; Philip Temple. 267: Philip Temple; Walter Imber. 268: top left and right, G. J. H. Moon; Walter Imber. 269: National Publicity Studios; Philip Temple. 270: Philip Temple. 271: top left and right, bottom left, Philip Temple; M. Bennetts. 272: Philip Temple; Walter Imber. 273: Walter Imber. 274-5: Philip Temple. 276: NZ Geological Survey; G. Woodward/Lands & Survey Department. 277: top left and right, G. Woodward/Lands & Survey Department; NZ Wildlife Service. 279: top left, M. Bennetts; bottom, Philip Temple. 281: G. Woodward/Lands & Survey Department; NZ Forest Service. 283, 284: Philip Temple. 285: Philip Temple; NZ Geological Survey. 286: Philip Temple. 287: Greig Royle; Geoff Mason. 288, 289: Andris Apse. 290: Philip Temple. 291: Greig Royle; A. F. Billing; Philip Temple. 292: Philip Temple; Greig Royle. 293: John Johns; Philip Temple. 294, 295: Philip Temple.

Paintings
The following works are reproduced from the collection of the Hocken Library, University of Otago:
Pink and White Terraces, Lake Rotomohana and Mt Tarawera, by J. B. C. Hoyte; – p. 62;
Mt Tarawera in Eruption, June 10 1886, after Charles Blomfield; – p. 62; and
Milford Sound looking North West from Freshwater Basin, by John Buchanan, – p. 266.

Typesetting by Craftsmen Typesetting, 170 Pacific Highway,
Greenwich, NSW 2065.

Colour separations by Gibbneys Graphics 1980
375 Hay Street, Perth, Western Australia 6000

Printed and bound in 1990 by Everbest Printing Co., Ltd,
Hong Kong for Reader's Digest (Australia) Pty Ltd,
26–32 Waterloo Street, Surry Hills, NSW 2010.